PENGUIN PASSNOTES

Modern Mathematics

Ian Dawbarn was educated at York University where he took a
B.A. (Hons) and at Oxford University where he received an M.Sc.
He has taught in schools in Oxford and is now Tutor in Mathe-
matics at Davies's College, London. He has also written
Mathematics in the Penguin Passnotes series, and is an examiner
for a major GCE examining board.

PENGUIN PASSNOTES

Modern Mathematics

IAN DAWBARN
ADVISORY EDITOR: S. H. COOTE, M.A., PH.D.

PENGUIN BOOKS

Penguin Books Ltd, Harmondsworth, Middlesex, England
Viking Penguin Inc, 40 West 23rd Street, New York, New York 10010, U.S.A.
Penguin Books Australia Ltd, Ringwood, Victoria, Australia
Penguin Books Canada Ltd, 2801 John Street, Markham, Ontario, Canada L 3 R 1 B 4
Penguin Books (N.Z.) Ltd, 182–190 Wairau Road, Auckland 10, New Zealand

First published 1985

Made and printed in Great Britain by
Richard Clay (The Chaucer Press) Ltd, Bungay, Suffolk
Filmset in Monophoto Times Roman by
Northumberland Press Ltd, Gateshead, Tyne and Wear

*The publishers are grateful to the following Examination Boards
for permission to reproduce questions from examination papers used
in individual titles in the Passnotes series:*

*Associated Examining Board, University of Cambridge Local Examinations Syndicate,
Joint Matriculation Board, University of London School Examinations Department,
Oxford and Cambridge Schools Examination Board, University of Oxford Delegacy of Local Examinations.*

*The Examination Boards accept no responsibility whatsoever for the accuracy or
method of working in any suggested answers given as models.*

Contents

Introduction

This is a comprehensive guide to O-level modern mathematics covering the syllabuses of all of the major examining boards. Your course may not require some of the topics – see the list on page 14.

The book is designed so that you can work through methodically building your knowledge of the subject. Alternatively you may wish to check up on certain topics. A detailed contents list is provided so that you can find the section you need. Page references throughout the text and a glossary of technical terms are also included to help you find your way around the book.

The theory is presented in a clear and concise way, and is illustrated by the many worked examples. You should study these examples carefully to see how the ideas are used and also to learn how to set out an argument in a methodical and accurate way.

Questions from past examination papers are given at the end of each topic. You should attempt most of these, as understanding in mathematics can only come through practice. These questions are identified by examination board, but you need not restrict yourself to those from one board only. All of the questions are chosen to show the main points of the theory. Numerical answers to many of the questions are given.

Examining Boards

AEB   *not*   Statistics/Probability (pages 348–75)
Iterative methods (pages 376–80)
Plans and elevation (pages 386–9)

CAM   *not*   Binary operations and groups (pages 57–66)
Differentiation and integration (pages 188–204)

JMB   *not*   Group axioms (pages 62–4)
Iterative methods (pages 376–80)
Plan and elevation (pages 386–9)

LON   *not*   Group axioms (pages 62–4)
Integration (pages 197–204)
Iterative methods (pages 376–80)
Plan and elevation (pages 386–9)

OXF   *not*   Binary operations and groups (pages 57–66)
Iterative methods (pages 376–80)

SMP   *not*   Differentiation and integration (pages 188–204)

Notation Used

$\mathbb{N}$	natural numbers
$\mathbb{Z}$	integers
$\mathbb{Q}$	rational numbers
$\mathbb{R}$	real numbers
$a * b$	the result of combining a and b with operation $*$
$<, \leqslant$	less than, less than or equal to
$>, \geqslant$	greater than, greater than or equal to
$\circ\text{———}\circ$	open interval on the number line
$\bullet\text{———}\bullet$	closed interval on the number line
$\in$	is an element of
$\notin$	is not an element of
$\cap$	intersection
$\cup$	union
A'	the complement of A
$\mathscr{E}$	the universal set
$\varnothing$	the empty set
$\subset \ or \ \subseteq$	is a subset of
$\not\subset$	is not a subset of
$n(A)$	number of elements in set A
$\{\ldots\}$	the set of … (elements listed in brackets)
a^{-1}	inverse of a
$m:A \rightarrow B$	mapping from set A to set B
$f:\mathbb{R} \rightarrow \mathbb{R}$	function with domain and range $\mathbb{R}$
$\left.\begin{array}{l} f:x \mapsto \\ \text{or} \\ f(x) \end{array}\right\}$	function with variable x
$fg \ or \ f \circ g$	composition of functions g and then f
f^{-1}	inverse of the function f
$\dfrac{dy}{dx}, f'(x)$	gradient function

$\int y\,dx$	integral of y with respect to x
$\int_a^b y\,dx$	definite integral with limits a and b
$\not= \not=$	equal lines
$\uparrow\uparrow$	parallel lines
$<$	equal angles
$T(A)$	image of point A under transformation T
T^{-1}	inverse of transformation T
M^{-1}	inverse of matrix M
M^{T}	transpose of M
$\mathbf{a}, \mathbf{b}$	vectors
$\begin{pmatrix} 1 \\ 2 \end{pmatrix}$	column vector
$|\mathbf{a}|$	modulus of $\mathbf{a}$
$p(A)$	probability of the event A

Section 1: Numbers

Sets

The basic numbers are those used for counting; 0, 1, 2, 3, 4, ... (the dots show that the list continues without end). They form the set of **natural numbers**, denoted by the letter $\mathbb{N}$. (But some texts use $\mathbb{N} \equiv \{1, 2, 3, ...\}$.)

In general, a set is a collection of **elements**, often listed between curly brackets. Sets are denoted by capital letters, and their elements are denoted by small letters.

Examples $\mathbb{N} = \{0, 1, 2, 3, 4, ...\}$, $A = \{a, b, c, d\}$,
$$C = \{\bigcirc, \triangle, \square, \triangledown\}.$$

The number 2 is an element, or **member**, of $\mathbb{N}$. We write $2 \in \mathbb{N}$. $a \in A$ means that the element a is in the set A. Conversely $b \notin A$ means that b is not a member of A. The elements of a set can be listed in any order, $\{a, b, c, d\}$ and $\{b, c, a, d\}$ are the same set. Two sets are **equal** if they contain exactly the same elements.

Properties of the Natural Numbers

Natural numbers can be combined by adding them together. The result is another natural number ($2 + 3 = 5$, for example). Addition, $+$, is a **binary operation** on the set $\mathbb{N}$. A binary operation on a given set is a rule for combining two members of the set. Since the result of addition is also in $\mathbb{N}$, we say that $\mathbb{N}$ is **closed** under the operation of addition.

Numbers can also be multiplied together. Multiplication is a binary operation on $\mathbb{N}$, and $\mathbb{N}$ is closed under this operation. Numbers that are multiplied to form a **product** are called the **factors** or **divisors** of that product. For example, since $2 \times 3 = 6$, 2 and 3 are factors of 6.

Numbers which have 2 as a factor are called **even numbers**. The even numbers form the set $\{0, 2, 4, 6, 8, 10, 12, \ldots\}$. Since $2 \times 0 = 0$, 2 is a factor of 0 and so 0 is even.

The remaining natural numbers, that do not have a factor of 2, are called **odd numbers**. They form the set $\{1, 3, 5, 7, 9, 11, \ldots\}$.

Some numbers have many factors. For example 12 has divisors 1, 2, 3, 4, 6 and 12 itself. Some numbers have only two factors, the least possible. A number that can only be divided by 1 or itself is called a **prime number**. 1 is not counted as a prime. The primes form the set $\{2, 3, 5, 7, 11, \ldots\}$. We can denote this set by P. The elements of P also appear in the list of members of $\mathbb{N}$. We say that P is a **subset** of $\mathbb{N}$, and write $P \subset \mathbb{N}$. $A \subset B$ means that A is a subset of B, the elements of A also belong to B. In this example, the set B is defined in terms of the properties of its elements. The notation $A \subseteq B$ means that A is either a subset of B *or* is the same set as B.

Example   If $A = \{2, 3\}$ and $B = \{x : x \text{ is a prime less than } 100\}$, then $A \subseteq B$.

The sets A and B of the last example are **finite sets**, you can count their members. $\mathbb{N}$ and P are **infinite sets**. If A is a finite set, then $n(A)$ means the number of elements in A. For the set A above, $n(A) = 2$.

Products of three or more numbers

The product $2 \times 3 \times 4$ can be worked out in two ways.
   (i) Find 2×3 and multiply the result by 4: $(2 \times 3) \times 4 = 6 \times 4 = 24$.
   (ii) Find 3×4 and multiply the result by 2: $2 \times (3 \times 4) = 2 \times 12 = 24$.
(Notice how brackets are used to indicate the order of the operations.) The answer is 24 in both cases. We say that multiplication is an **associative** operation, since $(a \times b) \times c = a \times (b \times c)$ for any numbers a, b and c.

Further, $2 \times 3 = 6$ and $3 \times 2 = 6$. Two numbers can be multiplied in either order, $a \times b = b \times a$ for any numbers a and b. We say multiplication is a **commutative** or **symmetric** operation. Addition is also commutative and associative. Later in the section you will come across operations that do not have these properties.

Any natural number can be expressed as a product of its prime factors. For example $12 = 2 \times 2 \times 3$ (2 and 3 are primes). 2 is a **repeated factor**. Repeated factors can be written with the **power** or **index** notation.

2×2 is written as 2^2, 2 to the power 2, or with index 2

$2 \times 2 \times 2$ is written as 2^3, 2 to the power 3

$4 \times 4 \times 4 \times 4 = 4^4$, and so on

The power counts the number of times that the factor appears in the product.

For a number a, a^2 is called the **square** of a, a^3 is called the **cube** of a. Notice that $2^1 = 2$. In general $a^1 = a$ for any number a.

Common Factors and Multiples

Example   12 has factors 1, 2, 3, 4, 6 and 12

18 has factors 1, 2, 3, 6, 9 and 18

1, 2, 3 and 6 appear in both lists of factors, and are called the **common factors** of 12 and 18. 6 is the largest of these and is called the highest common factor (**H C F**) of 12 and 18.

Given two numbers, a **common multiple** can be formed by multiplying them together, $10 \times 12 = 120$ is a common multiple of 10 and 12. Another number with this property is 60. 60 is the smallest number that has 10 and 12 as factors. We say that 60 is the least common multiple (**L C M**) of 10 and 12.

Example   When a certain natural number is divided by 4 or 6 the remainder is 3 in each case. Find the smallest such number.

Answer   The number must be of the form $A + 3$, where A is a multiple of both 4 and 6. The smallest is obtained when A is the L C M of 4 and 6. So $A = 12$ and the required number is $12 + 3 = 15$.

Example   The difference between the greatest and least primes between 30 and 60 is

(a) 26   (b) 27   (c) 28   (d) 29

Answer   The primes in the given range are 31, 37, 41, 43, 47, 53 and 59. The difference between the greatest and least is $59 - 31 = 28$. The answer is (c).

Examination questions

1. $D(n)$ denotes the sum of the divisors of n, including 1 but excluding n itself. (For example $D(20) = 1+2+4+5+10 = 22$.) The value of $D(28)$ is

(a) 14   (b) 21   (c) 28   (d) 30   [SMP]

2. Using each of the digits 1, 2, 3 once only
 (i) list all the numbers between 100 and 300 which are divisible by 3,
 (ii) list all the prime numbers between 100 and 300.

3. In the pattern shown, each number apart from the 1s and 2s is the sum of the number above it and the number to the left of that. (Examples are indicated by the arrows.)

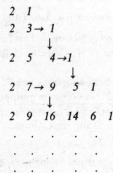

 (i) Write the next row.
 (ii) Describe (a) the second column, (b) the third column, (c) hence find the first three numbers in the 20th row.
 (iii) State the connection between each number in the fourth column and the numbers in the third column.   [SMP]

Answer
 3. (i) 2   11   25   30   20   7   1
   (ii) (a) The odd numbers   (b) the squares of the natural numbers
       (c) 2   39   361

Subtraction and Negative Numbers

When two natural numbers are added together, the result is also a natural number. This property is called **closure** (page 17). The natural numbers can be pictured as steps on a number line.

The addition $2 + 3$ for example, means first go 2 steps to the right of 0, and then a further 3 steps. The result is a total of 5 steps.

$2+3=5$

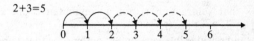

The steps are always taken to the right, and since the line continues indefinitely in this direction, the result is always on the line.

    Subtraction can be regarded as taking steps to the *left*. $3 - 2$ means take 3 steps to the right and then two left.

$3-2=1$

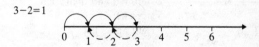

As long as the second number is less than or equal to the first, the result is on the line. However, if the second number is larger than the first, as in $2 - 3$

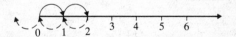

the result is off the end of the line, and so is not a natural number. $\mathbb{N}$ is *not* closed under subtraction.

    The line must be extended indefinitely to the left as well. The steps to the left of 0 are given by the **negative integers** $^-1, {}^-2, {}^-3, {}^-4, \ldots$ (sometimes the $-$ sign is written lower, as in -2, etc.).

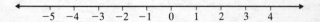

The **positive integers** can be written with $+$ signs in front to emphasize the positivity

$$^+1, ^+2, ^+3, \ldots$$ notice that $^-0 = {}^+0$

but usually the $+$ sign is not written.

The complete set $\{\ldots\ ^-4,\ ^-3,\ ^-2,\ ^-1, 0, 1, 2, 3, 4, \ldots\}$ is called the **set of integers**, denoted by the letter $\mathbb{Z}$.

$$\mathbb{N} \text{ is a subset of } \mathbb{Z}, \qquad \mathbb{N} \subset \mathbb{Z}$$

It is now possible to do the subtraction $2 - 3$

$$2 - 3 = -1$$

This shows that subtraction is not a commutative operation, since $3 - 2 = {}^+1$ while $2 - 3 = {}^-1$.

Negative and positive integers can be combined with the operations $+$ and $-$.

Examples

(a) $^-1 + 3$ 1 step left and then 3 right
    $= 2$ 2 steps right
(b) $^-2 - (^+3)$ 2 steps left and then 3 left
    $= {}^-5$ 5 steps left
(c) $1 + (^-3)$ 1 right and 3 left
    $= {}^-2$ 2 left

Signed numbers are often put in brackets to avoid mistakes when using them.

Adding $^-3$ is the same as subtracting $^+3$, $+(^-3) = {}^-3$. Since this rule applies for any number

$$+(-) = -$$

similarly

$$-(+) = -$$

Now consider $3 - (^-2)$. A minus in front of a positive number changes the direction from right to left. In the same way, a minus in front of a negative number changes the direction from left to right

$$3 - (^-2) = 3 + 2$$

The rule is

$$-(-) = +$$

A plus has no effect on the direction, so that

$$+ (+) = +$$

These four rules are the **rules of signs**. They are very important for manipulating numbers, and should be remembered.

You have seen that subtraction is not commutative, $2 - 3 = {}^-1$ while $3 - 2 = {}^+1$. Subtraction is also not associative

$$(1-2)-3 = ({}^-1)-3$$
$$= {}^-4$$

while
$$1-(2-3) = 1-({}^-1)$$
$$= 1+1 \qquad \text{from the sign rules}$$
$$= 2$$

Integers can also be combined using multiplication. The signs of the numbers are treated separately using the four sign rules.

Examples

(i) $({}^-2) \times ({}^+3) = (-)(+)(2 \times 3)$ separate the signs
$$= -6 \qquad\qquad\qquad\qquad \text{as } (-)(+) = -$$

(ii) $({}^-3) \times ({}^-5) = (-)(-)(3 \times 5)$
$$= {}^+15 \qquad\qquad\qquad\qquad \text{as } (-)(-) = +$$
$$= 15 \qquad\qquad\qquad\qquad \text{dropping the } + \text{ sign}$$

Division and Fractions

3 is a divisor of 12 since $12 = 3 \times 4$. We can say that 12 **divided** by 3 is 4, in symbols $12 \div 3 = 4$. Picture this on the number line as 12 steps divided into 3 pieces, each of length 4 steps

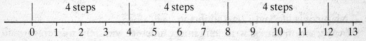

When negative integers are involved, the signs are separated and the four rules are used just as for multiplication. For example,

$$({}^-12) \div ({}^+4) = (-)(+)(12 \div 4)$$
$$= {}^-3$$

If an integer is divided by one of its factors, then the result is also an integer. However, if it is divided by a number that is not a factor, then the result is not an integer.

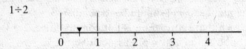

One has been divided into two equal pieces, each half a unit long. The result is a number half way between 0 and 1 which is not an integer. It is written as the **fraction** $\frac{1}{2}$ (one half). The bar separating the 1 and the 2 reminds you that $\frac{1}{2} = 1 \div 2$. In general, the division $a \div b$ gives rise to the fraction a/b. This means that $\mathbb{Z}$ is *not* closed under the operation $\div$.

Fractions can also have signs, for example the division $(^-1) \div 2$ results in the fraction $^-\frac{1}{2}$. Also $1 \div (^-2) = {}^-\frac{1}{2}$.

For a fraction

$$\frac{a}{b}$$

the top number a is called the **numerator** and the bottom number b is called the **denominator**.

The fraction $\frac{2}{1}$ indicates that 2 has been divided into 1 piece, which must be of length 2. So $\frac{2}{1} = 2$. In general for any integer a, $\frac{a}{1} = a$.

An integer can also be regarded as a fraction with denominator 1. The integers form a subset of the fractions. The fractions are often called the set of **rational numbers**, denoted by the letter $\mathbb{Q}$. We can write the **chain** of subsets $\mathbb{N} \subset \mathbb{Z} \subset \mathbb{Q}$. A length cannot be divided into pieces of length 0. No fraction may have a zero denominator.

Now consider the division $3 \div 6$, 3 divided into 6 equal pieces.

Each piece is of length $\frac{1}{2}$ unit. So $\frac{3}{6} = \frac{1}{2}$.

Any fraction can be written in many different ways, the numerator and denominator can *both* be multiplied by any quantity without changing the value of the fraction. In the example above

$$\frac{1}{2} = \frac{3 \times 1}{3 \times 2} = \frac{3}{6}$$

This turns out to be a very useful property of fractions. By repeatedly dividing out factors common to the numerator and denominator, a fraction can be put in its **lowest terms**, when the top and bottom have no further factors in common.

Example
$$\frac{24}{120} = \frac{12}{60} = \frac{6}{30} = \frac{3}{15} = \frac{1}{5}$$

When the result of a calculation is a fraction, it should always be expressed in its lowest terms.

Combining fractions

The operations $+$, $-$, $\times$ and $\div$ can be used on the set of rational numbers.

Adding and subtracting fractions: When two fractions have the same denominators, they can be added (or subtracted) by adding (or subtracting) the numerators.

Examples

(a)
$$\frac{1}{2} + \frac{3}{2} = \frac{1+3}{2}$$

$$= \frac{4}{2} \qquad \text{one half and 3 halves make 4 halves}$$

$$= \frac{2}{1} \qquad \text{put in lowest terms}$$

$$= 2 \qquad \text{write as an integer}$$

(b)
$$\frac{3}{5} - \frac{7}{5} = \frac{3-7}{5}$$

$$= \frac{^-4}{5} \qquad \text{a negative fraction}$$

However, most pairs of fractions have different denominators. We can use the property, that the top and bottom can be multiplied by any quantity, to give the fractions the same denominator.

Example
$$\frac{1}{2} + \frac{2}{3}$$

Answer   Multiply by 3 in the first fraction, and by 2 in the second. The denominators then become 6, which is the LCM of 2 and 3.

$$\frac{1}{2}+\frac{2}{3} = \frac{3\times 1}{3\times 2}+\frac{2\times 2}{2\times 3}$$

$$= \frac{3}{6}+\frac{4}{6} \qquad \text{denominators now equal}$$

$$= \frac{3+4}{6}$$

$$= \frac{7}{6}$$

A fraction like $\frac{7}{6}$ which has a larger numerator than denominator can also be written as a **mixed number**, which has a whole number part and a fractional part less than 1.

$$\frac{7}{6} = 1\frac{1}{6} \qquad \text{as } 7\div 6 = 1 \text{ remainder } 1$$

$$(1\frac{1}{6} \text{ stands for } 1+\frac{1}{6})$$

Conversely, a mixed number can be converted into a fraction

$$2\frac{3}{5} = 2+\frac{3}{5} = \frac{2\times 5+3}{5}$$

$$= \frac{10+3}{5} \qquad \text{do the multiplication first}$$

$$= \frac{13}{5}$$

When mixed numbers are involved in calculations, they can first be converted into fractions. But note also the examples

(i) $17\frac{1}{2}+4\frac{1}{4} \quad = 17+4+\frac{1}{2}+\frac{1}{4} = 21\frac{3}{4}$

(ii) $125\frac{1}{3}-15\frac{1}{2} = 124-15+1\frac{1}{3}-\frac{1}{2}$

$\qquad\qquad\quad = 109+\frac{4}{3}-\frac{1}{2}$

$\qquad\qquad\quad = 109+\frac{8}{6}-\frac{3}{6}$

$\qquad\qquad\quad = 109\frac{5}{6}$

Multiplying fractions: To multiply fractions, multiply the numerators and denominators separately

$$\frac{1}{2} \times \frac{3}{4} = \frac{1 \times 3}{2 \times 4}$$

$$= \frac{3}{8}$$

Dividing fractions: To divide by a fraction, turn it upside down and multiply

$$\frac{1}{2} \div \frac{3}{4} = \frac{1}{2} \times \frac{4}{3} \qquad \text{turn and multiply}$$

$$= \frac{1 \times 4}{2 \times 3}$$

$$= \frac{4}{6}$$

$$= \frac{2}{3} \qquad \text{dividing out the common factor 2}$$

When calculations also involve integers, convert them into fractions with denominator 1 and then use the rules above.

Example Evaluate
(a) $\frac{1}{3} + \frac{1}{9} - \frac{1}{27}$
(b) $3\frac{3}{4} \times 1\frac{1}{3}$

Answer

(a) $\dfrac{9}{27} + \dfrac{3}{27} - \dfrac{1}{27}$ 　　　　　LCM of 3, 9 and 27 is 27. Multiply by 9 in the first fraction and 3 in the second

$$= \frac{9 + 3 - 1}{27}$$

$$= \frac{11}{27}$$

(b) $3\dfrac{1}{4} \times 1\dfrac{1}{3} = \dfrac{13}{4} \times \dfrac{4}{3}$ 　　　　$3\frac{1}{4} = 3 + \frac{1}{4} = \frac{12}{4} + \frac{1}{4} = \frac{13}{4}$

$$= \frac{13 \times 4}{3 \times 4} \qquad\qquad 1\frac{1}{3} = 1 + \frac{1}{3} = \frac{3}{3} + \frac{1}{3} = \frac{4}{3}$$

$$= \frac{13}{3} \qquad \text{divide out by 4}$$

$$= 4\frac{1}{3}$$

Example   Write the following fractions in ascending order of magnitude

$$^3/_5, \quad ^4/_9, \quad ^7/_{15}$$

Answer   Write the fractions with the same denominators

$$\frac{3}{5} = \frac{3 \times 9}{5 \times 9} = \frac{27}{45} \qquad \text{LCM of 5, 9 and 15 is 45}$$

$$\frac{4}{9} = \frac{4 \times 5}{9 \times 5} = \frac{20}{45}$$

$$\frac{7}{15} = \frac{7 \times 3}{15 \times 3} = \frac{21}{45}$$

The order is $^{20}/_{45}$, $^{21}/_{45}$, $^{27}/_{45}$ which corresponds to $^4/_9$, $^7/_{15}$, $^3/_5$
(Alternatively you could convert all of the fractions to decimals, as shown
in the next section.)

Examination questions

1. *Write as a single fraction*
(i) $^1/_5 \div ^1/_4$ *(ii)* $^1/_5 - (^1/_4 \times ^1/_3)$ *(iii)* $^1/_5 + ^1/_4 + ^1/_3$ [CAM]

2. *Evaluate*   *(i)* $2^5/_8 - 1^{11}/_{16}$ *(ii)* $2^5/_8 \div 1^{11}/_{16}$ *giving your answers
as fractions in their lowest terms.*   [SMP]

3. *The result of arranging the fractions* $^2/_3$, $^4/_7$, $^7/_{10}$ *in descending order
of magnitude is*

A $^7/_{10}$, $^4/_7$, $^2/_3$ B $^4/_7$, $^7/_{10}$, $^2/_3$ C $^2/_3$, $^7/_{10}$, $^4/_7$ D $^7/_{10}$, $^2/_3$, $^4/_7$
E $^4/_7$, $^2/_3$, $^7/_{10}$ [LON]

4. *Which of the following does not lie between* $^1/_2$ *and* $^5/_7$?
A $^3/_5$ B $^7/_9$ C $^2/_3$ D $^8/_{15}$

Answers

1. (i) $^4/_5$ (ii) $^7/_{60}$ (iii) $^{47}/_{60}$
2. (i) $^{15}/_{16}$ (ii) $^{14}/_9$
3. D
4. B

The next example illustrates how brackets can be used to show the order of the steps of a calculation.

Example   Evaluate $\frac{1}{2}(1 + \frac{1}{2}(1 + \frac{1}{2}(1 + \frac{1}{2})))$

Answer   When a bracket appears between two numbers, a multiplication is intended. So $\frac{1}{2}(1) = \frac{1}{2} \times 1 = \frac{1}{2}$. The value of the expression inside the innermost brackets is found first.

$\frac{1}{2}(1 + \frac{1}{2}(1 + \frac{1}{2}(\frac{3}{2})))$ since $1 + \frac{1}{2} = \frac{3}{2}$

$\quad = \frac{1}{2}(1 + \frac{1}{2}(1 + \frac{3}{4}))$ $\frac{1}{2}(\frac{3}{2}) = \frac{1}{2} \times \frac{3}{2} = \frac{3}{4}$

$\quad = \frac{1}{2}(1 + \frac{1}{2}(\frac{7}{4}))$ $1 + \frac{3}{4} = \frac{7}{4}$

$\quad = \frac{1}{2}(1 + \frac{7}{8})$ $\frac{1}{2}(\frac{7}{4}) = \frac{7}{8}$

$\quad = \frac{1}{2}(1\frac{5}{8})$ $1 + \frac{7}{8} = 1\frac{5}{8}$

$\quad = {}^{15}\!/_{16}$ $\frac{1}{2}(1\frac{5}{8}) = {}^{15}\!/_{16}$

Irrational Numbers

The fractions fill in some of the spaces between the integers on the number line. They do not quite fill out the whole line.

A number with a square root which is an integer is called a perfect square. A number that is not a perfect square has a square root which is not even a fraction.

For example $\sqrt{2}$ is not a fraction ($\sqrt{2} \notin \mathbb{Q}$). It is an **irrational number**. Examples of other irrational numbers are

$$\sqrt{3}, \quad \sqrt{2}+1, \quad \sqrt{7}, \quad 1-\sqrt{101}$$

Together the rational and irrational numbers make up the whole number line, they form the set of **real numbers** $\mathbb{R}$.

Since an irrational number is not a fraction, it cannot be written exactly as a decimal. We can, however, write numbers such as $\sqrt{2}$ to any desired accuracy. To 4 decimal places $\sqrt{2} = 1\cdot4142$. (See page 31.)

Examination question

State two irrational numbers whose sum is rational.   [SMP]

Answer $1+\sqrt{2}$ and $1-\sqrt{2}$ for example

Sequences

We now look at an alternative answer to the example on p. 29. The result of the innermost part of the calculation is $\frac{1}{2}(1 + \frac{1}{2}) = \frac{3}{4}$, then taking the next set of brackets gives $\frac{1}{2}(1 + \frac{3}{4}) = \frac{7}{8}$. The successive parts of the calculation form a **sequence**

$$\frac{3}{4}, \frac{7}{8}, \ldots$$

clearly the next number in the sequence is $\frac{15}{16}$ (double the previous denominator and subtract one to give the numerator).

A sequence of numbers is a list of numbers with some rule for predicting further values in the list.

Example   Write down the next two numbers in the sequence

$$31, 23, 17, 13, \ldots$$

Answer   The difference between the first two numbers is 8, that between the second and third is 6, that between the third and fourth is 4, so the difference between the fourth and fifth is 2, and the difference between the fifth and sixth is 0. The sequence continues: 31, 23, 17, 13, 11, 11.

Example   The last digit of 3^{102} is

   (a) 1   (b) 3   (c) 7   (d) 9

Answer   Working out the first few powers of 3

$$3^1 = 3 \quad 3^2 = 9 \quad 3^3 = 27 \quad 3^4 = 81$$
$$3^5 = 243 \quad 3^6 = 729 \quad 3^7 = 2187 \quad 3^8 = 6561$$

The last digit follows the sequence 3, 9, 7, 1, 3, 9, 7, 1, 3, 9, 7, 1, ... $102 = 4 \times 25 + 2$, which is 25 complete cycles of 4 and one half cycle. The last digit is the second in the sequence 3, 9, 7, 1 which is 9. The answer is (d).

See also page 376 for some applications of sequences.

Decimal Numbers

These are used to express numbers in terms of some particular fractions. These fractions correspond to the divisions of the units of the number line into ten, a hundred, ..., parts. For example, measuring along a number line, length, or mark on the number scale, can be measured by taking finer and finer divisions until the required accuracy is reached.

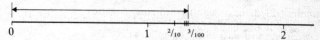

The length above is found by taking 1 unit, 2 tenths and then 3 hundredths. This is written as the **decimal number** 1·23. There are two digits after the **decimal point** (·) so that the number is said to have 2 **decimal places**.

Usually a length cannot be measured exactly, perhaps because the divisions would become so fine as to be impractical. The answer is given to a certain number of decimal places. For example, if only tenths are used to measure the length below

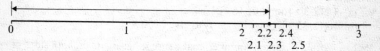

since the length is closer to 2·3 than to 2·2, it is counted as 2·3 to 1 decimal place. If in fact we can go to a further decimal place we would find the answer 2·27.

This shows the **rounding up** that often happens when the number of decimal places is to be reduced.

When the first digit to be ignored is 5 or more, the preceding digit is increased by 1.

Example   Write 122·3712
   (a) to 1 decimal place
   (b) to 2 decimal places

Answer
   (a) cut off the digits after the first decimal place

$$122·3|712$$

   since 7 is larger than 5 (in symbols 7 > 5) the 3 must be rounded up to give 122·4

   (b) cut off the digits after the second decimal place

$$122·37|12$$

   since 1 is less than 5 (in symbols 1 < 5) the 7 is not rounded up, the answer is 122·37

The accuracy of a number can also be specified as the number of **significant figures**, that is the number of digits starting from the first non-zero digit on the *left*.

Examples   21·32 has 4 significant figures (sig. fig.)
0·0012 has 2 sig. fig.
10 013·57 has 7 sig. fig.

When the number of sig. figs. is reduced, the same rounding up rule as for decimal places applies.

Examples   Express 1 012·35
   (a) to 5 sig. fig.
   (b) to 2 sig. fig.

Answer
   (a) 1 012·3|5 round up to 1 012·4
   (b) 10|12·35, fill out with zeros to give 1 000

When writing a decimal number, make sure it has digits on *both* sides of the decimal point, so write 21·0 and not 21·, 0·2 and not ·2.

From the definition of a decimal number it follows that it is a fraction, or rational number.

$$1·2 = 1 + \frac{2}{10} = \frac{12}{10}$$

In general, the number of zeros in the denominator is the same as the number of decimal places. For example $3·156 = \frac{3156}{1000}$ and $0·02 = \frac{2}{100}$.

It is also possible to write some fractions in decimal form

$$\frac{1}{2} = 0·5, \quad \frac{1}{4} = 0·25, \quad \frac{3}{4} = 0·75, \quad \frac{1}{5} = 0·2, \quad \ldots$$

(found by long division).

Other fractions, however, are not so simple. To find the decimal for $\frac{1}{3}$ by long division produces 0·3333 ... where the 3s never stop. This is an example of an **infinite**, and in this case a **recurring**, decimal. It can be written as $0·\dot{3}$ where the dot above the 3 means that it is to be repeated indefinitely. (In a recurring decimal, a sequence of digits is repeated indefinitely.)

It is only possible to express $\frac{1}{3}$ as a decimal to a certain number of decimal places, for example to 3 decimal places it is 0·333. The number of decimal places to be used for calculations will usually be specified in a question. Make sure that you use this accuracy.

Decimal Arithmetic

To add or subtract two decimals, make sure that the decimal points are aligned, and then continue as for whole numbers.

Examples

$$
\begin{array}{r} 1\cdot23 \\ +0\cdot6 \\ \hline 1\cdot83 \end{array}
\qquad
\begin{array}{r} 3\cdot71 \\ -2\cdot02 \\ \hline 1\cdot69 \end{array}
$$

To multiply decimal numbers, first multiply ignoring the points. The number of decimal places for the product is the *sum* of the numbers of decimal places of each part.

Example $1\cdot23 \times 0\cdot6$

First multiply 123×6 to give 738. $1\cdot23$ has 2 decimal places, $0\cdot6$ has 1, so the product has $1 + 2 = 3$ decimal places.

Answer The answer is $0\cdot738$ (notice that 0 is put in front).

To divide you can either
   (a) convert into fractions and use the rules for dividing fractions,
or
   (b) use long division, keeping careful track of the position of the decimal points,
or
   (c) use a calculator, tables or slide rule.

In most cases where a difficult division is required, you will be allowed (and advised) to use a calculating aid as in (c).

When a decimal number is multiplied by a power of 10, the point moves to the right as many times as given by the power

$$1\cdot23 \times 100 = 123\cdot0 \qquad 100 = 10^2, \text{ the point moves 2 places}$$

If the number is divided by a power of 10, the point moves to the left

$$1\cdot23 \div 100 = 0\cdot0123 \qquad \text{filling in with zeros to make up the places}$$

This is often useful in simplifying calculations.

Square Roots and More Powers

The statement

$$4 \text{ is the square of } 2 \quad (2^2 = 4)$$

can be rewritten as

$$2 \text{ is the \textbf{square root} of } 4 \quad (2 = \sqrt{4})$$

The square root of the quantity a, written as $\sqrt{a}$, is the number which when squared gives the answer a.

Examples

a	1	4	9	16	25	36	100	10 000
$\sqrt{a}$	1	2	3	4	5	6	10	100

Notice that when the square root of a power of 10 is taken, the number of zeros is halved. Of course this can only be done when the power is even.

Also, since for example $(-3)^2 = (-3)(-3) = +9$, -3 is another square root of 9 (using the sign rules given on pages 22–3).

In general, any positive number has two square roots. The $\sqrt{}$ symbol is usually taken to mean the **positive root**, so that 9 has the square roots $\sqrt{9}$ and $-\sqrt{9}$, that is 3 and -3.

The square root of a product can be found as the product of the separate roots $\sqrt{ab} = \sqrt{a} \times \sqrt{b}$.

Example
$$
\begin{aligned}
\sqrt{16} &= \sqrt{4 \times 4} \\
&= \sqrt{4} \times \sqrt{4} \\
&= 2 \times 2 \\
&= 4
\end{aligned}
$$

To find the square root of a fraction, take the root of the numerator and denominator separately

$$\sqrt{\frac{9}{25}} = \frac{\sqrt{9}}{\sqrt{25}} = \frac{3}{5}$$

To find the square root of a decimal number, write it as a fraction whose denominator is an even power of 10

$$\sqrt{1 \cdot 44} = \sqrt{\frac{144}{100}} = \frac{\sqrt{144}}{\sqrt{100}} = \frac{12}{10} = 1 \cdot 2$$

$$\sqrt{0 \cdot 0081} = \frac{\sqrt{81}}{\sqrt{10\,000}} = \frac{9}{100} = 0 \cdot 09$$

These calculations used the fact that 4, 9, 16, 25, 81 and 144 are perfect squares.

Tables and calculators must be used to find difficult square roots (see pages 381–5).

Cube roots: Since $2^3 = 2 \times 2 \times 2 = 8$, we say that 2 is the **cube root** of 8 and write $2 = \sqrt[3]{8}$. Similarly $\sqrt[3]{27} = 3$, $\sqrt[3]{1\,000} = 10$ and so on.

Summary $\qquad \sqrt{ab} = \sqrt{a}\sqrt{b}, \quad \sqrt{\frac{a}{b}} = \frac{\sqrt{a}}{\sqrt{b}}$

However $\sqrt{a+b}$ is *not* $\sqrt{a} + \sqrt{b}$. (Use a calculator to show that $\sqrt{10}$ is not equal to $\sqrt{5} + \sqrt{5}$.)

Table of squares and cubes

a	0	1	2	3	4	5	6	7	8	9	10
a^2	0	1	4	9	16	25	36	49	64	81	100
a^3	0	1	8	27	64	125	216	343	512	729	1 000

Rules for powers (indices)

Consider the multiplication

$$10^4 \times 10^3 = 10\,000 \times 1\,000$$
$$= 10\,000\,000$$
$$= 10^7$$

The separate powers have been added together, $4 + 3 = 7$.

In general, for any number a, and powers m and n,

$$a^m \times a^n = a^{m+n}$$

also

$$a^m \div a^n = a^{m-n}$$

and

$$(a^m)^n = a^{mn}$$

Examples

(a) $2^3 \times 2^5 = 2^8$ as $(2 \times 2 \times 2) \times (2 \times 2 \times 2 \times 2 \times 2)$
$= 2 \times 2 \times 2 \times 2 \times 2 \times 2 \times 2 \times 2$

(b) $3^7 \div 3^2 = 3^5$

(c) $(2^2)^3 = 2^6$

Now $2^2 \div 2^3 = 2^{2-3} = 2^{-1}$, a negative power! This means that

$$2^{-1} = \frac{2^2}{2^3} = \frac{1}{2}$$ dividing by the factors of 2

In general

$$a^{-1} = \frac{1}{a}$$

the **reciprocal** of a.

For other powers

$$a^{-2} = \frac{1}{a^2}, \quad a^{-3} = \frac{1}{a^3}, \quad \ldots$$

where a can be any non-zero number.

Square roots can also be expressed as powers

$$\sqrt{a} = a^{1/2}$$

from the index rules

$$(a^{1/2})^2 = a^{1/2 \times 2} = a^1 = a$$

(since $a^1 = a$).

Similarly $\sqrt[3]{a} = a^{1/3}$.

Also, $a^0 = 1$, no matter what the value of a. For example, for $a = 2$

$$2^1 \times 2^0 = 2^{1+0}$$ using the index rules

so $2^1 \times 2^0 = 2^1$

dividing by 2^1 (that is 2)

$$2^0 = 1$$

Standard Index Form (also known as Standard Form)

Power notation can be used for handling very large and very small numbers. For example, if the number 2 135 000 000 000 appears several times in a calculation it would be very easy to make a mistake by miscounting the zeros. This number can be written as $2 \cdot 135 \times 10^{12}$, remembering that each power of 10 shifts the decimal point one place to the right.

A number of the form $a \times 10^n$, where a is between 1 and 10 and n is a positive or negative whole number, is said to be in **standard index form**. When the power is positive the number is greater than or equal to 1 (written as $\geqslant 1$). If the power is negative the number is between 0 and 1.

To multiply or divide two numbers in standard form, deal with the number parts, any sign and the powers of 10 separately.

Examples

(i) $(3 \times 10^4) \times (4 \times 10^8) = (3 \times 4) \times (10^4 \times 10^8)$

$$= 12 \times 10^{12} \qquad \text{using the index rules}$$

(ii) $\dfrac{(1 \cdot 2 \times 10^3) \times (3 \cdot 5 \times 10^2)}{(1 \cdot 4 \times 10^4)} = \dfrac{(1 \cdot 2 \times 3 \cdot 5) \times (10^3 \times 10^2)}{1 \cdot 4 \times 10^4}$

$$= \frac{4 \cdot 2 \times 10^5}{1 \cdot 4 \times 10^4}$$

$$= \frac{4 \cdot 2}{1 \cdot 4} \times \frac{10^5}{10^4}$$

$$= 3 \times 10^{5-4}$$

$$= 3 \times 10^1 \qquad \text{in standard index form}$$

$$= 30 \qquad \text{in ordinary form}$$

When two numbers in standard form are to be added or subtracted, you should convert into ordinary form first. You must *not* simply add the numbers and powers separately!

Examples

(i) $1 \cdot 2 \times 10^3 + 3 \cdot 4 \times 10^5 = 1\,200 + 340\,000$

$$= 341\,200$$

$$= 3 \cdot 412 \times 10^5$$

But (ii) $5 \cdot 6 \times 10^3 - 2 \cdot 3 \times 10^3 = (5 \cdot 6 - 2 \cdot 3) \times 10^3$ because the powers
$$= 3 \cdot 3 \times 10^3$$ of 10 are the same

Estimation

When only a rough answer to a calculation is required (for example to 1
sig. fig.), all of the numbers in the calculation can be rounded up or down
to make this easier.

Example   Estimate to 1 sig. fig.

$$\frac{38\,300}{426 \times 1\,890}$$

Answer   Work out

$$\frac{38\,000}{400 \times 1\,900} = \frac{38}{40 \times 19} \qquad \text{dividing top and}$$
$$\text{bottom by } 1\,000$$

$$= \frac{2}{40} \qquad \text{dividing by 19}$$

$$= \frac{1}{20}$$

$$= 0 \cdot 05$$

When performing any calculation, it is a good habit to make a rough
estimate of the answer as a check for errors.

Examples
1.   Evaluate $1 \cdot 23 \times 3 \cdot 1$

Answer   123   2 decimal places
                          $\times\ \ 31$ + 1 decimal place

                             123
                             369
                           $3\,\overline{813}$ 3 decimal places

The answer is $3 \cdot 813$. (Estimate $1 \times 3 = 3$ as a check.)

2. 4 bags of sugar are weighed and the masses are recorded in kilograms to 4 sig. fig. The masses are

$$1 \cdot 987, \quad 1 \cdot 995, \quad 2 \cdot 010, \quad 2 \cdot 012$$

(a) What is the lowest possible value of the mass of the lightest bag?
(b) What is the highest possible weight of the heaviest bag?

Answer

(a) The masses are correct to 4 sig. fig. The lightest recorded mass is $1 \cdot 987$ kg.   Masses from $1 \cdot 9865$ to $1 \cdot 9875$ kg are measured as $1 \cdot 987$ kg (to 4 sig. fig.)

The smallest possible value is $1 \cdot 9865$ kg.

(b) The highest measured mass is $2 \cdot 012$ kg. The largest value it could have is $2 \cdot 012\,5$.

3. Given that $135 \cdot 12 \times 2931 = 396\,036 \cdot 72$, evaluate

(a) $134 \cdot 12 \times 2931$,   (b) $235 \cdot 12 \times 2931$,   (c) $13\,512 \times 293 \cdot 1$

without direct multiplication.

Answer

(a) $134 \cdot 12 \times 2931$

$$= (135 \cdot 12 - 1) \times 2931$$
$$= 135 \cdot 12 \times 2931 - 2931$$
$$= 396\,036 \cdot 72 - 2931$$
$$= 393\,105 \cdot 72$$

see page 40

$$\begin{array}{r} 396\,036 \cdot 72 \\ - \quad 2\,931 \cdot 00 \\ \hline 393\,105 \cdot 72 \end{array}$$

(b) $235 \cdot 12 \times 2931$

$$= (100 + 135 \cdot 12) \times 2931$$
$$= (100 \times 2931) + (135 \cdot 12 \times 2931)$$
$$= 293\,100 + 396\,036 \cdot 72$$
$$= 689\,136 \cdot 72$$

$$\begin{array}{r} 396\,036 \cdot 72 \\ + \quad 293\,100 \cdot 00 \\ \hline 689\,136 \cdot 72 \end{array}$$

(c) $13\,512 \times 293 \cdot 1$

Multiplication is commutative
$100 \div 10 = 10$

$$= 135 \cdot 12 \times 100 \times 2931 \div 10$$
$$= 135 \cdot 12 \times 2931 \times 10$$
$$= 396\,036 \cdot 72 \times 10$$
$$= 3\,960\,367 \cdot 2$$

This example used the result

$$(135 \cdot 12 - 1) \times 2931 = 135 \cdot 12 \times 2931 - 1 \times 2931$$

In general $(a + b) \times c = a \times c + b \times c$

for any numbers a, b and c. This result is called the **distributive law** (see also page 63).

4. $\sqrt{3 \cdot 7} = 1 \cdot 9235$ to 5 sig. fig. Calculate

(a) $\sqrt{0 \cdot 037}$ (b) $\sqrt{370}$ to 5 sig. fig.

Answer

(a) $\sqrt{0 \cdot 037} = \sqrt{\dfrac{3 \cdot 7}{100}}$

$\qquad = \dfrac{\sqrt{3 \cdot 7}}{\sqrt{100}} = \dfrac{\sqrt{3 \cdot 7}}{10} = \dfrac{1 \cdot 9235}{10}$

$\qquad = 0 \cdot 19235$

(b) $\sqrt{370} = \sqrt{3 \cdot 7 \times 100}$

$\qquad = \sqrt{3 \cdot 7} \times \sqrt{100}$

$\qquad = 1 \cdot 9235 \times 10$

$\qquad = 19 \cdot 235$

5. $\frac{1}{9}$ expressed as a decimal to 3 decimal places is

(a) $0 \cdot 111$ (b) $0 \cdot 110$ (c) $0 \cdot 101$ (d) $0 \cdot 100$

Answer   By long division

```
           0·1111
      9 )1·000000
         9↓|||
         ─────
          10
           9↓||
         ─────
           10
            9↓|
         ─────
           10
            9↓
         ─────
           10
            9↓
         ─────
           10
```

The answer is 0·111 to 3 decimal places, i.e. answer (a) (¹⁄₉ is the recurring decimal 0·1̇)

6. Simplify

(a) $\dfrac{16^{\frac{1}{2}} \times 2^{-1}}{9^{\frac{1}{2}}}$ (b) $8^{\frac{1}{3}} \times 3^0 \div 16^{\frac{1}{4}}$

Answer

(a)
$$16^{\frac{1}{2}} = \sqrt{16} = 4 \qquad \text{(page 36)}$$
$$2^{-1} = \frac{1}{2} = 0\cdot5$$
$$9^{\frac{1}{2}} = \sqrt{9} = 3$$

giving
$$\frac{4 \times 0\cdot5}{3} = \frac{2}{3}$$

(b)
$$8^{\frac{1}{3}} = \sqrt[3]{8} = 2 \text{ since } 2^3 = 8$$
$$3^0 = 1 \qquad \text{(page 36)}$$

and
$$16^{\frac{1}{4}} = \sqrt[4]{16} = 2 \text{ since } 2^4 = 16$$

giving
$$2 \times 1 \div 2 = 1$$

Examination questions

1. *Calculate the exact value of 2·7 × 3·7* [SMP]

2. *The masses of a set of objects (recorded in kilograms rounded to 4 significant figures) are*

1·532,   1·562,   1·562,   1·576,   1·592,   1·593,   1·596

(i) *State the lowest possible value of the smallest mass measured.*
(ii) *Find the largest possible difference between the least and greatest masses measured.* [SMP]

3. *Write down 0·080 6   (a) correct to 2 decimal places   (b) correct to 2 significant figures.* [AEB]

4. *You may assume that 124·6 × 1 357 = 169 082·2 without checking.*
(i) *Using the above result, evaluate 123·6 × 1 357 by a subtraction method only.*
(ii) *By a method similar to that used in (i), calculate 224·6 × 1 357. (No credit will be given for direct multiplication.)*

(iii) Write down the value of $169\,082 \cdot 2 \div 1\,246$. [SMP]

5. *Estimate, correct to 1 sig. fig., the value of*

$$\frac{(1 \cdot 98)^2 \times 4\,973}{102 \cdot 6}$$ [AEB]

6. *The mass of an electron in grams is*

$$0 \cdot 000\,000\,000\,000\,000\,000\,000\,000\,000\,91$$

Express this number in standard index form. [SMP]

7. $\sqrt{5 \cdot 4} = 2 \cdot 323\,8$ *correct to 5 sig. fig.*
Evaluate to the same degree of accuracy $\sqrt{0 \cdot 054}$. [SMP]

8. *Calculate (a)* $27^{1/3}$ *(b)* 4^{-2} *(c)* $3^{1/2} \times 3^{1/2}$. [AEB]

9. *The square root of $17\,956$ is $1\,a\,4$ (where a represents the tens digit).*
State the value of a. [SMP]

10. $\dfrac{2}{0 \cdot 004}$ *in standard form is*

A 8×10^{-3} *B* 5×10^{-2} *C* 2×10^2 *D* 5×10^2 *E* 8×10^4 [LON]

11. *z is the recurring decimal $0 \cdot 131\,313 \ldots$*
(i) Write down the numerical value of $100z - z$.
(ii) Express z as a fraction. [SMP]

Answers

1. $9 \cdot 99$
2. (i) $1 \cdot 531\,5$ (ii) $0 \cdot 065$
3. (a) $0 \cdot 08$ (b) $0 \cdot 081$
4. (i) $167\,725 \cdot 2$ (ii) $304\,782 \cdot 2$ (iii) $135 \cdot 7$
5. 200
6. $9 \cdot 1 \times 10^{-28}$
7. $0 \cdot 232\,38$
8. (a) 3 (b) $0 \cdot 062\,5$ or $1/16$ (c) 3
9. 3
10. D
11. (i) $13 \cdot 0$ (ii) $13/99$

Section 2: Percentage and Ratio

Percentages

Percentages are fractions with denominators of 100. The symbol % is used in place of the denominator

so

$$10\% = \frac{10}{100} = 0 \cdot 1 \qquad 12\% = \frac{12}{100} = 0 \cdot 12$$

$$50\% = \frac{50}{100} = 0 \cdot 5$$

To express a fraction as a percentage, multiply by 100%

$$\tfrac{2}{3} = \tfrac{2}{3} \times 100\% = \frac{200}{3}\% = 66 \cdot 7\%$$

Fraction	Decimal	%
$\frac{1}{2}$	$0 \cdot 5$	50
$\frac{1}{4}$	$0 \cdot 25$	25
$\frac{3}{4}$	$0 \cdot 75$	75
$\frac{1}{8}$	$0 \cdot 125$	12·5
$\frac{1}{10}$	$0 \cdot 1$	10
$\frac{1}{5}$	$0 \cdot 2$	20
$\frac{1}{3}$	$0 \cdot 333$	$33\frac{1}{3}$

To find a certain percentage of a given quantity, multiply by the corresponding fraction

$$12\% \text{ of } 120 = \frac{12}{100} \times 120 = 0 \cdot 12 \times 120 = 14 \cdot 4$$

Problems involving percentages may use the following

$$\text{percentage changes} = \frac{\text{actual change}}{\text{initial value}} \times 100\%$$

A special case is profit on a sale. Profit = sales − costs

$$\text{percentage profit} = \frac{\text{profit}}{\text{cost}} \times 100\%$$

If the profit is negative, it is a loss

$$\text{percentage loss} = \frac{\text{loss}}{\text{cost}} \times 100\%$$

Some problems concern rates of interest on money invested or borrowed.

$$\text{Interest paid} = \text{investment} \times \text{interest rate}$$

for each period over which interest is calculated. The interest rate is expressed as a percentage.

Simple interest is only paid on the original investment, while **compound interest** is added on to the investment and itself earns extra interest. See also page 136.

Local government rates are given as pence in the pound, but are equivalent to a percentage. The revenue from rates is calculated as

$$\text{rate} \times \text{rateable value}$$

When an error in measurement is involved

absolute error = difference between actual value and measured value

$$\text{percent error} = \frac{\text{absolute error}}{\text{actual value}} \times 100\%$$

Examples

1. Find 15% of 150.

Answer

$$\frac{15}{100} \times 150 = \frac{15 \times 150}{100}$$

$$= \frac{2\,250}{100}$$

$$= 22 \cdot 50$$

2. The price of a certain commodity falls from £2 to £1·60. Express this fall as a percentage of the original price.

Answer   Fall = £2 − 1·60 = £0·40

$$\% \text{ Fall} = \frac{0 \cdot 40}{2 \cdot 00} \times 100\%$$

$$= \frac{40}{2}\% = 20\%$$

3. 60% of a certain number is 150. Find this number.

Answer   60% of the number is 150

so
$$1\% \text{ is } \frac{1}{60} \times 150$$

$$100\% \text{ is } \frac{1}{60} \times 150 \times 100$$

The full amount is
$$\frac{150 \times 100}{60} = 250$$

4. V.A.T. in the kingdom of Percentia is calculated at 5% on the first £200 of the price of an item and 10% for the remainder of the price.
   (a) Calculate the V.A.T. on goods costing (i) £150 (ii) £250.
   (b) If the V.A.T. paid on an item is £25, calculate its price including the V.A.T.

Answer
   (a) (i) £150 is under £200
            V.A.T. of 5%

$$5\% \text{ of } £150 = £\frac{5}{100} \times 150$$

$$= £\frac{750}{100}$$

$$= £7.50$$

   (ii) £250 = £200 + £50

$$\text{V.A.T. of 5\% on £200} = £\frac{5}{100} \times 200 = £10$$

$$\text{V.A.T. of 10\% on £50} = £\frac{10}{100} \times 50 = £5$$

Total V.A.T. = £15

   (b) V.A.T. = £25 = £15 + £10
        £10 is the V.A.T. on the first £200 of the price
        £15 is the V.A.T. at 10% on the remainder

$$£15 = 10\%$$

$$£\frac{15}{10} = 1\%$$

$$£\frac{15 \times 100}{10} = 100\%$$

The remainder is £150
The total before V.A.T. is added is £200 + £150 = £350
V.A.T. = £25
Total including V.A.T. = £375

5. (i) In 1983, a certain bicycle model cost £180. The price increased by 15% in 1984. Find the increase in £.

(ii) A second model falls in price by 10% to £270. Calculate the price in 1983.

Answer   (i) Old price = £180

$$\text{Increase} = 15\% \text{ of } £180 = £\frac{15}{100} \times 180$$

$$= £27$$

$$\text{New price} = £180 + £27$$

$$= £207$$

(ii) New price = £270

Decrease = 10%, leaving 90% of the original price.

$\therefore$ £270 = 90% of 1983 price

$$£\frac{270}{90} = 1\%$$

so 100% of 1983 price is $£\dfrac{270 \times 100}{90}$

$$= £300$$

Note: This question can be answered another way.
An increase of 15% results in a new total 115% of the old.

Since $115\% = \dfrac{115}{100} = 1.15$, the new total is found by multiplying the old total by 1.15.

$$1.15 \times 180 = 207$$

Conversely, for part (ii) 270 is 90% of 1983 price

So $\qquad 270 = 0.9 \times 1983$ price

So the 1983 price is $270 \div 0.9 = 270 \div \dfrac{9}{10}$

$$= \frac{270 \times 10}{9}$$

$$= £300$$

6. £1 000 is invested at an interest rate of 10% per annum. Calculate the interest earned in 5 years at simple interest.

Answer

$$\text{Yearly interest} = 10\% \text{ of } £1\,000$$
$$= £0.1 \times 1\,000$$
$$= £100$$
$$\text{Interest for 5 years} = 5 \times £100$$
$$= £500$$

Examination questions

1. *In 1979, a man's annual salary was £6 400. He was allowed £1 800 of this tax free, and then paid 25% tax on the next £1 000 and 33% tax on the remainder. Calculate his monthly salary after payment of tax.* [LON]

2. *A shopkeeper sells an article for £64·50, thus making a profit of 7·5% on the cost price. Calculate the profit made.* [CAM]

3. *(a) A man spends 30 per cent of his weekly income on mortgage repayments. If his mortgage repayments are £42 per week, calculate his weekly income.*

(b) When his daughter goes to a football match she spends half of her weekly pocket money on admission, a tenth of her pocket money on a programme and is then left with £1·20. Calculate her weekly pocket money.

[AEB]

4. *After modification a car will do 25% more miles to the gallon. Calculate the resulting percentage saving in fuel for a given journey.* [SMP]

Answers
1. £413·50
2. £4·50
3. (a) £140   (b) £3·00
4. 20%

Ratios

A quantity is divided in a given ratio by dividing it into fractions. For example, if 200 is to be divided in the ratio 2 : 3 then it is split into two fractions using the following method.

  (i) Add the numbers of the ratio $2+3 = 5$
 (ii) Divide the total by this number $200 \div 5 = 40$
(iii) Multiply each of the ratio numbers by this amount

$$40 \times 2 = 80, \quad 40 \times 3 = 120$$

The two parts are 80 and 120 (notice that they add up to 200).
This method is illustrated in the diagram

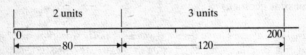

200 is to be made up of 5 units (2 on the left of the cut, 3 on the right) so each unit is 40. The same method works when the total is divided into more than 2 parts.

Example   Divide 1 600 in the ratios 2 : 3 : 5

Answer $2+3+5 = 10$
$$1\,600 \div 10 = 160$$
$$2 \times 160 = 320 \quad 3 \times 160 = 480 \quad 5 \times 160 = 800$$

giving the required parts.
Check: $320 + 480 + 800 = 1\,600$

Example   Every month I pay electricity, gas and rent bills. These bills for September were in the ratios 5 : 4 : 20.

  (a) If the bills totalled £290, calculate the amount paid for electricity.

(b) In October, the electricity bill increased by 10%, the rent increased by 5% and the gas bill fell 1%. Calculate the total I paid out in October.

(c) Express the increase from September to October for the total bill as a percentage of the September costs (to 1 decimal place accuracy).

Answer

(a) Divide £290 in ratios 5 : 4 : 20 $5 + 4 + 20 = 29$

$$\frac{290}{29} = 10, \quad 10 \times 5 = 50$$

The electricity bill was £50

(b) Gas bill was $10 \times 4 = £40$
Rent bill was $10 \times 20 = £200$
Increase in electricity = 10% of £50 = £5
Increase in rent = 5% of £200 = £10
Decrease in gas bill = 1% of 40 = £0·40
Total increase = £5 + 10 − 0·40 = £14·60
Total October bill = £290 + 14·60 = £304·60

(c) Increase = £14·60   % change

$$\% \text{ increase} = \frac{14 \cdot 60}{290} \times 100\% \qquad = \frac{\text{change}}{\text{initial value}} \times 100\%$$

$$= \frac{1\,460}{290}\%$$

$$= 5 \cdot 03\% \qquad \text{calculator or tables}$$

The % increase is 5·0% (to 1 decimal place).

Ratios share a property of fractions: the numbers of a ratio can be multiplied or divided by the same quantity.

$$1 : 2 : 5, \quad 2 : 4 : 10, \quad 6 : 12 : 30, \quad \tfrac{1}{4} : \tfrac{1}{2} : \tfrac{5}{4}$$

are all equivalent ratios.

Examination questions

1. *£1 800 is divided into three amounts in the ratios 4 : 5 : 6. The largest amount is*

A £360   B £480   C £600   D £720   E £900   [LON]

2. *A bottle contains red and blue sweets in the ratio 3 : 2. If there are 38 blue sweets, calculate the total number of sweets in the bottle.*

3. *Given that $x : y = 2 : 3$ and $y : z = 9 : 11$ find $x : z$*   [SMP]

4. *At the beginning of 1979 the cost of manufacture of a car was £4 000 and the manufacturer sold the car at a profit of 15% on his cost price.*

(a) Find the selling price.

The cost of manufacturing the car was made up of wages, raw materials, electricity and factory maintenance in the ratios 15 : 6 : 3 : 1. During 1979 wages rose by 20%, the cost of raw materials by 12½%, of electricity by 25% and of factory maintenance by 50%.

(b) Express the increase in the total cost of manufacturing during the year 1979 as a percentage of the total cost at the beginning of that year.

After the rise in costs, the manufacturer decided to sell the car at a profit of only 12% of the cost price.

(c) Find the new selling price.

(d) Calculate the increase in the selling price of the car and express this increase as a percentage, to one decimal place, of the original selling price.   [LON]

Answers

   1. D

   2. 95

   3. 6 : 11

   4. (a) £4 600   (b) 20%   (c) £5 376   (d) 16·9%

Section 3: Number Bases and Sets

Number Bases

We use a number system which depends on the **place value** of digits. For example, the number 123 means

one hundred, two tens and three units

The right-hand digit counts the units, the next digit counts the tens and the third counts the hundreds

$$123 = 1 \times 100 + 2 \times 10 + 3 \times 1$$
$$= 1 \times 10^2 + 2 \times 10^1 + 3 \times 1$$

Because the numbers are expressed in terms of powers of ten, we say that they are **base 10** numbers (or denary).

We could use other number bases. In fact base 2 (binary) and base 16 (hexadecimal) numbers are widely used by electronic computers. Another example is the measurement of time in hours, minutes and seconds, which is a base 60 system.

Examples 213_8 is in base 8 (the base is given by the subscript). It can be expressed in base 10 as

$$2 \times 8^2 + 1 \times 8^1 + 3 \times 1 = 2 \times 64 + 1 \times 8 + 3 \times 1$$
$$= 128 + 8 + 3$$
$$= 139 \text{ in base 10}$$

The number 8 is written as 10_8 in base 8.

Similarly $100_8 = 64$, $1\,000_8 = 512$, $10_3 = 3$, $100_2 = 4$ in base 10.

The ten digits 0, 1, 2, 3, 4, 5, 6, 7, 8, 9 are used in base 10 numbers. Base 8 numbers only use the digits 0, 1, 2, 3, 4, 5, 6, 7 and base 2 numbers can only use the two digits 0 and 1.

The equivalents of decimal points occur in other bases.

Examples

1. 'Bicimal numbers'

$$111 \cdot 101_2 = 1 \times 2^2 + 1 \times 2 + 1 \times 1 + 1 \times \frac{1}{2} + 0 \times \frac{1}{2}^2 + 1 \times \frac{1}{2}^3$$

$$= 4 + 2 + 1 + 0 \cdot 5 + 0 \cdot 125$$

$$= 7 \cdot 625 \text{ in base } 10$$

2. $0 \cdot 53_6 = 5 \times 6^{-1} + 3 \times 6^{-2}$ in base 10

$$= \frac{5}{6} + \frac{3}{36} \qquad \text{since } 6^{-1} = \frac{1}{6}, \quad 6^{-2} = \frac{1}{6^2} = \frac{1}{36}$$

$$= \frac{30}{36} + \frac{3}{36} \qquad \text{multiply by 6 in first fraction}$$

$$= \frac{33}{36}$$

$$= \frac{11}{12} \text{ in base } 10$$

This can be written as the decimal $0 \cdot 917$ (to 3 d.p.) ($^{11}/_{12}$ cannot be expressed exactly as a decimal).

Base 10 numbers can be converted to other bases by repeated division by the base number.

Example   Convert the base 10 number 254 into base 3

$$
\begin{array}{r}
3 \overline{)254} \\
3 \overline{)84} \quad \text{remainder 2} \\
3 \overline{)28} \quad \text{remainder 0} \\
3 \overline{)9} \quad \text{remainder 1} \\
3 \overline{)3} \quad \text{remainder 0} \\
3 \overline{)1} \quad \text{remainder 0} \\
\overline{0} \quad \text{remainder 1}
\end{array}
$$

The remainders are then read *upwards*

$$254_{10} = 100\,102_3$$

Arithmetic can be done in any base.

Examples

1.
$$\begin{array}{r} 101_2 \\ + \quad 11_2 \\ \hline 1\,000_2 \end{array}$$
carry 1 whenever the total is 2

2.
$$\begin{array}{r} 120_3 \\ - \quad 21_3 \\ \hline 22_3 \end{array}$$
'borrowing' 3s (as $10_3 = 3_{10}$)

3.
$$\begin{array}{r} 111_2 \\ \times 110_2 \\ \hline 000 \\ 1\,110 \\ 11\,100 \\ \hline 101\,010_2 \end{array}$$

Conversion between bases which are powers of 2

Example   Convert the binary number $101\,110_2$ into base 4.
$4 = 2^2$, group the digits into *pairs* starting from the right

$$10 \quad 11 \quad 10$$

then convert each two digit pair into base 10

$$232_4 \text{ is the required base 4 number}$$

To convert a binary number into base 8, since $8 = 2^3$, take groups of *three* digits, again counting from the right.

Example   Convert $1\,011\,110_2$ to base 8.

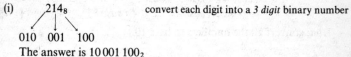

001	011	110	group into sets of 3, filling with zeros on the left if necessary
1	3	6	convert groups

The answer is 136_8.

To change back into binary, each digit is converted to a binary number.

Examples

(i) 214_8 convert each digit into a *3 digit* binary number
        010 001 100
The answer is $10\,001\,100_2$

(ii) 1321_4 convert each digit into a *2 digit* binary number
        01 11 10 01
The answer is $1\,111\,001_2$

When converting between other bases, it is often easiest to convert into base 10 first.

Example   Change 212_3 into a base 5 number.
First convert 212_3 into base 10

$$212_3 = 2 \times 3^2 + 1 \times 3^1 + 2 \times 1$$
$$= 2 \times 9 + 1 \times 3 + 2 \times 1$$
$$= 18 + 3 + 2$$
$$= 23$$

Now convert 23_{10} into base 5 by division

$$5\underline{)23}$$
$$4 \quad \text{remainder } 3$$
$$23_{10} = 43_5$$

Examination questions

1. $N = 10 \cdot 11$ is written in base 2.
   (i) Write, in base 2, the number which is twice as big as N.
   (ii) Calculate, in base 2, one and a quarter times N.   [SMP]

2. $23\Delta_8$ is divisible by eight. State the missing digit denoted by Δ.   [SMP]

3. Express $101\,010_2$ in base 8.   [SMP]

4. If $333_n + 444_n = 1221_n$, then the number base n is
   A 5   B 6   C 8   D 9   E 11   [LON]

5. Which is the smallest of the following numbers?
   A 0·2 (base 4)   B 0·22 (base 5)   C 0·3 (base 6)
   D 0·33 (base 7)   E 0·4 (base 8)   [LON]

   (*Hint*: convert all the numbers to base 10.)

6. Calculate, leaving your answer in base 6.
   (a) $534_6 + 54_6$ (b) $25_6 \times 21_6$ [AEB]

7. Which of the following numbers are multiples of 12_3?
   (i) 101_3 (ii) $1\,111_3$
   A (i) only   B (ii) only   C both (i) and (ii)   D neither (i) nor (ii)
   [AEB]

8. *Express as a binary number*

$$(i) \ 46_{10} \quad (ii) \ 46_8$$

[CAM]

Answers

1. (i) 101·1   (ii) 11·0111
2. 0
3. 52_8
4. B
5. B
6. (a) $1\,032_6$ (b) $1\,005_6$
7. C
8. (i) $101\,110_2$ (ii) $100\,110_2$

Modulo Arithmetic

Earlier, we saw that numbers were represented on a number line. They could also be pictured on a series of dials, as for example on a type of electricity meter.

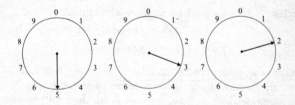

The number 532 is shown here.

This representation could also be used for numbers in different bases.

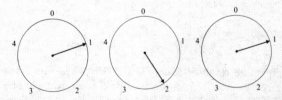

which shows the number 121_5.

Suppose that only the units dial is visible. Then many different numbers would show the same reading. For example, on the base 10 dials, 2, 12, 22, 222 would show as the single digit 2.

We write this as **12 ≡ 2 (modulo 10)**, 12 is **congruent** or **equivalent** to 2 (modulo 10). A number is equivalent to the *remainder* when it is divided by the *base*.

Examples $6 \equiv 1$ (modulo 5) $6 \div 5 = 1$ remainder 1

$34 \equiv 6$ (modulo 7) $34 \div 7 = 4$ remainder 6

Negative numbers correspond to going round the dial backwards.

This shows $-1 \equiv 5$ (modulo 6). Addition, subtraction and multiplication can be used modulo any natural number.

Examples $1+2+3+4 = 10 \equiv 0$ (modulo 5)

$2-7 = -5 \equiv 7$ (modulo 12)

$3 \times 4 = 12 \equiv 5$ (modulo 7)

Now take as an example addition modulo 5 on the set $\{0, 1, 2, 3, 4\}$ (since we are only concerned with the remainders after division by 5, these are all the digits needed). Form a table showing the result of adding any two numbers

+	0	1	2	3	4
0	0	1	2	3	4
1	1	2	3	4	0
2	2	3	4	0	1
3	3	4	0	1	2
4	4	0	1	2	3

For example, the result of adding 2 and 3 is where the 2 row and 3 column meet: $2+3 = 0$. Addition modulo 5 is an example of a binary operation on the set $\{0, 1, 2, 3, 4\}$ (see page 17).

Operations and Operation Tables

A binary operation on a set A is a rule for combining two elements of A. If the result is also in A then A is closed under the operation.

The operation is often denoted by a symbol such as *, $a * b$ is the result of combining a and b. If A is closed, then $a * b \in A$ for all $a, b \in A$.

Example Let $A = \{0, 1, 2, 3, 4\}$ with operation * which is addition modulo 5. A is closed under *.

Also
$$2 * 3 \equiv 2 + 3 \,(\text{mod } 5) \equiv 0 \,(\text{mod } 5)$$

and
$$3 * 2 \equiv 3 + 2 \,(\text{mod } 5) \equiv 0 \,(\text{mod } 5)$$

so that
$$2 * 3 = 3 * 2.$$

* is a commutative operation: $a * b = b * a$ for all $a, b \in A$. * is also associative: $a * (b * c) = (a * b) * c$ for all $a, b, c \in A$. For example

$$2 * (3 * 4) = 2 * 2 = 4$$
$$(2 * 3) * 4 = 0 + 4 = 4$$

Symmetry can be seen from the operation table. The table for a commutative operation is symmetric about the **main diagonal.**

*	0	1	2	3	4	5
0	0	0	0	0	0	0
1	0	1	2	3	4	5
2	0	2	4	0	2	4
3	0	3	0	3	0	3
4	0	4	2	0	4	2
5	0	5	4	3	2	1

* is multiplication modulo 6 on the set $\{0, 1, 2, 3, 4, 5\}$

main diagonal

Many types of set can have operations defined on them, for example: composition of functions (page 96), addition of vectors (page 329), multiplication of matrices (page 314).

Example Ordinary multiplication of numbers corresponds to finding the area of a rectangle (see page 208).

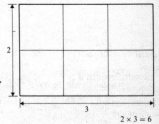

$2 \times 3 = 6$

We could define another operation on the natural numbers by taking the **perimeter** of the rectangle (that is the length all the way round the sides).

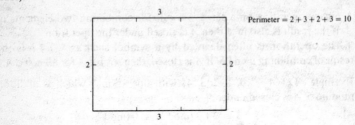

Perimeter = 2 + 3 + 2 + 3 = 10

Part of the table is shown below

*	1	2	3	4	5	.	.	.
1	4	6	8	10	12			
2	6	8	10	12	14			
3	8	10	12	14	16			
4	10	12	14	16	18			
5	12	14	16	18	20			
.								
.								
.								

(Only part can be shown since the table extends indefinitely.)

This operation can be described by the **formula**

$$a*b = 2(a+b) \quad \text{for any } a, b \in \mathbb{N}$$

Not all operations are commutative.

Example   * is defined on the set $\mathbb{N}$ by $a*b$ which means 'add 3 to a and multiply the result by b'. $2*3 = (2+3) \times 3 = 15$ while $3*2 = (3+3) \times 2 = 12$

Identity elements

For addition in $\mathbb{Z}$, $0+2 = 2$

$0-3 = -3$

in general $0+a = a$ for any $a \in \mathbb{Z}$

0 is the **identity** for $\mathbb{Z}$ under addition. 1 is the identity for $\mathbb{Z}$ under multiplication. The identity leaves the elements of the set unchanged when combined with them.

If the set A contains an element e with the property

$$e * a = a \quad \text{and} \quad a * e = a \quad \text{for any } a \in A$$

then e is the identity for A with operation $*$.

You can find the identity from the operation table – it corresponds to the row (or column) which exactly copies the top row (or first column).

Example   Find the identity element in the table

*	a	b	c	d	e
a	e	a	d	c	b
b	a	b	c	d	e
c	d	c	a	e	b
d	b	d	e	d	a
e	c	e	b	a	d

The b row copies the top row, and the b column copies the first column. b is the identity. (*Both* the column and row must satisfy this condition.)

A set need not have an identity under the particular operation.

Examples

1.

*	p	q	r	s
p	r	q	p	s
q	q	p	q	p
r	p	q	s	r
s	s	p	r	s

Inspection of the table shows that there is no identity

2. For $a, b \in \{0, 1, 2, 3\}$ define $a * b = 2a + 3b \pmod 4$ (which is *not* symmetric).

			b		
	*	0	1	2	3
a	0	0	3	2	1
	1	2	1	0	3
	2	0	3	2	1
	3	2	1	0	3

There is no identity.

Inverse elements

For $\mathbb{Z}$ under addition $2+(-2) = 0$, the identity.
For $\mathbb{Z}$ under multiplication $2 \times (\frac{1}{2}) = 1$, the identity.

$$-2 \text{ is the } \textbf{inverse} \text{ of } 2 \text{ under } +$$
$$\frac{1}{2} \text{ is the inverse of } 2 \text{ under } \times$$

When an element is combined with its inverse, the result is the identity element.

For a set A with operation * and identity e, if $a, b \in A$, $a * b = e$ and $b * a = e$ then a and b are **inverse elements**, and we write $b = a^{-1}$.

So $$a * a^{-1} = e = a^{-1} * a$$

(even when * is not commutative).

Warning: a^{-1} does *not* mean $1/a$ unless we are considering multiplication in $\mathbb{R}$ and $\mathbb{Q}$ (see page 36).

Not all elements have inverses.

Examples

1. Multiplication in $\mathbb{Z}$: 2 has no inverse since $\frac{1}{2} \notin \mathbb{Z}$.

2. Multiplication in $\mathbb{R}$: 0 has no inverse since division by 0 is undefined.

3. If A does not have an identity, then no element can have an inverse.

Note: The inverse of a is required to belong to A as well.

Inverses can be spotted from the operation table.

Example   Addition modulo 5 on the set $\{0, 1, 2, 3, 4\}$.

*	0	1	2	3	4
0	0	1	2	3	4
1	1	2	3	4	0
2	2	3	4	⓪	1
3	3	4	0	1	2
4	4	0	1	2	3

Identity is 0.

To find the inverse of 2, look for the identity 0 in the 2 row. It appears in the 3 column. 2 and 3 are inverses. Also 1 and 4 are inverses.

An element that is its own inverse is called **self-inverse**. The identity is self-inverse.

Finding the inverse of 2 is equivalent to solving the **equation**

$$2 * x = 0$$

see page 127

Example   For addition modulo 5, find an x in the set $\{0, 1, 2, 3, 4\}$ such that $3 * x = 4$.

Answer   From the table

*	0	1	2	3	4
0	0	1	2	3	4
1	1	2	3	4	0
2	2	3	4	0	1
3	3	④	0	1	2
4	4	0	1	2	3

Look for a 4 in the 3 row. This happens in the 1 column so $3 * 1 = 4$. The solution is $x = 1$.

Example $a * b$ denotes the remainder when $a \times b$ is divided by 13.

(i) Evaluate $3 * 5$ (ii) Find a positive integer n such that $5 * n = 7$

Answer   (i) $3 \times 5 = 15 \equiv 2 \,(\text{mod } 13)$

so $3 * 5 = 2$

(ii) Complete the 5 row of the table.

*	0	1	2	3	4	5	6	7	8	9	10	11	12
0													
1													
2													
3													
4													
5	0	5	10	2	⑦	12	4	9	1	6	11	3	8

7 appears in the 4 column. So $n = 4$.

Summary of Properties of Binary Operations

The group axioms

(i) A is **closed under** * if $a*b \in A$ whenever $a, b \in A$.

(ii) * is **associative on A** if $a*(b*c) = (a*b)*c$ for all $a, b, c \in A$.

(iii) A has an **identity element** e if $c \in A$ and $a*e = e*a = a$ for all $a \in A$.

(iv) $a \in A$ has an **inverse** $a^{-1} \in A$ if $a*a^{-1} = e = a^{-1}*a$ where e is the identity element.

A set A with operation * for which * is associative, A is closed under *, A has an identity element and each $a \in A$ has an inverse $a^{-1} \in A$, is called a **group**. The group is denoted by $(A, *)$.

* is **commutative** if $a*b = b*a$ for all $a, b \in A$.

A group for which * is commutative is called a **commutative group**.

Examples

1. The set $\{0, 1, 2, 3, 4\}$ with addition modulo 5 is a commutative group.
2. 2×2 non-singular matrices under multiplication (page 317).
3. Vectors under vector addition (page 329).
4. Invertable functions under composition (page 96).
5. The symmetries of triangles, squares, etc. (page 250).

Isomorphisms

Sometimes the operation tables of two different groups are strikingly similar.

Example   Two group operation tables are given as

*	a	b	c	d	e
a	b	c	d	e	a
b	c	d	e	a	b
c	d	e	a	b	c
d	e	a	b	c	d
e	a	b	c	d	e

∘	P	Q	R	S	T
P	P	Q	R	S	T
Q	Q	R	S	T	P
R	R	S	T	P	Q
S	S	T	P	Q	R
T	T	P	Q	R	S

Relabelling $P \to e$, $Q \to d$, $R \to c$, $S \to b$, $T \to a$ in the second table results in

	e	d	c	b	a
e	e	d	c	b	a
d	d	c	b	a	e
c	c	b	a	e	d
b	b	a	e	d	c
a	a	e	d	c	b

which is the same as the first table when the elements are reordered.

We say that the two groups are **isomorphic** if the table for one can be obtained from that of the other by renaming the elements and reordering if necessary.

The distributive law

The set $\mathbb{R}$ has the two operations $\times$ and $+$ defined on it. The two operations are linked by the distributive law

$$a \times (b+c) = a \times b + a \times c$$

for any numbers a, b and c.

Example
$$2 \times (3+4) = 2 \times 7 = 14$$
$$(2 \times 3) + (2 \times 4) = 6 + 8 = 14$$

If the set S has the operations $*$ and $\circ$ defined on it, then we say $*$ *is distributive over $\circ$ on the left* if

$$a * (b \circ c) = (a * b) \circ (a * c) \qquad \text{for any } a, b, c, \in S$$

$*$ *is distributive over $\circ$ on the right* if

$$(b \circ c) * a = (b * a) \circ (c * a) \qquad \text{for any } a, b, c, \in S$$

Multiplication in $\mathbb{R}$ (or $\mathbb{Q}$) is both left and right distributive over addition.

Example Define $*$ on $\mathbb{N}$ by $a * b = a \times b + 1$. Then $*$ is not distributive over $+$.

Take $a = 1, b = 2, c = 3$ then

$$1 * (2+3) = 1 * 5 = 1 \times 5 + 1 = 6$$

whereas
$$(1 * 2) + (1 * 3) = (1 \times 2 + 1) + (1 \times 3 + 1)$$
$$= 3 + 4$$
$$= 7$$

so
$$1 * (2+3) \neq (1 * 2) + (1 * 3)$$

Completing tables

The operation table for a group can often be completed using the group properties without detailed knowledge of the operation.

Example   Complete the table for $A = \{a, b, c, d\}$, given that the operation is commutative and a is the identity, and that a and c are the only self-inverse elements.

*	a	b	c	d
a				
b				
c	c	d	a	b
d				

Answer   For a group, each element appears exactly once in each row. a is the identity and the table is symmetric

*	a	b	c	d
a	a	b	c	d
b	b		d	
c	c	d	a	b
d	d		b	

since b is not self-inverse then $b * b \neq a$, so $b * b$ must be c, $b * d$ is then a. The table becomes

*	a	b	c	d
a	a	b	c	d
b	b	c	d	a
c	c	d	a	b
d	d	a	b	

Finally $d * d = c$ (as d is not self-inverse).

Examination questions

   1. *Give that $a * b$ means 'add 3 to a and multiply the result by b' then the value of $(4 * 3) * 5$ is*

        A 60   B 75   C 78   D 105   E 120   [LON]

2. *Three 'subtractions' are done by a pupil as follows:*

989	909	923
123	183	138
866	886	815

Evidently in each case the pupil takes the smaller digit from the larger in each column. Denote this operation by $\ominus$

(i) *Evaluate (a)* $835 \ominus 000$ *(b)* $353 \ominus 268$ *(c)* $115 \ominus 846$

(ii) *(a)* *State the identity for* $\ominus$

     (b) *Give the inverse of 123 for this operation*

(iii) *Give an example to show that* $\ominus$ *is not associative.*   [SMP]

3. *The commutative operation* * *is defined on the set* $S = \{a, b, c, d\}$. *The identity element is a, and every element of S is its own inverse.*

(i) *Copy and complete the table for* *

*	a	b	c	d
a				
b			d	c
c				
d				

(ii) *Express* $(b * c) * b$ *as a single element of S.*

(iii) *Solve the equation* $c * x = d$, *where* $x \in S$.   [SMP]

4. *Operations* $\circ$ *and* * *are defined on the set* $S = \{a, b, c, d\}$. *The combination tables are shown below.*

$\circ$	a	b	c	d
a	d	a	b	c
b	a	b	c	d
c	b	c	d	a
d	c	d	a	b

*	a	b	c	d
a	c	b	a	d
b	b	b	b	b
c	a	b	c	d
d	d	b	d	b

(a) *Assuming that both operations* $\circ$ *and* * *are associative on S, explain fully why* $(S, \circ)$ *forms a group and give one of the group axioms that is not satisfied by* $(S, *)$.

(b) *Find x if* $x = a * (c \circ d)$.

     Demonstrate using a, c and d that * *is distributive over* $\circ$ *from the left.*

(c) *The set S under the operation † forms a group which is not isomorphic to the group (S, ∘). Given that in this new group a is the identity element and that b is self inverse, draw up the group table for (S, †). Demonstrate using b, c and d that † is not distributive over ∘.*

[AEB]

5. $p * q$ denotes $p \times 10^q$. Write $7 * (-2)$ as a decimal.   [CAM]

Answers
   1. E
   2. (i)(a) 835   (b) 115   (c) 731
       (ii)(a) 000   (b) 123
       (iii) Consider $(111 \ominus 222) \ominus 333$ for example
   5. 0·07

Summary of Number Types

The natural numbers	$\mathbb{N} = \{0, 1, 2, 3, 4, \ldots\}$
The integers	$\mathbb{Z} = \{\ldots, {}^-3, {}^-2, {}^-1, 0, 1, 2, 3, \ldots\}$
The rational numbers	$\mathbb{Q} = \{\text{fractions}\}$
Irrationals	$\{{}^\pm\sqrt{2}, {}^\pm\sqrt{3}, {}^\pm\sqrt{5}, {}^\pm\sqrt{7}, 1+\sqrt{2}, \ldots\}$
The real numbers	$\mathbb{R} = \{\text{all numbers}\}$
Prime numbers	$P = \{2, 3, 5, 7, 11, \ldots\}$ (numbers whose only factors are 1 and themselves)
Even numbers	$E = \{0, 2, 4, 6, 8, \ldots\}$ (multiples of 2)
Odd numbers	$O = \{1, 3, 5, 7, \ldots\}$ (2 is not a factor)

Sets and Venn Diagrams

The chain of subsets $\mathbb{N} \subset \mathbb{Z} \subset \mathbb{Q} \subset \mathbb{R}$ can be illustrated on a **Venn diagram**.

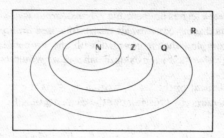

This kind of diagram is used to show the relationships between sets.

Examples   (i) $\mathbb{N} \subset \mathbb{Z}$ (ii) T = multiples of 3 and E = even numbers.

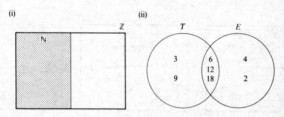

In example (ii), the sets E and T have elements in common, they **overlap**.
Listing the elements

$$E = \{0, 2, 4, 6, 8, 10, 12, 14, 16, 18, \ldots\}$$
$$T = \{0, 3, 6, 9, 12, 15, 18, \ldots\}$$

The elements common to both lists are $\{0, 6, 12, 18, \ldots\}$ (multiples of 6).
This set is called the **intersection** of E and T written as $E \cap T$.

Definition: $A \cap B$, the intersection of sets A and B, is the set of all elements common to both A and B. It is a subset of A and also a subset of B.

Definition: $A \cup B$, the **union** of A and B, is the set formed from all of the elements of the sets A and B.

Example   If $A = \{a, b, c\}$ and $B = \{c, d, e\}$ then $A \cap B = \{c\}$ and $A \cup B = \{a, b, c, d, e\}$ (no repetitions in the list).

A set can contain *any* type of element (numbers, letters, functions, shapes).

Note: $\cup$ and $\cap$ are binary operations on sets.

The **empty set** $\emptyset$ has no elements, $\emptyset = \{\ \}$.

The **universal set** $\mathscr{E}$ contains all the objects used for a particular problem. For example, when concerned with the properties of the whole numbers take $\mathscr{E} = \mathbb{N}$. In the example above, we would take $\mathscr{E} = \{$letters of the alphabet$\}$.

The **complement** of the set A, written as A', is the set of all elements *not* in A. It is found by crossing out the elements of A from the universal set.

Example   If $A = \{0, 1, 2, 3, 7\}$ and $\mathscr{E} = \{0, 1, 2, 3, 4, 5, 6, 7, 8\}$ then $A' = \{4, 5, 6, 8\}$.

These relationships can be pictured as

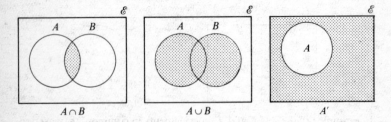

$A \cap B$ $A \cup B$ A'

If $A \subset B$ then a useful picture is

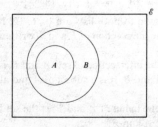

It is often useful to write the elements of the sets in the appropriate places on the Venn diagram.

Definition: $n(A) = $ the number of elements in set A.

Example   If $A = \{1, a, \square, c, 3, 5,\}$ then $n(A) = 6$.

Examples

1. If
$$\mathscr{E} = \{\text{integers between 3 and 30}\}$$
$$P = \{\text{prime numbers}\}$$
$$A = \{\text{multiples of 3}\}$$
$$B = \{\text{multiples of 5}\}$$

list the elements of

(a) P (b) $P \cap A$ (c) $A \cap B$ (d) $(A \cup B) \cap P'$

Answer (a) $P = \{3, 5, 7, 11, 13, 17, 19, 23, 29\}$ (see page 66)

(b) Since $A = \{3, 6, 9, 12, 15, 18, 21, 24, 27, 30\}$ then $P \cap A = \{3\}$.

(c) $B = \{5, 10, 15, 20, 25, 30\}$, $A \cap B = \{15, 30\}$.

(d) $(A \cup B) = \{3, 5, 6, 9, 10, 12, 15, 18, 20, 21, 24, 25, 27, 30\}$
$P' = \{4, 6, 8, 9, 10, 12, 14, 15, 16, 18, 20, 21, 22, 24, 25, 26, 27, 28, 30\}$
$(A \cup B) \cap P' = \{6, 9, 10, 12, 15, 18, 20, 21, 24, 25, 27, 30\}$

2.
$$\mathscr{E} = \{0, 1, 2, 3, 4, 5, 6, 7, 8, 9, 10, 11, 12\}$$
$$A = \{\text{multiples of 3}\}$$
$$B = \{\text{multiples of 4}\}$$
$$C = \{\text{odd numbers}\}$$

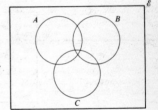

Insert the numbers 0, to 12 in the diagram.

Answer

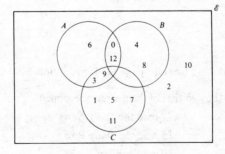

Comments: 0 and 12 are multiples of both 3 and 4 and so are placed in the intersection of A and B. $A \cap B \cap C = \emptyset$ since no odd number can also be a multiple of 4.

3. 100 people answered a survey. 80 said that they drank coffee, 60 said that they drank tea and 5 said that they had neither. How many drank both tea and coffee?

Answer

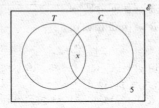

$$T = \{\text{tea drinkers}\}, C = \{\text{coffee drinkers}\}$$

In this example, the *number* of elements in each subset is shown on the diagram. Suppose that x people drink both, so that $n(T \cap C) = x$. Then $80 - x$ drink just coffee, and $60 - x$ drink just tea.

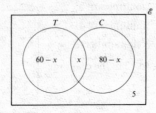

Totalling:

$$60 - x + x + 80 - x + 5 = 100$$
$$60 + 80 + 5 - x = 100$$
$$145 - x = 100$$

so

$$x = 45$$

45 people drink both (see also page 114 for equations).

4. A survey showed that of the people questioned

27 read the *Daily News*

15 read the *Daily Post*

10 read neither

14 read both

How many people answered the survey?

Answer Let $N = \{$those who read the *Daily News*$\}$

$P = \{$those who read the *Daily Post*$\}$

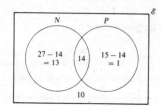

Totalling: $13 + 14 + 1 + 10 = 38$, 38 people answered.

5. If $\mathscr{E} = \{$people in a certain room$\}$

$A = \{$people taller than $1 \cdot 5$ m$\}$

$B = \{$left-handed people$\}$

$C = \{$people wearing hats$\}$

Express each of the following statements in symbols.

(a) No left-handed person wears a hat.

(b) All people over $1 \cdot 5$ m tall wear hats.

Answer (a) $B \cap C = \varnothing$ (b) $A \subset C$

6. (a)

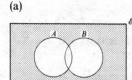

(b)

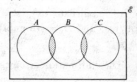

Describe the sets indicated by the shaded region, using set notation.

Answer

(a) The unshaded region is $A \cup B$, so the shaded region is $(A \cup B)'$.

(b) The two shaded parts are $A \cap B$ and $B \cap C$. The combined set is $(A \cap B) \cup (B \cap C)$.

7. $\mathscr{E} = \{$families living in Smith Street$\}$

$C = \{$families who have a car$\}$

$$T = \{\text{families with a colour television}\}$$
$$V = \{\text{families with video recorders}\}$$

(a) Write the following statements without using set notation

    (i) $C' \cap T = \emptyset$ (ii) $V \subset T$

(b) Draw a Venn diagram showing the sets $\mathscr{E}$, C, T and V.

Answer

  (a) (i) All families without cars also have no colour television.

     (ii) All families with video recorders also have colour television.

  (b)

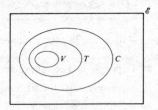

Note: that $C' \cap T = \emptyset$ is equivalent to $T \subset C$.

8. Quadrilaterals are four-sided figures. Parallelograms are quadrilaterals with pairs of parallel sides. Rectangles are parallelograms with angles of 90°. Squares are equal-sided rectangles. A rhombus is an equal-sided parallelogram.

If $\mathscr{E} = \{\text{all quadrilaterals}\}$, $P = \{\text{parallelograms}\}$, $R = \{\text{rectangles}\}$, $S = \{\text{squares}\}$ and $H = \{\text{rhombi}\}$, show these sets in a Venn diagram (see also page 226).

Answer   The information given can be expressed as

$$S \subset R \subset P \subset \mathscr{E}$$
$$H \subset P$$

and $$S = R \cap H$$

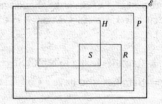

9. Of 140 students, 70 study mathematics, 60 study physics and 50 study chemistry. 20 study both mathematics and physics, 15 study physics and chemistry and 12 study mathematics and chemistry.

How many study all three subjects?

Answer

Let

$$M = \{\text{maths students}\}$$
$$P = \{\text{physics students}\}$$
$$C = \{\text{chemistry students}\}$$

Let

$$x = n(M \cap C \cap P)$$

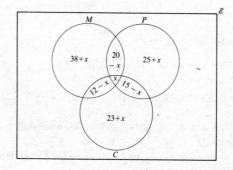

$n(M \cap P) = 20$ so $20 - x$ study maths and physics but not chemistry

$n(M \cap C) = 12$ so $12 - x$ study maths and chemistry but not physics

$n(P \cap C) = 15$ so $15 - x$ study physics and chemistry but not maths

$n(M) = 70$ so $70 - (20 - x) - x - (12 - x)$ study only maths, etc.

Simplifying, $38 + x$ study maths only; also $25 + x$ and $23 + x$ for P, C.

Adding the numbers in the diagram

$$(38 + x) + (20 - x) + (25 + x) + (15 - x) + (23 + x) + (12 - x) + x = 140$$
$$38 + 20 + 25 + 15 + 23 + 12 + x - x + x - x + x - x + x = 140$$
$$133 + x = 140$$
$$x = 7$$

(see page 114 for equations).

7 students study all three subjects.

Examination questions

1. *Given that x is an integer, and* $\mathscr{E} = \{x: 1 < x < 13\}$ *with subsets P, D and E such that*

$$P = \{prime\ factors\ of\ 330\},$$
$$D = \{odd\ numbers\ less\ than\ 10\},$$
$$E = \{even\ numbers\ less\ than\ 12\},$$

list the members of

  (a) P *(b)* D *(c)* $P \cup D$ *(d)* $P \cap D$ *(e)* $P \cap D \cap E$
  (f) $(P \cup D \cup E)'$ [AEB]

2. *If* $A = \{s, h, o, e\}$, $B = \{s, o, c, k\}$ *and* $C = \{l, a, c, e, s\}$ *then* $n\,((A \cap B) \cup C) =$

  A 2 *B* 6 *C* 7 *D* 8   [AEB]

3. *For two sets A and B, A * B means* $(A \cap B)'$.
$A' * B'$ *is equivalent to*

  (a) $A \cup B$ *(b)* $A \cap B$ *(c)* $A' \cup B'$ *(d)* $A' \cap B'$ [SMP]

4. $\mathscr{E} = \{1, 2, 3, 4, 5, 6, 7, 8, 9, 10\}$, $B = \{even\ numbers\}$,
$C = \{multiples\ of\ 3\}$.
  (i) *Complete the Venn diagram by inserting the numerals 1 to 10 in the*
     appropriate regions.
  (ii) *List the set* $B' \cap C$.

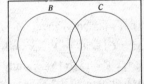

5.

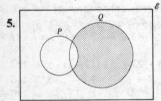

The shaded area in the diagram represents

A $P' \cap Q'$ *B* $P' \cap Q$ *C* $P \cap Q'$ *D* $P \cap Q$ *E* *None of these*
                                                        [LON]

6. $\mathscr{E}$ = the set of integers. Sets A and B are defined by $A = \{x: x \geqslant 5\}$, $B = \{x: -2 < x \leqslant 8\}$.
List the elements of $A \cap B$.

7. In a school of 2 000 pupils, 1 200 study history and 900 study geography. 300 study both subjects. The number who study neither is

A 100   B 200   C 300   D 400   E 500   [LON]

8. The sets A, B and C are shown in the Venn diagram.

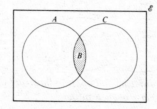

(i) Write down an expression for the shaded area in the form

$$\ldots \cap \ldots \cap \ldots$$

(ii) If $\mathscr{E}$ = {positive integers less than 40},

   A = {even numbers},

   B = {6, 18, 30},

   C = {multiples of 3},

list the elements represented by the shaded region.   [SMP]

9. In a village a survey was made of the possibility of supplying gas, electricity, water and drainage to all the houses, none of which had any of these services. It was found that each house could be supplied with water and electricity only, or water and drainage only, or gas and drainage only. Given that

$\mathscr{E}$ = {all the houses in the village},

G = {houses which can be supplied with gas},

E = {houses which can be supplied with electricity},

W = {houses which can be connected to a main water supply},

D = {houses which can be connected to the main drainage system}, *state which one of the sets $\mathscr{E}$, G, E, W, D, $\varnothing$ is equal to each of*

(i) E', (ii) G', (iii) G ∩ E, (iv) W ∪ D, (v) E ∩ W.

It is impossible to supply more than 70 houses with water or to connect more than 80 houses to a drainage system.

If the water and drainage supplies are to be fully used, find

(a) *the largest possible number of houses there could be in the village,*

(b) *the smallest possible number of houses there could be in the village.*

State in each case the number of houses which could be supplied with electricity and the number which could be supplied with gas.   [LON]

10.

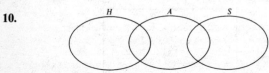

Copy the above Venn diagram and use it to illustrate the following information, indicating the number in each subset.

$n(H \cap A) = 15$, $n(A \cap S) = 24$, $n(A) = 69$, $n(H) = 49$,
$\mathscr{E} = H \cup A \cup S$ *and* $n(\mathscr{E}) = 120$.

Find (i) $n(A')$, (ii) $n(A \cup H)$, (iii) $n[(H \cap A) \cup S]$.   [CAM]

11. Use set notation to identify the shaded set in each of the given Venn diagrams.

(ii)

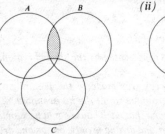

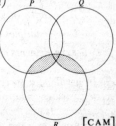

[CAM]

Answers

2. B

3. (a)

4. (ii) {3, 9}

5. B

6. {5, 6, 7, 8}

7. B

8. (i) $A \cap B' \cap C$ (ii) {12, 24, 36}

11. (i) $A \cap B \cap C'$ (ii) $(P \cap R) \cup (Q \cap R)$

Section 4: Mappings, Functions and Formulae

Mappings

The elements of one set are often related to those of another.

Examples

1. The set $\{A, B, C, D, \ldots\}$ of capital letters and the corresponding set $\{a, b, c, d, \ldots\}$ of small letters.

2. The set $\{$John, Mary, Peter, Ann$\}$ of first names and their corresponding surnames $\{$Smith, Brown, Jones, Green$\}$.

3. The set of colours $\{$red, amber, green$\}$ and the set of traffic light commands $\{$Stop, Wait, Go$\}$.

4. A telephone directory associates a set of names with a set of numbers.

The association between sets can be shown by listing their elements in order in a table:

The corresponding elements must be written in the correct order.

Colour	Command
Red	Stop
Amber	Wait
Green	Go

However, the elements of a set can be listed in any order (see page 17). A way of showing corresponding sets which does not depend on their order is the **mapping diagram**, where corresponding pairs are connected by arrows.

The sets are usually enclosed by loops or circles.

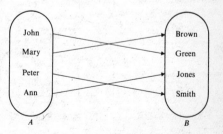

The diagram above shows the **mapping**, or correspondence, of the set
A = {John, Mary, Peter, Ann} to the set B = {Brown, Green, Jones, Smith}. The mapping can be denoted by a single letter, m for instance, and we write

$$m: A \rightarrow B$$

to mean that m maps set A to set B. A is called the **domain** of the mapping, its elements are at the blunt ends of the arrows. B is called the **range** of the mapping, its elements are at the pointed ends of the arrows.

An element of the domain set is connected by an arrow to its **image** in the range set. For example, Brown is the image of Mary under the mapping m. We write this as m: Mary $\mapsto$ Brown, or as m(Mary) = Brown. (Read these statements as 'm maps Mary to Brown', and 'm of Mary is Brown' respectively.)

Here, *each* surname corresponds to exactly *one* first name, it is an example of a **one-to-one** mapping. Not all mappings are one-to-one. For example, if some of the people have the same surnames

Exercise: How many different people are represented here? Make a list of their full names.

This is an example of a **many-to-many** mapping.

The different kinds of mapping are shown by the diagrams

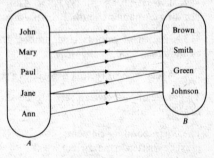

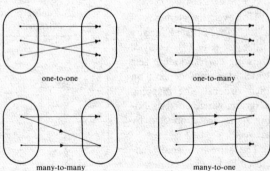

one-to-one

one-to-many

many-to-many

many-to-one

Exercise: Try to find everyday examples of each type of mapping.

All of these are mappings *onto* the domains. Each range element is connected by an arrow to at least one domain element.

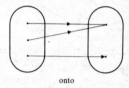

onto

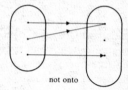

not onto

Example The mapping l from the set $A = \{2, 3, 4, 5, 6\}$ to the set $B = \{2, 3, 5, 7\}$ associates a positive integer with its prime factors (see page 66). This can be shown in the mapping diagram $l: A \to B$

7 is not the image of any of the members of A. If we restrict the range set to $C = \{2, 3, 5\}$, then the mapping $l: A \to C$ is onto.

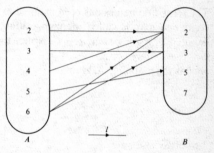

Composition of maps

Suppose that a class of students is to be formed into three groups according to the first letter of their surname. Those whose surnames start with a letter between A and H are in group I, those between I and P are in group II, and the rest are in group III. The mapping n, from the set of surnames {Alexander, Brown, Jones, Smith} to the set {I, II, III} has diagram

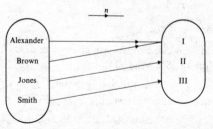

Starting with the set of first names {John, Ann, Peter, Mary, Michael} map to the set {Smith, Brown, Jones, Alexander} with mapping *m*. Then map to the set {I, II, III} with map *n*. The combined result can be shown on the diagram

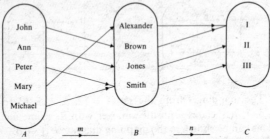

The set of first names has been mapped to the set of group numbers. The combined map is called the **composition** of the maps *m* and *n*, and is denoted by *n* ∘ *m*, or *nm*: *A* → *C*. Notice that the map *m* is used first – *nm* means *m followed by n*.

nm has the mapping diagram

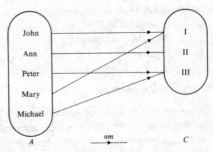

Composition is a binary operation on the set of maps (see page 57). (The domain of *n* must be a subset of the range of *m*.)

Inverse and identity maps

A mapping *m*: *A* → *B* can be reversed, giving a map *m*$^{-1}$: *B* → *A*. This is the inverse mapping. (See page 60.)

Example   A set of metal rods labelled *A*, *B*, *C*, *D* and *E* are measured. Their lengths, in cm to the nearest mm, form the set

$$M = \{20 \cdot 0, 20 \cdot 1, 20 \cdot 5, 21 \cdot 2, 22 \cdot 0\}$$

Denoting the set of labels by *L*, the measuring process gives a mapping
$m: L \rightarrow M$. Suppose that the diagram is

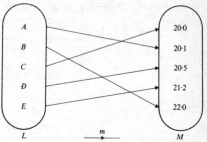

(so that rod *A* is 20·1 cm
long).
Note: it would be more
usual to display these results
in a table.

The map *m* associates a length with each label. Reversing the diagram
gives the inverse map m^{-1} which associates a rod with each length.

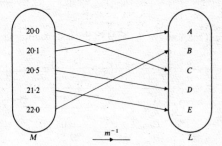

The mapping $m: L \rightarrow M$ can be combined with the mapping $m^{-1}: M \rightarrow L$

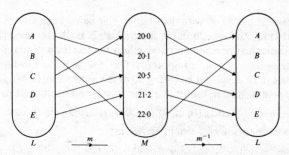

The resulting composition is the map $m^{-1}m: L \rightarrow L$. By the definition of
inverse, m^{-1} must be the identity mapping (see page 60).

The diagram above can be reduced to the single mapping

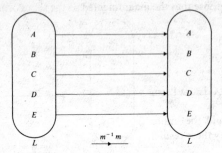

The identity mapping associates each element with itself, it leaves the elements unchanged.

Ordered pairs

The measurement mapping $m: L \to M$ of the last example could be shown as the table

Rod	Length
A	20·1
B	22·0
C	20·0
D	20·5
E	21·2

The labels are paired off with the lengths. This pairing can also be shown as $(A, 20 \cdot 1), (B, 22 \cdot 0), (C, 20 \cdot 0), (D, 20 \cdot 5), (E, 21 \cdot 2)$. Each bracketed pair has a label in the first position and a length in the second position. Because the order within a pair is important, they are called **ordered pairs**. A mapping can be described by listing all of the ordered pairs. We say that the mapping is *equal* to the set of all the corresponding ordered pairs

$$m = \{(A, 20 \cdot 1), (B, 22 \cdot 0), (C, 20 \cdot 0), (D, 20 \cdot 5), (E, 21 \cdot 2)\}$$

The inverse mapping m^{-1} can be shown as

$$m^{-1} = \{(20 \cdot 1, A), (22 \cdot 0, B), (20 \cdot 0, C), (20 \cdot 5, D), (21 \cdot 2, E)\}$$

The word **relation** is often used instead of mapping when it is defined as a set of ordered pairs.

Example The mapping $l: A \to C$ of page 79, which associates numbers with their prime factors, can be represented as the set of ordered pairs

$$l = \{(2, 2), (3, 3), (4, 2), (5, 5), (6, 2), (6, 3)\}$$

A particular class of mapping is the function.

Functions

A **function** is a mapping of numbers to numbers which associates only *one* image number with each domain number. Functions are usually denoted by the letters f, g and h, and usually map $\mathbb{R}$ to $\mathbb{R}$ or $\mathbb{Q}$ to $\mathbb{Q}$.

Note: Some texts allow the domain and range of a function to be general sets. Here we follow the conventional approach, restricting to number sets.

Note: The mapping $l: A \to C$ above is *not* a function, even though it only involves numbers. The number 6 is mapped to the two factors 2 and 3.

Examples of functions
1. If $A = \{-1, 0, 1, 2, 3, 4\}$, $B = \{0, 1, 4, 9, 16\}$ and the mapping f associates a number with its square, then f is a function.

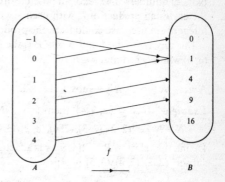

2. $A =$ the set of years of birth, $B =$ the set of possible ages in years, then the mapping that associates a date of birth with an age is a function. For example, $f(1968) = 16$, if the year is now 1984.

3. For $x \in \mathbb{N}$, $f(x) =$ the number of different prime factors of x

$$f(51) = 2$$

since
$$51 = 3 \times 17$$

Exercise: If $f: \mathbb{R}^+ \to \mathbb{R}$ associates a positive number with its square root, then is f a function? (See page 34.)

You can tell if a mapping is a function by looking at the mapping diagram. Functions can have arrows meeting at the pointed ends but not at the blunt ends.
(We define functions as either one-to-one or many-to-one mappings.)

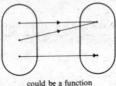

could be a function

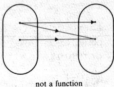

not a function

Cartesian Products

A function is also a mapping and so can be represented as a set of ordered pairs of numbers. The set of all possible ordered pairs of numbers is called the **cartesian product** of $\mathbb{R}$ with itself – written as $\mathbb{R} \times \mathbb{R}$. If only positive integers are used, we could form the product $\mathbb{N} \times \mathbb{N}$.

For any two sets A and B, $A \times B$ is the set of all possible ordered pairs (a, b) where $a \in A$ and $b \in B$.

Note: A function is a subset of $\mathbb{R} \times \mathbb{R}$.

Example   If $N = \{2, 3, 4\}$, then

$$N \times N = \{(2, 2), (2, 3), (2, 4), (3, 2), (3, 3), (3, 4), (4, 2), (4, 3), (4, 4)\}$$

Define the relation $R = \{(x, y): x \text{ is a factor of } y\}$ on $N \times N$. Then R is the subset $\{(2, 2), (2, 4), (3, 3), (4, 4)\}$.

Formulae

A function can also be displayed as a table of values. Tables of logarithms, squares and square roots for example (see also page 381). However, this is not always the most practical form of a function.

For example, if a physicist requires to know the length of a certain rod at various temperatures he could consult a table of values of the lengths at various temperatures. The table would necessarily contain many numbers and would be awkward to use.

Fortunately a function can often be represented more conveniently as a **formula**.

Example Let l = length of the rod, in cm to 1 decimal place, t = temperature, in °C to 1 decimal place. The formula

$$l = 24 \cdot 0 + 1 \cdot 1 \times (t - 14 \cdot 0)$$

relates temperature and length for this particular rod.
Given a temperature (value of t), the length (value of l) can be calculated.
When temperature = 16 °C, put $16 \cdot 0$ in place of t in the formula

$$l = 24 \cdot 0 + 1 \cdot 1 \times (16 \cdot 0 - 14 \cdot 0)$$

The brackets show that the subtraction should be done first

$$l = 24 \cdot 0 + 1 \cdot 1 \times 2 \cdot 0$$

The multiplication is done next

$$l = 24 \cdot 0 + 2 \cdot 2$$
$$= 26 \cdot 2$$

The length is $26 \cdot 2$ cm when the temperature is $16 \cdot 0$ °C.

Because t can take different values, it is called the **variable** or **argument** of the formula.

It is essential to do the steps of the calculation in the correct order.

(i) Any quantity in brackets should be worked out first. If there are several sets of nested brackets, the innermost ones should be taken first.

(ii) Multiplications should then be done.

(iii) Finally additions and subtractions should be done.

Powers, such as 2^2, $4 \cdot 5^4$, and so on, are repeated multiplications and so should come before addition and subtraction. The importance of these **priority rules** is illustrated in the following examples.

Examples

1.
$$(2+3)^2 = 5^2 \qquad \text{brackets first}$$
$$= 25 \qquad 5^2 = 5 \times 5$$

2.
$$2 + 3^2 = 2 + 9$$
$$= 11$$

3. $2 + 3 \times 5 = 2 + 15$ multiply first

$= 17$

4. $(2 + 3) \times 5 = 5 \times 5$ brackets

$= 25$

5. $1 + (1 + \tfrac{1}{2}(1 + \tfrac{1}{2})) = 1 + (1 + \tfrac{1}{2}(\tfrac{3}{2}))$ innermost brackets first

$= 1 + (1 + \tfrac{3}{4})$ $\tfrac{1}{2}(\tfrac{3}{2})$ means $\tfrac{1}{2} \times \tfrac{3}{2}$

$= 1 + \tfrac{7}{4}$

$= 1\tfrac{1}{4}$

(See pages 25–7 for combining fractions.)

Notice that the multiplication sign $\times$ is not written next to brackets. In fact $\times$ is not used in formulae. Quantities written next to each other are taken to be *multiplied* together.

Brackets are very useful for showing the correct sequence of the operations. You should make sure that you use them in your working.

Square root signs can also appear in formulae.

Examples

6. $\sqrt{(2 \times 5 - 1)} = \sqrt{(10 - 1)}$ multiply first

$= \sqrt{9}$ evaluate bracketed expression

$= 3$

7. $\sqrt{(2 \times 5)} - 1 = \sqrt{10} - 1$

$= 3 \cdot 162 - 1$ see page 381

$= 2 \cdot 162$

Division is always shown in the form of a fraction. The dividing bar of the fraction has the effect of a bracket.

Examples

8. $3 + \tfrac{1}{2} = 3 + 0 \cdot 5 = 3 \cdot 5$

9. $\dfrac{3 + 1}{2} = \dfrac{(3 + 1)}{2}$

$= \dfrac{4}{2}$ $3 + 1$ is in brackets

$= 2$

A function has associated with it

   (i) Some domain of numbers.

   (ii) A corresponding range of values.

   (iii) A formula for working out the value of the function given a value of the variable.

A given value of the variable is fed into the formula, the correct sequence of operations is followed, and the result is the value of the function. We can think of a function as a calculating machine.

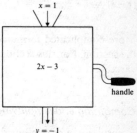

The output value is often described by the letter y. So when $x = 1$, $y = -1$. The diagram shows the function $f(x) = 2x - 3$, with variable x. (Remember that $2x$ means the multiplication $2 \times x$.)

Using the mapping notation of page 77, we could also write

$$f : x \mapsto 2x - 3$$

Any letter can be used for the variable of a function, but x is the most common one. Other examples of formulae are

(i) $\qquad\qquad f(x) = 2x^2 + 3x - 1 \qquad\qquad$ with domain $\mathbb{R}$

(ii) $\qquad\qquad g(z) = \dfrac{\sqrt{z} + 2}{z + 1} \qquad\qquad$ with domain $\mathbb{R}, z \neq -1$

(iii) $\qquad\qquad h(x) = (2x)^2 + 3x - 1 \qquad\qquad$ with domain $\mathbb{R}$

Note the difference between f and h. Only x is squared in f, while in h, x is doubled first and then the result is squared.

$$\begin{aligned}
f(3) &= 2(3)^2 + 3(3) - 1 \\
&= 2 \times 9 + 3 \times 3 - 1 \\
&= 18 + 9 - 1 \qquad\qquad \text{multiply first} \\
&= 26
\end{aligned}$$

While
$$\begin{aligned}
h(3) &= (2 \times 3)^2 + 3 \times 3 - 1 \\
&= 6^2 + 9 - 1 \\
&= 36 + 9 - 1 \\
&= 44
\end{aligned}$$

When calculating the value of a function, set out *all* of the steps neatly like this. You are then less likely to make a mistake.

Example   If $f: p \mapsto 1 - 2p^2$, evaluate $f(-3)$.

$$f(-3) = 1 - 2(-3)^2 = 1 - 2(9) = 1 - 18 = -17$$

(*Note* the use of brackets)

More complicated formulae with several variables are covered later in the section. For this section, we shall only consider formulae with single variables.

Combining and simplifying formulae

Formulae can be combined together, for example by adding them.

$$(2x + 1) + (x^2 - 3x - 1)$$

This expression can be simplified by removing the brackets and adding **like terms**. The terms of an expression are the products of powers of the variable and numbers.

The terms of the expression $x^2 - 3x - 1$ are x^2, $-3x$ and -1. Terms are said to be *like* if they have the same power. For example $2x^2$ and $5x^2$, or $3x^3$ and $10x^3$. Like terms can be added by simply adding the numerical factors

$$2x^2 + 5x^2 = 7x^2$$
$$3x^3 - 10x^3 = -7x^3$$

Unlike terms cannot be added together in this way. For example the expression $2x^2 - 3x - 1$ *cannot* be simplified further.

Returning to the combined formulae

$$(2x + 1) + (x^2 - 3x - 1) = 2x + 1 + x^2 - 3x - 1$$
$$= x^2 + 2x - 3x + 1 - 1$$
$$= x^2 - x$$

The last step combined the like terms $2x - 3x = -x$ and also $1 - 1 = 0$.

Whenever expressions are added or subtracted, they should be simplified in this way.

Examples

1. $$(3x^3 - 5x^2 + 6x - 2) - (2x^3 + 2x - 4)$$

The minus sign changes the signs of all the terms in the second set of brackets (from the sign rules on page 23). When the brackets are removed the expression becomes

$$3x^3 - 5x^2 + 6x - 2 - 2x^3 - 2x + 4 = 3x^3 - 2x^3 - 5x^2 + 6x - 2x - 2 + 4$$

The terms have been shuffled around so as to put like terms together. This is allowed because $+$ is a commutative operation (page 62). Combining like terms

$$x^3 - 5x^2 + 4x + 2$$

is the final expression.

2.
$$(3a^4 - 4a^3 + 2a - 1) + (a^5 - 2a^2 + 3a + 9)$$
$$= 3a^4 - 4a^3 + 2a - 1 + a^5 - 2a^2 + 3a + 9$$

(The $+$ in front of the brackets has no effect on the signs)

$$= a^5 + 3a^4 - 4a^3 - 2a^2 + 2a + 3a - 1 + 9$$

where the terms have been rearranged

$$= a^5 + 3a^4 - 4a^3 - 2a^2 + 5a + 8$$

where like terms have been combined.

The terms in the final expression have been written in *descending order* of the powers. The term with the highest power a^5 is written first. You should always write expressions in either descending order like this, *or* with the powers increasing (ascending order).

Expressions can also be multiplied together.

Examples

1. Multiplying x and $2 - 3x$. The product is written as

$$x(2 - 3x)$$

using brackets, and omitting the multiplication sign.

The x outside the brackets multiplies *each term* inside the brackets

$$x2 - x3x$$

Since multiplication is also a commutative operation, the letters and numbers in each term can be shuffled around.

$$2x - 3xx$$

The product xx can be written as x^2

$$2x - 3x^2$$

is the final form.

2. $3x(2x^2 + x + 1) = 3x2x^2 + 3xx + 3x1$ multiply through by $3x$

$$= (3)(2)xx^2 + 3xx + (3)(1)x$$

where the numbers in each term have been shuffled to the front, brackets being used to indicate multiplication.

$$= 6x^3 + 3x^2 + 3x$$ since $xx^2 = xxx = x^3$

3. $(1 + 2x)(2 - x) = (1 + 2x)2 - (1 + 2x)x$

The whole expression inside the first set of brackets multiplies each term inside the second set of brackets. Now multiply by the terms outside the brackets

$$(1)(2) + 2x2 - 1x - 2xx$$

remember that the minus in front of a set of brackets changes the signs of the terms inside. This expression simplifies to

$$2 + 4x - x - 2x^2 = 2 + 3x - 2x^2$$ combining like terms

The answer is written in ascending order of the powers. It could also be put in descending order

$$-2x^2 + 3x + 2$$

but it is not usual to begin an expression with a minus sign, and so the alternative ascending order is used here (a minus at the beginning of an expression is too easy to miss off by mistake).

4. $(x + 3)(x^2 - 2x - 1) = (x + 3)x^2 - (x + 3)2x - (x + 3)1$

$$= xx^2 + 3x^2 - x2x - 3(2)x - x1 - 3(1)$$

$$= x^3 + 3x^2 - 2x^2 - 6x - x - 3$$ $1x = x$

$$= x^3 + x^2 - 7x - 3$$

Make sure that you write down every step of this kind of calculation, being particularly careful with the signs. Use the sign rules of page 23. Only combine *like* terms.

The next two examples show how powers, such as squares, are dealt with.

Examples

1. $(3x)^2 = (3x)(3x)$ definition of square

$$= (3)(3)xx$$

$$= 9x^2$$

This is the same as squaring both the 3 and the x.

2.
$$(3+x)^2 = (3+x)(3+x)$$
$$= (3+x)3+(3+x)x$$
$$= 3(3)+x3+3x+xx$$
$$= 9+3x+3x+x^2$$
$$= 9+6x+x^2$$

which is *not* the result of squaring the 3 and x separately!

Expressions can be divided to form **algebraic fractions**.

Examples
$$\frac{1+x}{1-x} \qquad 1+\frac{2}{x}$$

Note: that if
$$f:x\mapsto 1+\frac{2}{x}$$

then the number 0 is not a possible value for x. Division by zero is not allowed, 0 must be excluded from the domain of f. Similarly, 1 must be excluded from the domain of the function

$$g: x\mapsto \frac{1+x}{1-x}$$

Fractions with letters obey the same rules as numerical fractions (see page 25).

Examples

1.
$$\frac{1}{x}+\frac{3}{x}=\frac{1+3}{x}$$
same denominator

2.
$$\frac{1}{2a}-\frac{3}{5a}=\frac{5}{10a}-\frac{6}{10a}$$
make the denominators the same
$$=\frac{5-6}{10a}$$
$$=\frac{-1}{10a}$$

3.
$$\frac{1}{x}+\frac{3}{2+x}=\frac{(2+x)}{x(2+x)}+\frac{3x}{x(2+x)}$$
common denominator $x(2+x)$
$$=\frac{(2+x)+3x}{x(2+x)}$$

$$= \frac{2+x+3x}{x(2+x)}$$

$$= \frac{2+4x}{x(2+x)}$$

4. $$\frac{2}{x} \times \frac{(1+x)}{(1-x)} = \frac{2 \times (1+x)}{x \times (1-x)}$$

$$= \frac{2(1+x)}{x(1-x)}$$

which can also be written as $$\frac{2+2x}{x-x^2}$$

when the brackets are multiplied out.

5. $$\frac{2}{x} \div \frac{(1+x)}{(1-x)} = \frac{2}{x} \times \frac{(1-x)}{(1+x)}$$

$$= \frac{2(1-x)}{x(1+x)}$$

$$= \frac{2-2x}{x+x^2}$$

6. $$\left(\frac{2}{1+z}\right)^2 = \frac{2^2}{(1+z)^2} = \frac{4}{(1+z)^2}$$

Flow Diagrams

A function like $$f: x \mapsto \frac{2x-3}{5}$$

can be shown as a sequence of operations, the inner workings of the 'function machine' on page 87. These operations are displayed in a **flow diagram**

$f:$ input x value $\rightarrow$ | double it | $\rightarrow$ | subtract 3 | $\rightarrow$ | divide by 5 | $\rightarrow f(x)$

or more simply as

$$f: x \rightarrow \boxed{\times 2} \rightarrow \boxed{-3} \rightarrow \boxed{\div 5} \rightarrow f(x)$$

the steps correspond to pressing buttons on a calculator.

If the variable of a function appears only once in the formula, then a flow diagram can be made. However, if the variable appears several times, so that the value of x is to be 'input' in different places, we cannot make a flow diagram. For example, the function

$$f(x) = \frac{1+x}{1-x}$$

does not have a diagram, unless the formula is rewritten as

$$f(x) = \frac{2}{1-x} - 1$$

It is essential that the steps are written in the correct order. For example, the diagram

$$g: x \rightarrow \boxed{-3} \rightarrow \boxed{\times 2} \rightarrow \boxed{\div 5} \rightarrow g(x)$$

(which interchanges the first two steps of the function f) corresponds to the formula

$$g(x) = \frac{2(x-3)}{5}$$

which is different from the formula for f.

To see how this formula was derived, follow the diagram through step by step

$$
\begin{array}{cc}
\text{input } x & x \\
\downarrow & \downarrow \\
-3 & x-3 \\
\downarrow & \downarrow \\
\times 2 & 2(x-3) \\
\downarrow & \downarrow \\
\div 5 & \dfrac{2(x-3)}{5} \\
\downarrow &
\end{array}
$$

Notice how each successive operation acts on the result of all the previous ones.

Example   The flow chart

$$x \rightarrow \boxed{\begin{array}{c}\text{multiply} \\ \text{by 4}\end{array}} \rightarrow \boxed{\text{add 3}} \rightarrow f(x)$$

shows the function f.
  (i) Complete $f : x \mapsto \ldots$

  (ii) Given that $g : x \mapsto \dfrac{1}{2(x-1)}$

complete the diagram

$$x \rightarrow \boxed{} \rightarrow \boxed{} \rightarrow \boxed{\text{divide into 1}} \rightarrow g(x)$$

Answer
  (i) Step by step: x, $4x$, $4x+3$ so $f : x \mapsto 4x+3$
  (ii) $x \rightarrow \boxed{-1} \rightarrow \boxed{\times 2} \rightarrow \boxed{\text{divide into 1}} \rightarrow g(x)$

Some functions and their flow diagrams

(1) $f(x) = x^2 - 2$ $x \rightarrow \boxed{\text{square}} \rightarrow \boxed{-2} \rightarrow$

(2) $f(x) = (x-2)^2$ $x \rightarrow \boxed{-2} \rightarrow \boxed{\text{square}} \rightarrow$

(3) $f(x) = \dfrac{1}{x} + 3$ $x \rightarrow \boxed{\begin{array}{c}\text{take} \\ \text{reciprocal}\end{array}} \rightarrow \boxed{+3} \rightarrow$

(4) $f(x) = \dfrac{1}{x+3}$ $x \rightarrow \boxed{+3} \rightarrow \boxed{\begin{array}{c}\text{take} \\ \text{reciprocal}\end{array}} \rightarrow$

(5) $f(x) = \dfrac{1}{x^2+3}$ $x \rightarrow \boxed{\text{square}} \rightarrow \boxed{+3} \rightarrow \boxed{\begin{array}{c}\text{take} \\ \text{reciprocal}\end{array}} \rightarrow$

(6) $f(x) = \dfrac{1}{x^2} + 3$ $\quad x \rightarrow$ [square] $\rightarrow$ [take reciprocal] $\rightarrow$ [$+3$] $\rightarrow$

(7) $f(x) = 1 - x$
$\quad\quad\quad = -x + 1$ $\quad x \rightarrow$ [$\times(-1)$] $\rightarrow$ [$+1$] $\rightarrow$

(8) $f(x) = 2 - x^2$
$\quad\quad\quad = -x^2 + 2$ $\quad x \rightarrow$ [square] $\rightarrow$ [$\times(-1)$] $\rightarrow$ [$+2$] $\rightarrow$

(9) $f(x) = \dfrac{2}{1-x^2}$ $\quad x \rightarrow$ [square] $\rightarrow$ [$\times(-1)$] $\rightarrow$ [$+1$] $\rightarrow$ [divide into 2] $\rightarrow$

(10) $f(x) = \sqrt{(3-x^2)} + 2$ $\; x \rightarrow$ [square] $\rightarrow$ [$\times(-1)$] $\rightarrow$ [$+3$] $\rightarrow$ [$\sqrt{}$] $\rightarrow$ [$+2$] $\rightarrow$

Note also that [divide into 2] is an alternative for

[take reciprocal] $\rightarrow$ [$\times 2$]

Also [take from 2] can be used instead of [$\times(-1)$] $\rightarrow$ [$+2$]

Combining functions

All the different functions form a set, which we can denote by the letter $\mathscr{F}$. Several binary operations (see page 57) can be defined on $\mathscr{F}$. In other words, there are several ways in which two functions can be combined together to form a third function.

1. Addition: Define the function $f+g$ by $f+g: x \mapsto f(x) + g(x)$.

Example If $f(x) = 2x^2 + 1$ and $g(x) = x^2 + 2x + 3$, then
$$f+g: x \mapsto 2x^2 + 1 + x^2 + 2x + 3$$
This formula can be simplified by combining like terms, as on page 88
$$f+g: x \mapsto 3x^2 + 2x + 4$$

2. Multiplication: Define the function $f \times g$ by $f \times g: x \mapsto f(x)g(x)$.

Example   For the functions f and g defined in the example above

$$f \times g(x) = (2x^2 + 1)(x^2 + 2x + 3)$$
$$= (2x^2 + 1)x^2 + (2x^2 + 1)2x + (2x^2 + 1)3$$
$$= 2x^2x^2 + x^2 + 2x^22x + 2x + 2x^23 + 3$$
$$= 2x^4 + x^2 + 4x^3 + 2x + 6x^2 + 3$$
$$= 2x^4 + 4x^3 + 7x^2 + 2x + 3$$

See page 88 for the methods used to simplify the expressions.

3. Composition of functions: This is defined in the same way as composition of mappings (page 80). $f \circ g(x)$, or $fg(x)$, means work out the value of $g(x)$ *and then put the result into the* f *formula*. Remember that, in the composition fg, g *is done first*.

Example $f(x) = 2x^2 - 3$ and $g(x) = 5x + 1$. The easiest method is to make the flow diagrams for f and g first

$f: x \rightarrow$ | square | $\rightarrow$ | $\times 2$ | $\rightarrow$ | -3 | $\rightarrow$

$g: x \rightarrow$ | $\times 5$ | $\rightarrow$ | $+1$ | $\rightarrow$

Now put these diagrams one after the other (g first)

$fg: x \rightarrow$ | $\times 5$ | $\rightarrow$ | $+1$ | $\rightarrow$ | square | $\rightarrow$ | $\times 2$ | $\rightarrow$ | -3 | $\rightarrow$

Forming the formula step by step

$$x, \ 5x, \ 5x + 1, \ (5x + 1)^2, \ 2(5x + 1)^2, \ 2(5x + 1)^2 - 3$$

so
$$fg(x) = 2(5x + 1)^2 - 3$$

which can then be simplified

$$fg(x) = 2(5x + 1)(5x + 1) - 3$$
$$= 2[(5x + 1)5x + (5x + 1)1] - 3$$
$$= 2[5x5x + 5x + 5x + 1] - 3$$
$$= 2[25x^2 + 10x + 1] - 3$$
$$= 50x^2 + 20x + 2 - 3$$
$$fg(x) = 50x^2 + 20x - 1$$

The formula can be found in another way, without using diagrams. This is particularly important since not all functions have diagrams.

Examples

1. If
$$f(x) = 2x - 1$$
$$f(2x) = 2(2x) - 1 \qquad \text{replace } x \text{ by } 2x \text{ in the formula}$$
$$= 4x - 1$$

2. $$f(x) = \frac{2x - 1}{x + 1} \qquad g(x) = x^2 - 2$$

Put the $g(x)$ formula into the f formula in place of the argument x

$$
\begin{aligned}
fg(x) &= f(g(x)) \\
&= f(x^2 - 2) \\
&= \frac{2(x^2 - 2) - 1}{(x^2 - 2) + 1} \\
&= \frac{2x^2 - 4 - 1}{x^2 - 2 + 1} \\
&= \frac{2x^2 - 5}{x^2 - 1}
\end{aligned}
$$

Note: Although multiplication and addition are commutative operations on the set of function $\mathscr{F}$, composition is *not*. fg and gf are usually different functions.

Exercise: If $f(x) = 2x^2 - 3$ and $g(x) = 5x + 1$, find $gf(x)$ and verify that it is not the same as $fg(x)$.

Composition is the most common way of combining two functions.

The identity function

The **identity function** leaves each element of the domain unchanged, it has formula $I: x \mapsto x$ or $I(x) = x$.

Inverse functions and equations

Functions are mappings and so may have inverses (page 81). A function f

associates a value of x with its image y. The **inverse function** f^{-1} produces a value of x given a value of y.

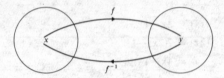

Example   If $f(1) = 3$ then $f^{-1}(3) = 1$.

If the function has a flow diagram, its inverse can be found by
  (i) replacing each step by its opposite, and
  (ii) reversing the flow.

Example $f : x \mapsto \dfrac{2x-1}{3}$ has diagram

$$x \to \boxed{\times 2} \to \boxed{-1} \to \boxed{\div 3} \to f(x)$$

inverting

$$f^{-1}(x) \leftarrow \boxed{\div 2} \leftarrow \boxed{+1} \leftarrow \boxed{\times 3} \leftarrow x$$

The resulting formula is $f^{-1}(x) = \dfrac{3x+1}{2}$

Suppose that we know the image of x is 2. Then $f(x) = 2$. This leads to the **equation**

$$\frac{2x-1}{3} = 2$$

Using the inverse, $x = f^{-1}(2)$. This can be calculated from the f^{-1} formula

$$f^{-1}(2) = \frac{3(2)+1}{2}$$

$$= \frac{7}{2}$$

$$= 3 \cdot 5$$

The **solution** of the equation $(2x-1)/3 = 2$ is $x = 3 \cdot 5$. A more complete discussion of equations and their solutions begins on page 114.

The following table lists operations and their opposites, which you will need to know when reversing flow diagrams.

Operation	+	−	×	÷	square	$\sqrt{}$	cube	$\sqrt[3]{}$	take reciprocal
Inverse	−	+	÷	×	$\sqrt{}$	square	$\sqrt[3]{}$	cube	take reciprocal

Taking the reciprocal is its own opposite since

$$\frac{1}{\dfrac{1}{x}} = 1 \div \frac{1}{x} = 1 \times \frac{x}{1} = \frac{x}{1} = x$$

The inverse of f ∘ g

The diagram for $f \circ g$ can be shown in the form

$$x \rightarrow \boxed{\quad g \quad} \rightarrow \boxed{\quad f \quad} \rightarrow fg(x)$$

Reversing this and replacing each block by its reverse

$$\leftarrow \boxed{\quad g^{-1} \quad} \leftarrow \boxed{\quad f^{-1} \quad} \leftarrow x$$

gives

$$(f \circ g)^{-1} = g^{-1} \circ f^{-1} \qquad\qquad \text{the order of } f \text{ and } g \text{ is reversed}$$

Example If $f: x \mapsto 2x^2 - 3$ and $g: x \mapsto 1 + x$, find formulae for $fg(x)$ and $(fg)^{-1}(x)$.

Answer
$$x \rightarrow \boxed{\quad +1 \quad} \rightarrow \boxed{\text{ square }} \rightarrow \boxed{\quad \times 2 \quad} \rightarrow \boxed{\quad -3 \quad} \rightarrow$$

$$\underbrace{\qquad\qquad}_{g} \qquad \underbrace{\qquad\qquad\qquad\qquad\qquad}_{f}$$

so $fg(x) = 2(x+1)^2 - 3$.
Reversing the diagram

$$\leftarrow \boxed{\quad -1 \quad} \leftarrow \boxed{\quad \sqrt{} \quad} \leftarrow \boxed{\quad \div 2 \quad} \leftarrow \boxed{\quad +3 \quad} \leftarrow x$$

which has formula

$$(fg)^{-1}(x) = \sqrt{\frac{x+3}{2} - 1}$$

A method for finding inverses of more complicated functions like

$$f(x) = \frac{1+x^2}{1-x}$$

can be found on page 136.

Examples

1. If $f: x \mapsto \dfrac{x-3}{x^2+2}$, evaluate $f(^-3)$.

Answer

$$f(^-3) = \frac{(^-3)-3}{(^-3)^2+2} \qquad \text{put } x = ^-3 \text{ in the formula, use brackets}$$

$$= \frac{^-6}{9+2} \qquad\qquad (^-3)^2 = {}^+9$$

$$= \frac{^-6}{11}$$

2. The domain of the mapping $f: x \mapsto 2+x^2$ is $^-2 \leqslant x \leqslant {}^+2$. Describe the range of this function as an inequality.

Answer

The range is given by

$$2 \leqslant y \leqslant 6$$

where $y = f(x)$

$^-2 \leqslant x$ means that x is greater than or equal to $^-2$ (see page 143)
$(^-2)^2 = {}^+4 = (^+2)^2$

3. $f: x \mapsto 1/x^2$ and g: $x \mapsto 2x+3$. Express gf as a formula in x.

Answer

$$gf(x) = g(f(x))$$

$$= g\left(\frac{1}{x^2}\right) \qquad \text{put } 1/x^2 \text{ in place of } x \text{ in the } g \text{ formula}$$

$$= 2\left(\frac{1}{x^2}\right)+3$$

$$= \frac{2}{x^2}+3$$

4. If $f: x \mapsto 1 - 3x$, find $f(3)$ and complete the statement $f^{-1}: x \mapsto \dots$

Answer

$$f(3) = 1 - 3(3) \qquad \text{insert } x = 3$$
$$= 1 - 9$$
$$= {}^-8$$

f has diagram

$$x \rightarrow \boxed{\times 3} \rightarrow \boxed{\text{take from } 1} \rightarrow 1 - 3x$$

reversing

$$\leftarrow \boxed{\div 3} \leftarrow \boxed{\text{take from } 1} \leftarrow x$$

(Notice that 'take from 1' is its own opposite.)

which has formula

$$f^{-1}: x \mapsto \frac{1-x}{3}$$

5. The function f has domain $\mathbb{N}$ and range $\{0, 1, 2, 3, 4\}$ and is defined by $f: n \mapsto$ the remainder when n is divided by 5.
   (a) write down the set of values of $f(2n)$,
   (b) write down the set of values of $f(n^2)$.

Answer
   (a) $f(n)$ has range $\{0, 1, 2, 3, 4,\}$
      0, 5, 10, 15, ... are all mapped to 0   find the remainders
      1, 6, 11, 16, ... are mapped to 1
      2, 7, 12, 17, ... are mapped to 2
      3, 8, 13, 18, ... are mapped to 3
      4, 9, 14, 19, ... are mapped to 4

   Doubling the numbers first
      0, 10, 20, 30, ... are mapped to 0   to find $f(2n)$
      2, 12, 22, 32, ... are mapped to 2
      4, 14, 24, 34, ... are mapped to 4
      6, 16, 26, 36, ... are mapped to 1
      8, 18, 28, 38, ... are mapped to 3

   The possible values of $f(2n)$ are
   $\{0, 1, 2, 3, 4\}$

(b) Squaring the numbers first
0, 25, 100, ... are mapped to 0
1, 36, 121, 256, ... map to 1
4, 49, 144, 289, ... map to 4
9, 64, 169, ... map to 4
16, 81, 196, 361, ... map to 1

the range of values of $f(n^2)$ is
$\{0, 1, 4\}$.

6. $A = \{1, 2, 3, 4\}$ and $B = \{2, 4, 6, 7\}$. Write down the cartesian product $A \times B$. If the relation R is defined as

$$R = \{(x, y): x \text{ and } y \text{ have a common factor other than } 1\}$$

where $x \in A$ and $y \in B$, list the elements of R, and also R^{-1}.

Answer

$A \times B = \{(1, 2), (1, 4), (1, 6), (1, 7), (2, 2),$ $A \times B$ = all possible ordered pairs
            $(2, 4), (2, 6), (2, 7), (3, 2), (3, 4), (3, 6),$
            $(3, 7), (4, 2), (4, 4), (4, 6), (4, 7)\}$

   $R = \{(2, 2), (2, 4), (2, 6), (3, 6), (4, 2), (4, 4), (4, 6)\}$

$R^{-1} = \{(2, 2), (4, 2), (6, 2), (6, 3), (2, 4), (4, 4), (6, 4)\}$ reverse order in the pairs

Notice that neither R nor R^{-1} are functions. 2 has more than one image in each case.

7. $N = \{0, 1, 2, 3\}$. Relations f and g are defined on $N \times N$ by

$$f = \{(x, y): 2y = 3x \pmod 4\}$$
$$g = \{(x, y): 2y = x + 1 \pmod 4\}$$

Write down the set of ordered pairs defining
   (a) $N \times N$ (b) f (c) g (d) f^{-1} (e) g^{-1}

State which of f, g, f^{-1} and g^{-1} are functions, giving reasons for your answers.

Answer

(a) $N \times N = \{(0, 0), (0, 1), (0, 2), (0, 3), (1, 0), (1, 1), (1, 2),$ all possible pairs
              $(1, 3), (2, 0), (2, 1), (2, 2), (2, 3), (3, 0), (3, 1),$
              $(3, 2), (3, 3)\}$

(b) $f = \{(0, 0), (2, 1), (0, 2), (2, 3)\}$ $2 \times 3 = 6 = 2 \pmod 4 = 2 \times 1$, and so on

(c) $g = \{(1, 1), (1, 3), (3, 0), (3, 2)\}$ 2×1 and $1 + 1$ are both $\equiv 2 \pmod 4$

(d) $f^{-1} = \{(0, 0), (1, 2), (2, 0), (3, 2)\}$ — reverse the pairs of f

(e) $g^{-1} = \{(1, 1), (3, 1), (0, 3), (2, 3)\}$ — reverse the pairs of g

f is not a function, since 0 is mapped to both 0 and 2.

a function must only map an element to a single image

g is not a function since 3 is mapped to both 0 and 2.

f^{-1} maps 2 to 1 and 0, and so is not a function. Similarly g^{-1} maps 3 to 0, 1 and 2.

Examination questions

1. Find $f(^-3)$ if $f: a \to a^2 - 4$ [SMP]

2. Multiply out $(a+2)(a+3)$, simplifying your answer [SMP]

3. $x^2 - 6x + 17$ may be written as

A $(x-6)^2 - 19$ B $(x-3)^2 + 8$ C $(x-3)^2 + 26$ D $(x-6)^2 + 53$

[AEB]

4. Given that $f(x) = \dfrac{2x+5}{x^2-2}$, the value of $f(^-2)$ is

A $-\tfrac{1}{2}$ B $-\tfrac{1}{6}$ C $\tfrac{1}{6}$ D $\tfrac{1}{2}$ E $\tfrac{3}{2}$ [LON]

5. Given that $f: x \mapsto \dfrac{1}{x}$ and $g: x \mapsto (x+1)^2$ then $gf(2) =$

A $\tfrac{1}{9}$ B $1\tfrac{1}{4}$ C $2\tfrac{1}{4}$ D $4\tfrac{1}{2}$ E $9\tfrac{1}{2}$ [LON]

6. Given that $f: x \mapsto \dfrac{1}{x}$ and $g: x \mapsto x + 2$ then $gf: x \mapsto$

A $\dfrac{1}{x} + 2$ B $\dfrac{x}{x+2}$ C $x + \dfrac{2}{x}$ D $\dfrac{1}{x+2}$ E $1 + \dfrac{2}{x}$ [LON]

7. $\qquad\qquad\qquad f: x \mapsto 3 - 2x$

(i) Calculate $f(2)$

(ii) Express f^{-1} in the form $f^{-1}: x \mapsto$ [SMP]

8. The flow chart $x \to \boxed{\text{multiply by 3}} \to \boxed{\text{add 2}} \to f(x)$ shows the function f.

(i) Complete $f: x \mapsto \dots$

(ii) Given that $g: x \mapsto \dfrac{1}{2(x-1)}$ complete its flow chart

$$x \to \boxed{} \to \boxed{} \to \boxed{\text{divide into 1}} \to g(x) \text{ for } g$$

(iii) Find $fg(0)$ [SMP]

9. $f(p)$ denotes the final digit of a positive integer p. For example $f(13) = 3$.

(i) Write down the set of possible values of $f(p^2)$.

(ii) Hence write down the set of possible values of $f(2p^2)$.   [CAM]

10. A function is defined for positive values of x by $f: x \mapsto (4+x^2)/3$. Find $f^{-1}(x)$, $1/f(x)$ and $f(-x)$.

11. If $P = \{0, 1, 2\}$ list the set of ordered pairs which define the cartesian product $P \times P = \{(x, y) : x \in P, y \in P\}$.

U and V are subsets of $P \times P$ defined by

$$U = \{(0,0), (1,2), (2,1)\}$$

$$V = \{(0,2), (1,0), (2,1)\}$$

Define each of U and V in the form $\{(x, y) : ax + by \equiv c \pmod{3}\}$ where a, b, $c \in P$.   [AEB]

Answers

1. 5

2. $a^2 + 5a + 6$

3. B

4. D

5. C

6. A

7. (i) -1 (ii) $\dfrac{3-x}{2}$

8. (i) $3x+2$ (ii) $\boxed{-1} \to \boxed{\times 2} \to \boxed{\text{divide into 1}} \to$

(iii) $\frac{1}{2}$

9. (i) $\{0, 1, 4, 5, 6, 9\}$ (ii) $\{0, 2, 8\}$

10. $\sqrt{3x-4}$, $3/(4+x^2)$, $(4+x^2)/3$

11. $\{(0,0), (0,1), (0,2), (1,0), (1,1), (1,2), (2,0), (2,1), (2,2)\}$

$U = \{(x, y) : x+y \equiv 0 \pmod{3}\}$ $V = \{(x, y) : 2x+y \equiv 2 \pmod{3}\}$

Section 5: Factorizing

Factorizing Expressions

The ease with which the value of a function can be calculated depends very much on the form of the expression.

Example   The formula

$$f(x) = 2x^4 - 4x^3 - 10x^2 + 12x$$

can also be expressed in the form

$$f(x) = 2x(x-1)(x+2)(x-3)$$

As an exercise, multiply out the brackets in this expression to verify that it gives the same answer as the first formula. Now evaluate $f(3)$. *Using the first formula*

$$
\begin{aligned}
f(3) &= 2(3^4) - 4(3^3) - 10(3^2) + 12(3) \\
&= 2 \times 81 - 4 \times 27 - 10 \times 9 + 12 \times 3 \\
&= 162 - 108 - 90 + 36 \\
&= 0
\end{aligned}
$$

This took several steps and you could easily make a mistake. Now use the second formula.

$$
\begin{aligned}
f(3) &= 2(3)(2)(5)(0) \\
&= 0 \qquad \text{since one of the factors is zero}
\end{aligned}
$$

The second expression is much more convenient for calculating values of the function. This expression is said to be in **factorized** form, as a product of factors. (The factors are 2, x, $x-1$, $x+2$, and $x-3$.)

In this section, methods for factorizing various types of expression are developed.

Common factors: Terms may have factors in common.

$$2x^2, 4x^3 \text{ and } 8x \text{ have common factors 2 and } x$$

(recall that $x^2 = x \times x$, $x^3 = x \times x \times x$). $2x$ is then also a common factor, it is the HCF of $2x^2$, $4x^3$ and $8x$ (see page 19).

Methods for Factorizing

The simplest expressions to factorize have just two terms.

Examples

1.
$$x + x^2$$

This can be written as $x + xx$.
The HCF of x and xx is x. Dividing out the HCF leaves

$$\cancel{x} + \cancel{x}x = 1 + x \qquad\qquad \text{since } x \div x = 1$$

this is the second factor

$$x + x^2 = x(1 + x) \qquad \text{separate factors in brackets}$$

2.
$$4x^2 + 2x^3$$

Write as $4xx + 2xxx$
HCF is $2xx = 2x^2$, dividing out leaves

$$^2\cancel{4}\cancel{x}\cancel{x} + 2\cancel{x}\cancel{x}x = 2 + x$$
$$4x^2 + 2x^3 = 2x^2(2 + x)$$

3.
$$6p^4 + 15p^{10}$$

HCF is $3p^4$. Divide out using the index laws of page 36

$$2 + 5p^6 \qquad\qquad p^4 \div p^4 = p^{4-4} = p^0 = 1$$
$$p^{10} \div p^4 = p^{10-4} = p^6$$
$$6p^4 + 15p^{10} = 3p^4(2 + 5p^6)$$

The next group of examples use the **difference of squares** formula.

$$(x - y)(x + y) = x^2 - y^2$$

Check this by multiplying out the brackets.

Examples

1.
$$x^2 - 16 = x^2 - 4^2$$
$$= (x - 4)(x + 4)$$

2. $3y^2 - 75 = 3(y^2 - 25)$ dividing out the common factor 3

$= 3(y^2 - 5^2)$

$= 3(y - 5)(y + 5)$

3. $4a^2 - 1 = (2a)^2 - 1^2$ since $(2a)^2 = 4a^2$

$= (2a - 1)(2a + 1)$

4. $9b^2 - 16 = (3b)^2 - 4^2$

$= (3b - 4)(3b + 4)$

5. $x^2 - \frac{1}{4} = x^2 - (\frac{1}{2})^2$

$= (x - \frac{1}{2})(x + \frac{1}{2})$

6. $(x - 1)^2 - 9 = (x - 1)^2 - 3^2$

$= (x - 1 - 3)(x - 1 + 3)$

$= (x - 4)(x + 2)$

Note: There is *no* equivalent factorization formula for $x^2 + y^2$.

Expressions of the form

$$x + 1, \quad 2x - 3, \quad \frac{9x + 2}{4}$$

are called **linear** expressions. They involve only the first power of the variable. If the second power is also included then the expression is **quadratic**, $3x^2 - x - 2$, $1 - 4x^2$, $2a^2 + 3a + 15$ are quadratic expressions. Some expressions with more than two terms are shown in the following examples.

Examples

1. $3x^2 - 6x + 9x^3 = 3xx - 6x + 9xxx$

The HCF is $3x$. Dividing out

$$3\!\!\!/xx - \overset{2}{6\!\!\!/x} + \overset{3}{9\!\!\!/}xxx = x - 2 + 3xx$$

The expression in factorized form is

$$3x(x - 2 + 3x^2)$$

2. $a^4 + 3a^3 - 6a^2 + a$

HCF is a. Dividing by a leaves

$$a^3 + 3a^2 - 6a + 1$$

$$a^4 + 3a^3 - 6a^2 + a = a(a^3 + 3a^2 - 6a + 1)$$

Quadratic Expressions

Quadratic expressions with two terms have already been dealt with. The most general quadratic expression has three terms, $ax^2 + bx + c$ where a, b and c are constant numbers called the **coefficients** of the expression.

The method for factorizing these expressions is quite complicated. The next examples should be studied carefully.

Examples

1. $x^2 - 3x + 2$ has an x^2 term

a middle term $-3x$

a constant term $+2$ including signs

The x^2 term factorizes as $x \times x$. Split these factors and place in brackets with the factorized constant term (unsigned)

$$(x \quad 1)(x \quad 2)$$

The sign of the constant term factorizes as $+ = (+)(+)$

$$\text{or } + = (-)(-)   \text{page 23}$$

Since the sign of the *middle term* is $-$, we choose $+ = (-)(-)$. Put these signs into the brackets.

$$(x - 1)(x - 2)$$

Check: by multiplying out

$$(x - 1)(x - 2) = (x - 1)x - (x - 1)2$$
$$= xx - x - x2 + 2$$
$$= x^2 - x - 2x + 2$$
$$= x^2 - 3x + 2$$

which is correct. Therefore $x^2 - 3x + 2 = (x - 1)(x - 2)$

The terms of some expressions may be factorized in several ways. Use a process of 'trial and error' to discover the correct one.

2. $x^2 + x - 6$ x^2 term is x^2
middle term is $+x$
constant term is -6

Split the x^2 term $(x \quad)(x \quad)$

6 factorizes as either 1×6 or as 2×3. Try 1×6

$$(x \quad 1)(x \quad 6)$$

The sign of the constant term is $- = (+)(-)$
Try

page 23

$$(x+1)(x-6)$$

Check by multiplying out, a quick method is to write

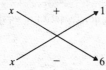

'Cross multiply' to get the x terms.
Multiply paired terms and add

$$-6 \times x + 1 \times x = -5x$$

Which is *not* correct.
If the $+$ and $-$ are changed round $(x-1)(x+6)$ the middle term would then be $+5x$ which is also wrong. We now try factorizing $6 = 2 \times 3$

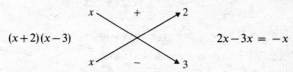

which is not correct. Change the $+$ and $-$ over

which is correct. Thus

$$x^2 + x - 6 = (x-2)(x+3)$$

You should still check by multiplying out the whole expression.

3. $\qquad\qquad\qquad 2x^2 + 5x - 7$

Factorize the x^2 term $\qquad (2x \quad)(x \quad)$

Factorize the constant term $7 = 1 \times 7$

and $- = (+)(-)$

First try

$(2x+1)(x-7)$

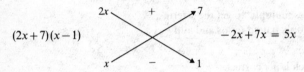

$x - 14x = -13x$

which is not correct.

Swapping the $+$ and $-$ will only result in a middle term $+13x$, which is also wrong.

Change the 1 and 7 over

$(2x+7)(x-1)$

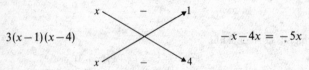

$-2x+7x = 5x$

which is correct

so, $2x^2+5x-7 = (2x+7)(x-1)$

4. $3x^2 - 15x + 12$

The terms have a common numerical factor 3.

Dividing out

$3(x^2-5x+4)$ as $3 \div 3 = 1$, $15 \div 3 = 5$, $12 \div 3 = 4$

$3(x\quad)(x\quad)$ splitting the x^2 term

$4 = 1 \times 4$ or $4 = 2 \times 2$, $+ = (+)(+)$ or $+ = (-)(-)$

Since the middle term has a minus sign, choose $+ = (-)(-)$

Try

$3(x-1)(x-4)$

$-x-4x = -5x$

which is correct.

With practice you should be able to choose the correct factorization fairly quickly. *Always check you answer by multiplying out.*

Exercises: Factorize the expressions

(i) $x^2 - 4x$ (ii) $x^2 - 4$ (iii) $x^2 - 4x + 3$ (iv) $3x^2 + 7x + 2$
(v) $3x^2 + 9x + 6$

Now consider $x^2 + 6x + 9$ which factorizes as

$$(x+3)(x+3) \qquad\qquad \text{Check this!}$$

We can write $(x+3)(x+3)$ as $(x+3)^2$

so $$(x+3)^2 = x^2 + 6x + 9$$

(A common mistake is to give $x^2 + 9$, you must multiply out fully!)
This is a special case of the general result

$$(x+y)^2 = x^2 + 2xy + y^2$$

also $$(x-y)^2 = x^2 - 2xy + y^2$$

You should remember these results as well as the difference of squares formula on page 106.

Example   Factorize $2x^2 + 8x + 8$

$$= 2(x^2 + 4x + 4)$$
$$= 2(x^2 + 2(2x) + 2^2)$$
$$= 2(x+2)^2 \qquad\qquad \text{as } y = 2 \text{ in the formula}$$

Simplifying Algebraic Fractions

To simplify a fraction like

$$\frac{x^2 - 1}{2x^2 + 2x}$$

factorize the numerator and denominator separately

$$x^2 - 1 = (x-1)(x+1) \qquad \text{difference of squares}$$
$$2x^2 + 2x = 2x(x+1)$$

The fraction becomes

$$\frac{(x-1)(x+1)}{2x(x+1)}$$

The factor $(x+1)$ is common to both top and bottom. We can divide out this factor to leave

$$\frac{(x-1)}{2x}$$

and the fraction is now in its lowest terms.

Note: You must factorize the numerator and denominator before you can divide out. For example, the fraction

$$\frac{x^2+1}{x^2-1}$$

cannot be simplified by 'cancelling' the x^2 terms.

When simplifying a fraction, you must multiply or divide the top and bottom by the same quantity.

Examination questions

1. $$3x^2-10x-8=$$
   A $(3x-4)(x-2)$ B $(3x-4)(x+2)$ C $(3x+4)(x-2)$
   D $(3x-2)(x+4)$ E $(3x+2)(x-4)$ [LON]

2. (i) Factorize $3x^2-48$,   (ii) simplify $\dfrac{x+4}{3x^2-48}$.   [JMB]

3. Which of the following divide $12x^2+5x-2$ exactly?
   A $6x-1$ B $6x+1$ C $3x-2$ D $3x+2$ [AEB]
   (A factor divides the expression exactly.)

4. Simplify as far as possible

$$\frac{x^2-1}{(2x-1)-(x-2)}.$$ [CAM]

5. Functions p and q are defined for all values of u by $p: u \mapsto 2u^2+3u+2$, $q: u \mapsto 3(u-1)$.
   (a) Find $p(1)$ and $q(p)1$.   (b) Write down and simplify an expression for

$q \circ p(u)$. *Show that this expression can be written as* $a(bu+c)(du+e)$ *for constants* a, b, c, d *and* e.

Answers
1. E
2. (i) $3(x-4)(x+4)$ (ii) $\dfrac{1}{3(x-4)}$
3. D
4. $(x-1)$
5. (a) 7, 18   (b) $3(2u+1)(u+1)$

Section 6: Equations

The equation on page 98 corresponds to an inverse function problem. More generally, a problem may specify certain conditions that the variable must satisfy. These conditions could be in the form of

Equations   such as $x - 3 = 1$, $x^2 + 2x - 3 = 0$, $x + \dfrac{1}{x} = 4$.

Inequalities $x < 3$, $x + 1 \geqslant 0$, $2x - 5 \leqslant 8$ (see page 143).

Other conditions could specify that the variable belongs to
                   certain sets. $x \in \mathbb{N}, x \in \mathbb{Q}$
                   $\{a \in N, a \text{ is divisible by } 3\}$

The values of the variable that satisfy all the conditions of the problem are called the **solutions** and form the **solution set**. Solutions of an equation are also called **roots**.

Solution Sets for Equations

In general, an equation is of the form $f(x) = g(x)$ where f and g are functions. If $f(x)$ and $g(x)$ are linear expressions then it is called a **linear equation**. The equation on page 98 is linear. It was solved by using a reverse flow diagram. It is not necessary to construct the diagram to follow this method.

Example   Find the solution set of the equation

$$\frac{2x + 7}{3} = 1$$

Multiply by 3

$$3\left(\frac{2x + 7}{3}\right) = 3$$

Dividing out the factors of 3

$$2x + 7 = 3$$

Subtract 7

$$2x + 7 - 7 = 3 - 7$$
$$2x = -4$$

Divide by 2

$$\frac{2x}{2} = -\frac{4}{2}$$
$$x = -2$$

The solution set is $\{^{-}2\}$

Each operation $(+, -, \times, \div)$ must act on *both* sides of the equation. The effect of each operation is to transfer a number from one side of the equation to the other.

The steps must be performed in the correct order. The 3 is dividing on the left. To reverse this *multiply* both sides by 3. To cancel the addition of 7, *subtract* 7 from both sides.

Examples

1.

$$\frac{3x - 5}{4} = \frac{2}{3}$$

$$3x - 5 = 4 \times \frac{2}{3} \qquad \text{multiply by 4}$$

$$3x - 5 = \frac{8}{3}$$

$$3x = \frac{8}{3} + 5 \qquad \text{add 5}$$

$$3x = \frac{8 + 15}{3}$$

$$3x = \frac{23}{3}$$

$$x = \frac{23}{9} \qquad \text{divide by, } \frac{23}{3} \div 3 = \frac{23}{3} \times \frac{1}{3} = \frac{23}{9}$$

The solution could also be given as a decimal.
To 2 decimal places the solution is $x = 2 \cdot 56$.

The solution may be restricted to $\mathbb{N}$, or $\mathbb{Q}$ as in the next example.

2. Find the solution of

$$\frac{2x+7}{3} = 3x-12$$

in the sets (a) $\mathbb{Q}$ (b) $\mathbb{N}$

$$
\begin{aligned}
2x+7 &= 3(3x-12) & \text{multiply by 3}\\
2x+7 &= 9x-36 & \text{multiply brackets out}\\
2x-9x &= -7-36 & \text{subtract } 9x \text{ and } 7\\
-7x &= -43 &\\
x &= \frac{-43}{-7} & \text{divide by } -7\\
x &= \frac{43}{7} & \text{cancel} - \text{signs}
\end{aligned}
$$

(a) The solution set is $\left\{\dfrac{43}{7}\right\} \subset \mathbb{Q}$.

(b) There are no solutions in $\mathbb{N}$.

The general idea is to get all the x terms on one side and the constant terms on the other.

3.
$$
\begin{aligned}
3\cdot5(2\cdot0x+1\cdot5) &= 7\cdot4 &\\
7\cdot0x+5\cdot25 &= 7\cdot4 & \text{as } \begin{cases} 3\cdot5\times2\cdot0 = 7\cdot0 \\ 3\cdot5\times1\cdot5 = 5\cdot25 \end{cases}\\
7\cdot0x &= 7\cdot4-5\cdot25 &\\
7\cdot0x &= 2\cdot15 &\\
x &= \frac{2\cdot15}{7\cdot0} &\\
x &= 0\cdot31 \quad \text{to 2 decimal places} &
\end{aligned}
$$

Notice that this method is more general than the flow diagrams used before.

The next set of examples are not linear equations, but can be transformed into linear equations.

Examples

1.
$$\sqrt{2-x} = 5 \qquad \text{square both sides to remove the } \sqrt{}$$
$$2-x = 25$$
$$2-25 = x$$
$$-23 = x$$

The solution set is $\{-23\}$.

2.
$$\frac{2}{1-x} = \frac{3}{x} \qquad \text{take the reciprocal of both sides, so that the fractions are turned over (see page 27)}$$

$$\frac{1-x}{2} = \frac{x}{3}$$

$$3(1-x) = 2x \qquad \text{cross multiply}$$
$$3-3x = 2x$$
$$3 = 2x+3x$$
$$3 = 5x$$
$$\frac{3}{5} = x$$

The solution set is $\left\{\dfrac{3}{5}\right\}$.

Sometimes the equation may not be completely known, but the solution is given.

Example
$$\frac{2x+3}{4} = \frac{x-a}{5}$$

has solution set $\{2\}$. Find the value of a,
Substituting $x = 2$

$$\frac{2(2)+3}{4} = \frac{2-a}{5}$$

$$\frac{4+3}{4} = \frac{2-a}{5}$$

$$\frac{7}{4} = \frac{2-a}{5} \qquad \text{an equation in } a$$

$$35 = 4(2-a) \qquad \text{cross multiplying}$$

$$35 = 8 - 4a$$
$$4a = 8 - 35$$
$$4a = -27$$
$$a = -\frac{27}{4}$$

Quadratic equations

The basic form of a quadratic equation is $ax^2 + bx + c = 0$ where a, b and c are constants, the coefficients of the equation. a cannot be zero, but b or c could be.

Examples

1. $x^2 = 4$ the same as $x^2 - 4 = 0$

This is the simplest type. Take square roots

$$x = \pm\sqrt{4}$$
$$x = 2 \quad \text{or} \quad x = -2 \qquad \text{remember } \textit{negative} \text{ roots also}$$

The solution set is $\{-2, 2\}$.

2. $z^2 = 3$

Take square roots

$$z = \sqrt{3} \quad \text{or} \quad z = -\sqrt{3}$$

The solution set is $\{-\sqrt{3}, +\sqrt{3}\}$. To 3 decimal place accuracy, the solutions are ± 1.732. There are no solutions in $\mathbb{Q}$.

3. $p^2 - 1 = 8$
$$p^2 = 9 \qquad \text{add 1 to both sides}$$
$$p = \pm\sqrt{9}$$
$$p = 3 \quad \text{or} \quad p = -3$$

Solution set is $\{-3, 3\}$.

4.
$$(x-1)^2 = 4$$
$$x-1 = 2 \quad \text{or} \quad x-1 = -2$$
$$x = 3 \quad \text{or} \quad x = -1 \qquad\qquad -2+1 = -1$$
Solution set is $\{-1, 3\}$.

The next examples are of the form $f(x) = 0$.

5.
$$x(x-1) = 0$$

The product of x and $x-1$ is zero. This means that one of them is itself zero.
$$x = 0 \quad \text{or} \quad x-1 = 0$$
$$x = 1$$
The solution set is $\{0, 1\}$.

6.
$$a^2 + 2a = 0$$

Factorize the left-hand side (see page 108)
$$a(a+2) = 0$$
So $\qquad\qquad a = 0 \quad \text{or} \quad a+2 = 0$
$$a = -2$$
The solution set is $\{-2, 0\}$.

7.
$$2x^2 = -3x$$

Put all the terms on the left, leaving 0 on the right
$$2x^2 + 3x = 0$$
$$x(2x+3) = 0 \qquad\qquad \text{factorizing}$$
$$x = 0 \quad \text{or} \quad 2x+3 = 0$$
$$2x = -3$$
$$x = -\frac{3}{2}$$
The solution set is $\left\{ -\frac{3}{2}, 0 \right\}$.

Note: The solution is $\{0\}$ as a subset of $\mathbb{N}$.

8.
$$3q^2 + 2q = 1$$
$$3q^2 + 2q - 1 = 0 \qquad \text{subtract 1 over}$$
$$(3q - 1)(q + 1) = 0 \qquad \text{factorize (see page 108)}$$
$$3q - 1 = 0 \quad \text{or} \quad q + 1 = 0$$
$$3q = 1 \quad \text{or} \quad q = -1$$
$$q = \frac{1}{3} \quad \text{or} \quad q = -1$$

The solution set is $\{-1, \frac{1}{3}\}$
It is important to make sure that the right-hand side is 0.
If you factorize the left-hand side first
$$3q^2 + 2q = 1$$
$$q(3q + 2) = 1$$
You *cannot* deduce anything like $q = 1$ or $3q + 2 = 1$!

9.
$$(2x - 1)(x + 3) = 15$$
$$(2x - 1)(x + 3) - 15 = 0 \qquad \text{right-hand side is now zero}$$
$$(2x - 1)x + (2x - 1)3 - 15 = 0 \qquad \text{multiply brackets}$$
$$2x^2 - x + 6x - 3 - 15 = 0 \qquad 2xx = 2x^2$$
$$2x^2 + 5x - 18 = 0$$
$$(2x + 9)(x - 2) = 0 \qquad \text{factorize}$$
$$2x + 9 = 0 \quad \text{or} \quad x - 2 = 0$$
$$2x = -9 \quad \text{or} \quad x = 2$$
$$x = -\frac{9}{2}$$

The solution set is $\left\{-\frac{9}{2}, 2\right\}$.

10.
$$x^2 - 6x + 9 = 0$$
$$(x - 3)(x - 3) = 0 \qquad \text{factorize}$$
so
$$(x - 3)^2 = 0$$
$$x - 3 = 0 \qquad \text{taking } \sqrt{\ } \text{ of both sides } (\sqrt{0} = 0)$$
$$x = 3$$

This equation has only *one* solution, $x^2 - 6x + 9$ is a perfect square.

Whenever $ax^2 + bx + c$ is a perfect square then the equation

$$ax^2 + bx + c = 0$$

has only one solution.

Not all quadratic expressions can be factorized. The next set of examples show the method of **completing the square**.

Examples

1. $\qquad x^2 + 2x + 1 = 7$ $\qquad\qquad x^2 + 2x - 6$ does *not* factorize

The left-hand side is a perfect square (see page 111)

$$(x+1)^2 = 7$$

take $\sqrt{\ }$ (+ and −) $\qquad x + 1 = \pm\sqrt{7}$

$$x = -1 \pm \sqrt{7}$$

One solution is found by taking the +, $x = -1 + \sqrt{7}$
the other by taking the −, $\qquad\qquad x = -1 - \sqrt{7}$
which are irrational numbers.

2. $\qquad x^2 + 2x = 3$

The left-hand side is not a perfect square. Add 1 to both sides.

$$x^2 + 2x + 1 = 4 \qquad\qquad \text{the left-hand side is now a square}$$

$$(x+1)^2 = 4 \qquad\qquad \text{take square roots}$$

$$x + 1 = 2 \quad \text{or} \quad x + 1 = -2$$

$$x = 1 \quad \text{or} \qquad x = -3$$

3. $\qquad z^2 + 4z = 7$

Compare the left-hand side with $(z+a)^2 = z^2 + 2az + a^2$ so that $4z = 2az$, $a = 2$

Add a^2 to both sides ($a^2 = 2^2 = 4$)

$$z^2 + 4z + 4 = 11 \qquad\qquad \text{the left-hand side is } (z+2)^2$$

$$(z+2)^2 = 11$$

take $\sqrt{\ }$ $\qquad (z+2) = \pm\sqrt{11}$

$$z = -2 \pm \sqrt{11}$$

4. $$x^2 - 5x + 1 = 4$$

The left-hand side is not a square.

$$x^2 - 5x = 3 \qquad \text{Subtract 1 over}$$

Divide the coefficient of x by 2, $-\dfrac{5}{2}$

square this number $$\left(-\frac{5}{2}\right)^2 = \frac{25}{4}$$

add to both sides $$x^2 - 5x + \frac{25}{4} = 3 + \frac{25}{4}$$

This makes the left-hand side a perfect square

$$\left(x - \frac{5}{2}\right)^2 = 3 + \frac{25}{4}$$

$$\left(x - \frac{5}{2}\right)^2 = \frac{12 + 25}{4}$$

$$\left(x - \frac{5}{2}\right)^2 = \frac{37}{4}$$

$$x - \frac{5}{2} = \pm\sqrt{\frac{37}{4}}$$

$$x = \frac{5}{2} \pm \sqrt{\frac{37}{4}}$$

$$x = \frac{5}{2} \pm \frac{\sqrt{37}}{2}$$

$$x = \frac{5 \pm \sqrt{37}}{2}$$

The solution set is $\left\{\dfrac{5 - \sqrt{37}}{2}, \dfrac{5 + \sqrt{37}}{2}\right\}$.

If the solutions are required as decimals

$$x = \frac{5 - 6\cdot083}{2} \quad \text{or} \quad x = \frac{5 + 6\cdot083}{2}$$

$$x = -0\cdot54 \quad \text{or} \quad x = 5\cdot54 \text{ to 2 decimal places}$$

5. $2x^2 + 6x + 1 = 0$ divide each term by 2
$x^2 + 3x + \frac{1}{2} = 0$ so that the coefficient of x^2 becomes 1

$$x^2 + 3x + 0{\cdot}5 = 0$$

$$x^2 + 3x = -0{\cdot}5$$ subtract the $0{\cdot}5$ over
$x^2 + 3x + 1{\cdot}5^2 = 1{\cdot}5^2 - 0{\cdot}5$ divide coefficient of x by 2, $\frac{3}{2} = 1{\cdot}5$
square $1{\cdot}5$ and add to both sides

$$(x + 1{\cdot}5)^2 = 1{\cdot}75$$

$$x + 1{\cdot}5 = \pm\sqrt{1{\cdot}75}$$

$$x = -1{\cdot}5 \pm \sqrt{1{\cdot}75}$$

The solutions are $x = -0{\cdot}172$ and $x = -1{\cdot}823$ (to 3 decimal places).
(*Note* again that $(x+1{\cdot}5)^2$ is *not* the same as $x^2 + 1{\cdot}5^2$, see page 111.)

When this method is used for the general case

$$ax^2 + bx + c = 0$$

the result is the *formula*

$$x = \frac{-b \pm \sqrt{(b^2 - 4ac)}}{2a}$$

This is an important result and should be remembered. Be very careful when substituting values of a, b and c particularly when they are negative.

Examples

1. $\qquad\qquad 2x^2 - 3x - 2 = 0$

$a = 2, \quad b = -3, \quad c = -2$ include the signs of the coefficients

$$x = \frac{-(^-3) \pm \sqrt{(^-3)^2 - 4(2)(^-2)}}{2(2)}$$ use brackets

$$= \frac{3 \pm \sqrt{9 + 16}}{4}$$ $-(^-3) = {}^+3$
$-(^-3)^2 = (^-3)(^-3) = {}^+9$

$$= \frac{3 \pm \sqrt{25}}{4} = \frac{3 \pm 5}{4}$$

$$x = \frac{3 + 5}{4} = \frac{8}{4} = 2$$

or $\qquad x = \dfrac{3 - 5}{4} = -\dfrac{2}{4} = -\dfrac{1}{2}$

The solution set is $\{-\frac{1}{2}, 2\}$.

2. $$3x^2 + 7x - 5 = 0$$

$a = 3, \quad b = 7, \quad c = -5$

$$x = \frac{-7 \pm \sqrt{7^2 - 4(+3)(-5)}}{2(3)}$$

$$= \frac{-7 \pm \sqrt{49 + 60}}{6}$$

$$= \frac{-7 \pm \sqrt{109}}{6}$$

$$= \frac{-7 \pm 10 \cdot 44}{6} \qquad\qquad \sqrt{109} = 10\cdot44 \text{ to 4 sig. fig.}$$

$$x = 0\cdot573 \quad \text{or} \quad x = -2\cdot91 \qquad\qquad \text{to 3 sig. fig.}$$

An examination question will often specify what accuracy to use for the solution. *If you do not follow their instructions you will lose credit.*

Show all of your working when solving an equation. Check your answers by substituting into the original equation to verify that it is satisfied.

The Factor and Remainder Theorems

The expression $f(x) = x^2 - 3x + 4$ can be factorized as

$$f(x) = (x-4)(x+1)$$

Each factor provides a solution of the equation $f(x) = 0$

$$x - 4 = 0 \quad \text{or} \quad x + 1 = 0$$

$$x = 4 \quad \text{or} \quad x = -1$$

so that $\qquad\qquad f(4) = 0 \quad \text{and} \quad f(^-1) = 0$

In general, if $f(x)$ is a polynomial (an expression which is a sum of terms in powers of x) and a is a solution of the equation $f(x) = 0$, then $x - a$ is a factor of $f(x)$.

This is called the **factor theorem**.

Example Show that $x - 4$ is a factor of

$$f(x) = 6x^3 - 23x^2 - 6x + 8$$

Answer Put $x = 4$

$$f(4) = 6 \times 4^3 - 23 \times 4^2 - 6 \times 4 + 8$$
$$= 6 \times 64 - 23 \times 16 - 6 \times 4 + 8$$
$$= 384 - 368 - 24 + 8$$
$$= 0$$

so $x - 4$ is a factor.

The expression can now be completely factorized. The factor $x - 4$ is taken out by long division

$$x - 4 \overline{)\ 6x^3 - 23x^2 - 6x + 8}$$

divide $6x^3$ by x to get $6x^2$
place $6x^2$ on top

$$\begin{array}{r} 6x^2 \qquad\qquad\qquad\quad \\ x - 4 \overline{)\ 6x^3 - 23x^2 - 6x + 8} \end{array}$$

multiply $x - 4$ by $6x^2$, and place below

$$\begin{array}{r} 6x^2 \qquad\qquad\qquad\quad \\ x - 4 \overline{)\ 6x^3 - 23x^2 - 6x + 8} \\ -\underline{6x^3 - 24x^2 \qquad\qquad\quad} \end{array}$$

$6x^2(x - 4) = 6x^3 - 24x^2$
subtract

$$\begin{array}{r} 6x^2 \qquad\qquad\qquad\quad \\ x - 4 \overline{)\ 6x^3 - 23x^2 - 6x + 8} \\ -\underline{6x^3 - 24x^2 \qquad\qquad\quad} \\ x^2 \qquad\qquad\quad \end{array}$$

$-23x^2 - (-24x^2) = x^2$
bring down the $-6x$ term

$$\begin{array}{r} 6x^2 \qquad\qquad\qquad\quad \\ x - 4 \overline{)\ 6x^3 - 23x^2 - 6x + 8} \\ -\underline{6x^3 - 24x^2 \qquad\qquad\quad} \downarrow \\ x^2 - 6x \qquad\quad \end{array}$$

divide x^2 by x to give x
put in the top expression

$$\begin{array}{r} 6x^2 + x \qquad\qquad\quad \\ x - 4 \overline{)\ 6x^3 - 23x^2 - 6x + 8} \\ \underline{6x^3 - 24x^2 \qquad\qquad\quad} \Big\downarrow \\ x^2 - 6x \qquad\quad \\ -\underline{x^2 - 4x \qquad\quad} \downarrow \\ -2x + 8 \end{array}$$

multiply $x(x - 4) = x^2 - 4x$
subtract

bring down $+8$

$$6x^2 + x - 2$$
$$x-4\overline{)\,6x^3 - 23x^2 - 6x + 8}$$
$$\underline{6x^3 - 24x^2}$$
$$x^2 - 6x$$
$$\underline{x^2 - 4x}$$
$$-2x + 8$$
$$\underline{-2x + 8}$$

$-2x \div x = -2$
multiply, $-2 \times (x-4)$
$= -2x + 8$

$$6x^3 - 23x^2 - 6x + 8 = (x-4)(6x^2 + x - 2)$$

Now factorize $6x^2 + x - 2 = (3x+2)(2x-1)$ page 108

So $f(x) = (x-4)(3x+2)(2x-1)$ is completely factorized.

The division was done in great detail, the next example shows how to set out a division:

Example   Divide $3x^3 - 2x^2 + 5x + 1$ by $x - 1$

Answer

$$3x^2 + x + 6$$
$$x-1\overline{)\,3x^3 - 2x^2 + 5x + 1}$$
$$\underline{3x^3 - 3x^2}$$
$$x^2 + 5x$$
$$\underline{x^2 - x}$$
$$6x + 1$$
$$\underline{6x - 6}$$
$$7$$

In this case $x-1$ does not divide exactly, a *remainder* of 7 is left.

Remainder theorem: When $(x-a)$ is not a factor of $f(x)$, a remainder is left when the division is carried out. The value of the remainder is given by $f(a)$.

We can use this result to check the remainder of the last example.

$$f(x) = 3x^3 - 2x^2 + 5x + 1 \qquad \text{divide by } x-1$$

when $x - 1 = 0, \quad x = 1$

Evaluate $f(1) = 3 - 2 + 5 + 1$

$$= 7$$

which is the required remainder.

Example   Find the remainder when $f(x) = 3x^3 - 2x^2 + x + 4$ is divided by $x - 2$.

Answer   When $x - 2 = 0$, $x = 2$. Evaluate

$$f(2) = 3 \times 2^3 - 2 \times 2^2 + 2 + 4$$
$$= 3 \times 8 - 2 \times 4 + 2 + 4$$
$$= 24 - 8 + 2 + 4$$
$$= 22$$

The remainder is 22.

Exercises:

1. Check this by dividing $f(x)$ by $x - 2$.
2. Do question 3 on page 109 using the factor theorem.

Equations and Modulo Operations   see page 56

Examples

1.
$$2x + 4 = 0 \ (\text{mod } 5)$$ this is also known as a congruence
$$2x = -4 \ (\text{mod } 5)$$

But $-4 = 1 \ (\text{mod } 5)$

So $2x = 1 \ (\text{mod } 5)$

$2x$ belongs to the set $\{1, 6, 11, 16, 21, \ldots\}$ since $\{1, 6, 11, 16, 21, \ldots\}$ are all equivalent to 1 modulo 5. Dividing by 2

$$x \text{ belongs to the set } \{\tfrac{1}{2}, 3, 11\tfrac{1}{2}, 8, 21\tfrac{1}{2}, \ldots\}$$

Taking solutions in $\mathbb{N}$, the solution set is $\{3, 8, \ldots\}$, which is infinite.

2.
$$3x - 5 = 1 \ (\text{mod } 7)$$
$$3x = 6 \ (\text{mod } 7)$$
$$3x \in \{6, 13, 20, 27, \ldots\}$$
$$x \in \{2, 13/3, 20/3, 9, \ldots\}$$

The solution set is

(a) $\{\ldots -5, {}^{-8}\!/3, {}^{-1}\!/3, 2, {}^{13}\!/3, {}^{20}\!/3, 9, \ldots\}$ as a subset of $\mathbb{Q}$

(b) $\{\ldots -5, 2, 9, \ldots\}$ as a subset of $\mathbb{Z}$

(c) $\{2, 9, \ldots\}$ as a subset of $\mathbb{N}$

Note: If a is a solution then so are $a+7, a+14, \ldots$

3. $$x^2 \equiv 4 \pmod 7$$

Find solutions in $\mathbb{N}$.

Answer x^2 is a member of $\{4, 11, 18, 25, 32, 39, 46, 53, 60, \ldots\}$
(which are all congruent to 4 modulo 7)
Taking square roots,

x is a member of $\{2, \sqrt{11}, \sqrt{18}, 5, \sqrt{32}, \sqrt{39}, \sqrt{46}, \sqrt{53}, \sqrt{60}, \ldots\}$

The solution set is $\{2, 5, 9, \ldots\} \subset \mathbb{N}$
An easier method is

$$x^2 \equiv 4 \pmod 7$$

so $\qquad x \equiv 2 \quad\text{or}\quad x \equiv -2 \qquad \pmod 7$

$\qquad \therefore x \in \{2, 9, 16, 23, \ldots\} \quad\text{or}\quad x \in \{-2, 5, 12, 19, \ldots\}$

Combining these sets and taking solutions in $\mathbb{N}$ the solution set is $\{2, 5, 9, 12, 16, 19, 23, \ldots\}$.

Examination questions

1. *Find the elements of the set* $N = \{n: n^2 - 9n = 0\}$.   [AEB]

2. *Solve the equations (a)* $7 - 3p = 2$ *(b)* $4q = q^2$
(c) $2x^2 - 9x - 5 = 0$ [AEB]

3. *Solve the equation* $x^2 + x + 3 = 0$ *(mod 5)*
 (i) when $x \in \{0, 1, 2, 3, 4\}$
 (ii) when $x \in \{227, 228, 229, 230, 231\}$ [AEB]

4. *Solve the equations (i)* $x^2 - 4 = 0$,   *(ii)* $x^2 - 4x = 0$,
(iii) $x^2 - 4x + 3 = 0$.   [LON]

5. Solve the equation $\dfrac{2}{x} - \dfrac{3}{2} = \dfrac{1}{3}$.

6. Find the values of x for which $\dfrac{(x+3)}{(x-2)} = \dfrac{(3x+2)}{x}$.

7. The sum of 3, −5 and a is zero. Find a. [SMP]

8. One solution of $2x(x\ldots) = 0$ is $x = 3$. Complete the equation.

9. Given that x is a real number, the equation $x(x^2+9) = 0$ has
(a) no solutions, (b) 1 solution, (c) 2 solutions, (d) 3 solutions.

[SMP]

10. Solve the equation $1 \cdot 76(x-5) = 6 \cdot 60$. [SMP]

11. (i) Write the number 143_8 in base ten.
  (ii) Express the number 143_n in terms of n.
  (iii) If $143_n = 99_{ten}$, use your answer to (ii) to write down an equation for n.
  (iv) Multiply out $(n+1)(n+3)$.
  (v) By taking possible pairs of factors of 99, or otherwise, find the (positive) value of n which is a solution of the equation of part (iii). [SMP]
(See page 51)

12. Given the equation $x^2 - 10x + k = 0$, find the value of k in each of the following cases.
  (i) The roots of the equation are 0 and 10.
  (ii) The roots of the equation are equal. [CAM]
Note: The equation has equal roots when the expression is a perfect square.

13. Solve the equation $\dfrac{p-2}{4} - \dfrac{9-p}{3} = 0$ [CAM]

14. It is stated that you can find the temperature by counting the chirps of the snowy tree cricket. The relationship is given by

$$T = 40 + \dfrac{N}{4}$$

where *T* is the temperature in °F and *N* is the number of chirps per minute.

  (i) State the temperature when the chirping rate is 60 per minute.
 (ii) What chirping rate would give the temperature of $T = 65$?
(iii) At what temperature will the cricket cease to chirp?
(iv) The relation between *T*, temperature in °F, and *C*, temperature in °C, is

$$T = 32 + \tfrac{9}{5}C$$

Find a formula for *C* in terms of *N*, giving your answer as simply as you can.   [SMP]

15. Solve the equations

(i) $4(x-3)-(x-2) = 5$,   (ii) $\dfrac{3}{y}+9 = 0$,   (iii) $z^2+4z = 0$ [CAM]

16. Show that $x-4$ is a factor of $6x^3-23x^2-6x+8$ and factorize this expression completely. Hence write down the solutions of the equation $6x^3-23x^2-6x+8 = 0$

(a) in the set of rational numbers,
(b) in the set of integers.   [LON]

Answers

  1. $\{0, 9\}$
  2. (a) $\tfrac{5}{3}$ (b) $\{0, 4\}$ (c) $\{-\tfrac{1}{2}, 5\}$
  3. (i) $\{1, 3\}$ (ii) $\{228, 231\}$
  4. (i) ± 2 (ii) $0, 4$ (iii) $1, 3$
  5. $\tfrac{12}{11}$
  6. $-0{\cdot}5, 4$
  7. 2
  8. $2x(x-3) = 0$
  9. (b)
 10. $8{\cdot}75$
 11. (i) 99 (ii) n^2+4n+3 (iii) $n^2+4n+3 = 99$ (iv) n^2+4n+3
     (v) 8
 12. (i) 0 (ii) 25
 13. 6
 14. (i) $55°F$ (ii) 100 (iii) $40°F$ (iv) $C = \tfrac{40}{9} + \tfrac{5N}{36}$
 15. (i) 5 (ii) $-\tfrac{1}{3}$ (iii) $0, -4$
 16. (a) $\{-\tfrac{1}{2}, \tfrac{2}{3}, 4\}$ (b) $\{4\}$

Section 7: Identities, Simultaneous Equations and Inequalities

---

Identities

When an expression is rewritten in a different form

$$(x+2)^2 \equiv x^2 + 4x + 4$$

both sides are equal for *any* value of x. This is called an **identity** and the 3-bar $\equiv$ sign is used to distinguish it from an equation. An equation is satisfied by a subset of the values of x while an identity is satisfied by all of them.

Examples

1.

$$x(x+1) \equiv x^2 + x \qquad \text{obtained by multiplying out brackets}$$

2.

$$2(x+1)^2 - 5 \equiv 2x^2 + 4x - 3$$

3. Find the value of k for which

$$(3x - k)^2 + 1 \equiv 9x^2 - 12x + 5$$

for all values of x.

Answer Left-hand side $= 9x^2 - 6kx + k^2 + 1$

Comparing with the right-hand side, we must have

$$9 = 9 \quad -6k = -12 \quad \text{and} \quad k^2 + 1 = 5$$

which is satisfied only when $k = 2$.

Formulae and Expressions with Several Variables

The formula on page 123 giving solutions of a quadratic equation contains the variables a, b and c. Given the values of a, b and c the value of x

can be calculated (as in the examples on page 123). Be very careful when substituting numbers into a formula. Put negative numbers in brackets.

Example   Find the value of

$$V = \frac{2ab + c^2}{3d}$$

when $a = {}^-1, b = 2, c = {}^-3$ and $d = 4$.

Answer
$$V = \frac{2({}^-1)(2) + ({}^-3)^2}{3(4)}$$

$$= \frac{{}^-4 + 9}{12}$$

$$= \frac{5}{12}$$

The variable V is calculated from the values of the variables a, b, c and d. It is called the **subject** of the formula.

Flow diagrams can be used in the **rearrangement** of formulae.

Example

$$V = \frac{2ab + c^2}{3d}$$

is a formula giving values of V. Rearrange this to give a in terms of b, c, d and V.

Answer   Draw a flow diagram for V, treating b, c and d *as if they were constants* and a as the variable

$$a \rightarrow \boxed{\times 2b} \rightarrow \boxed{+c^2} \rightarrow \boxed{\div 3d} \rightarrow V$$

$$\text{reverse } a \leftarrow \boxed{\div 2b} \leftarrow \boxed{-c^2} \leftarrow \boxed{\times 3d} \leftarrow V$$

The corresponding formula builds up as

$$V, 3dV, 3dV - c^2$$

following the steps of the diagram. Finally

$$a = \frac{3dV - c^2}{2b}$$

Examples

1. Make x the subject of the formula

$$y = \sqrt{\frac{x-1}{2}}$$

(that is, write x in terms of y)
Flow diagram

$$x \rightarrow \boxed{-1} \rightarrow \boxed{\div 2} \rightarrow \boxed{\sqrt{}} \rightarrow y$$

$$x \leftarrow \boxed{+1} \leftarrow \boxed{\times 2} \leftarrow \boxed{\text{square}} \leftarrow y \qquad \text{reverse}$$

$$2y^2 + 1 \leftarrow 2y^2 \leftarrow y^2$$

$$x = 2y^2 + 1$$

2. Rearrange $\qquad z = \dfrac{a+b}{a-b}$

to give a in terms of b and z.
Since a appears twice in the formula, there is no obvious flow diagram. We use the method developed for solving equations – regard a as the variable and b and z as constants.

$$z = \frac{a+b}{a-b}$$

$$(a-b)z = a+b \qquad\qquad \text{multiply by } (a-b)$$

$$az - bz = a+b \qquad\qquad \text{multiply out}$$

$$az - a = bz + b \qquad\qquad \text{put } a \text{ terms on the left}$$

$$a(z-1) = b(z+1) \qquad\qquad \text{factorize}$$

$$a = \frac{b(z+1)}{(z-1)} \qquad\qquad \text{divide by } (z-1)$$

3. Make s the subject of the formula

$$r = \left(\frac{s+1}{2t}\right)^2$$

$$\sqrt{r} = \frac{s+1}{2t} \qquad\qquad \text{take } \sqrt{} \text{ of both sides}$$

$$2t\sqrt{r} = s+1 \qquad\qquad \text{multiply } 2t \text{ across}$$

$$2t\sqrt{r-1} = s \text{ or } s = 2t\sqrt{r-1} \qquad \text{subtract 1}$$

Simplifying and factorizing

The methods are just the same as for single variable expressions.

Examples

1. Simplify $(2x+3y)(x-5y)$

$$\begin{aligned} &= (2x+3y)x-(2x+3y)5y &&\text{multiply by first set of brackets}\\ &= 2xx+3yx-2x5y-3y5y &&-(+) = -\\ &= 2x^2+3xy-10xy-15y^2 &&\text{multiplication is commutative}\\ &= 2x^2-7xy-15y^2 \end{aligned}$$

$3xy$ and $-10xy$ have the same variables with the *same powers*. They are like terms and can be combined to make $3xy-10xy = -7xy$.

2. Simplify $(2a+b)^2$

$$\begin{aligned} (2a+b)^2 &= (2a+b)(2a+b)\\ &= (2a+b)2a+(2a+b)b\\ &= 2a2a+b2a+2ab+bb &&\text{distributive law (page 63)}\\ &= 4a^2+2ab+2ab+b^2\\ &= 4a^2+4ab+b^2 &&\text{adding } 2ab+2ab = 4ab \end{aligned}$$

Alternatively, use the formula $(x+y)^2 = x^2+2xy+y^2$ (page 111) with $x = 2a$ and $y = b$.

$$\begin{aligned} (2a+b)^2 &= (2a)^2+2(2a)b+b^2\\ &= 4a^2+4ab+b^2 \end{aligned}$$

3. Simplify (a) $\dfrac{18a^3}{16b^4} \times \dfrac{3a}{4b}$ (b) $\dfrac{18a^3}{16b^4} \div \dfrac{3a}{4b}$

(a) $\dfrac{18a^3 \times 3a}{16b^4 \times 4b} = \dfrac{18 \times 3 \times a^3 \times a}{16 \times 4 \times b^4 \times b}$

$$= \frac{^9\cancel{18} \times 3 \times a^4}{_8\cancel{16} \times 4 \times b^5} \qquad \begin{array}{l} a^3a = a^4, b^4b = b^5\\ \text{divide common factor 2} \end{array}$$

$$= \frac{27a^4}{32b^5}$$

(b) $\dfrac{18a^3}{16b^4} \div \dfrac{3a}{4b} = \dfrac{18a^3}{16b^4} \times \dfrac{4b}{3a}$ (page 27)

$$= \dfrac{18a^3 \times 4b}{16b^4 \times 3a}$$

$$= \dfrac{18 \times 4 \times a^3 \times b}{16 \times 3 \times a \times b^4}$$

$$= \dfrac{{}^6\cancel{18} \times \cancel{4} \times a^2}{{}^4\cancel{16} \times \cancel{3} \times b^3}$$ $a^3 \div a = a^2$

$b^4 \div b = b^3$

$$= \dfrac{6a^2}{4b^3}$$ $18 \div 3 = 6$

$16 \div 4 = 4$

$$= \dfrac{3a^2}{2b^3}$$ divide by 2

Factorization also follows the methods used before.

Examples

1. $x^2 - 16y^4 = x^2 - (4y^2)^2$ difference of squares (page 106)

$$= (x - 4y^2)(x + 4y^2)$$

2. $x^2 + 4xy - 5y^2 = (x \quad\quad)(x \quad\quad)$ $x^2 = x \times x$

$(x \quad 5y)(x \quad y)$ $5y^2 = 5y \times y$

$= (x + 5y)(x - y)$ $- = (+)(-)$

Check by multiplying out.

3. $3abc + 6a^2b^3c^2d - 9ab^3c^2d^2$

$\dfrac{1}{3\cancel{abc}} + \dfrac{2}{\cancel{6}a^{2^1}b^{3^2}c^{2^1}d} - \dfrac{3}{\cancel{9}ab^{3^2}c^{2^1}d^2}$ HCF is $3abc$, divide out

$$= 1 + 2ab^2cd - 3b^2cd^2$$

The factorized form is $3abc(1 + 2ab^2cd - 3b^2cd^2)$

4. $3p^3q^2 + 2p^2q = 3pppqq + 2ppq$ HCF is $ppq = p^2q$

divide out ppq

$$= 3\cancel{pp}pq\cancel{q} + 2\cancel{pp}\cancel{q}$$

$$= 3pq + 2$$

$$3p^3q^2 + 2p^2q = p^2q(3pq + 2)$$

5.
$$xa - 2ya + 2bx - 4yb$$

Take the terms in pairs and factorize each pair

$$xa - 2ya = a(x - 2y) \quad 2bx - 4yb = 2b(x - 2y)$$

Giving
$$a(x - 2y) + 2b(x - 2y)$$

$(x - 2y)$ is now a common factor, divide out

$$a(x - 2y) + 2b(x - 2y) = (a + 2b)$$
$$xa - 2ya + 2bx - 4yb = (x - 2y)(a + 2b)$$

We are now in a position to find the inverse of functions such as

$$f(x) = \frac{(1 + x)}{(1 - x)}$$

(see page 100). The method is

(i) Set $y = \dfrac{(1 + x)}{(1 - x)}$

(ii) Rearrange this formula to give x in terms of y.

$$(1 - x)y = (1 + x) \qquad \text{cross multiply}$$
$$y - xy = 1 + x \qquad \text{remove brackets}$$
$$y - 1 = xy + x \qquad \text{put all } x \text{ terms on the right}$$
$$y - 1 = x(y + 1) \qquad \text{factorize}$$
$$\frac{y - 1}{y + 1} = x \qquad \text{divide by } (y + 1)$$

Hence
$$f^{-1}(y) = \frac{y - 1}{y + 1}$$

The argument of a function is usually x, so rewriting with x in place of y

$$f^{-1}(x) = \frac{x - 1}{x + 1} \text{ is the required inverse.}$$

Compound interest (see page 44)

Problems involving compound interest can be solved using the formula

$$A = P\left(1 + \frac{R}{100}\right)^n \text{ where}$$

A = amount accumulated after n years, P = initial investment (**principal**),
R = interest rate (as a percentage), n = number of years of investment

Example   £1 000 is invested at 10% compound interest per annum.
Calculate the interest earned in 5 years. (See also example 6 on page 47.)

Answer $A = 1\,000 \times (1 + {}^{10}\!/_{100})^5$ $(P = 1\,000, R = 10, n = 5)$

so $A = 1\,000 \times ({}^{110}\!/_{100})^5$

$\qquad = 1\,000 \times 1 \cdot 1^5$

$\qquad = 1\,610 \cdot 51$ (calculator with $\boxed{x^y}$ key)

The investment grows to £1 610·51 in 5 years.

Examination questions

1. $\dfrac{1}{p} - \dfrac{5}{4q} =$

$A\,\dfrac{4}{4q-p}$ $B\,\dfrac{4q-5}{p}$ $C\,\dfrac{-1}{pq}$ $D\,\dfrac{4q-5p}{4pq}$

2. $r^2\theta = \pi l, r =$

$A \pm \sqrt{\pi l - \theta}$ $B\,\dfrac{\pi^2 l^2}{\theta^2}$ $C \pm \sqrt{\dfrac{\pi l}{\theta}}$ $D\,\dfrac{\pi l}{\theta^2}$

3. *Factorize completely (a)* $4a^2 b - 6ab^2$ *(b)* $2xy - 7y + 4x^2 - 14x$
(c) $x^2 - 16y^4$ [AEB]

4. *Make b the subject of the formula* $y = \dfrac{m(a-b)}{a+b}$ [LON]

5. $w = \dfrac{x-y}{2a}$. *Express x in terms of a, w and y.*   [SMP]

6. $V = \dfrac{1}{2\pi\sqrt{L}}$. *Which expression for L is correct?*

(a) $\dfrac{1}{2\pi\sqrt{V}}$ *(b)* $\dfrac{1}{2\pi V}$ *(c)* $\dfrac{1}{2\pi^2 V^2}$ *(d)* $\dfrac{1}{4\pi^2 V^2}$ [SMP]

7. Express $\dfrac{a}{3} + \dfrac{b}{2}$ as a single fraction.　　　　　　[SMP]

8. Factorize (i) $3t - 6$　(ii) $pq + p$　(iii) $x(y+1) + (y+1)$.　[CAM]

9. *(a)* Given that $p + 1 = \dfrac{q}{r}$, express r in terms of p and q.

(b) Simplify, as far as possible, $\dfrac{x^2 - 1}{(2x - 1) - (x - 2)}$　　　[CAM]

10. *(a)* A reserved seat for a school concert costs £1·20, an unreserved seat 70p. If 40% of the seats are unreserved, calculate the mean *(average)* price of a seat if all are sold.

(b) If $x\%$ of the seats were sold at q pence and the rest at r pence, write down a formula for the mean price, m pence. Show that the formula can be rearranged in the form

$$x = 100\frac{(m-r)}{(q-r)}$$　　　[SMP]

(See page 349 for means.)

11. Given that quantities a, b, c, and d are connected by the relation $a = bc(a + d)$, express a in terms of b, c and d.

12. $x(y - 6·36) = 22·25$
 (i) Calculate the value of x when $y = 10$.
 (ii) Calculate the value of y when $x = 9·1$.
 (iii) There is one value that y cannot take, whatever the value of x. State this value.
 (iv) For what range of values of y is x negative?　　　[SMP]

13. Make x the subject of the formula $y = \dfrac{(x^2 - 7)f}{p}$　　　[LON]

14. £500 is invested in a three-year fixed interest bond. The interest is calculated at the end of every year at the rate of 10·25% per annum, and then added to the existing investment so that it also earns interest in subsequent years. Calculate the total value of the investment
(i) at the end of the first year, *(ii)* at the end of the three-year period.

　　　[SMP]

Answers
1. D
2. C
3. (a) $2ab(2a-3b)$ (b) $(2x+y)(2x-7)$ (c) $(x-4y^2)(x+4y^2)$
4. $a\left(\dfrac{m-y}{m+y}\right)$
5. $2aw+y$
6. (d)
7. $\dfrac{2a+3b}{6}$
8. (i) $3(t-2)$ (ii) $p(q+1)$ (iii) $(x+1)(y+1)$
9. (a) $\dfrac{q}{p+1}$ (b) $(x-1)$
10. (a) £1·00
11. $bcd/(1-bc)$
12. (i) 6·11 (ii) 8·81 (iii) 6·36 (iv) $y < 6·36$
13. $\sqrt{\dfrac{py}{f}+7}$
14. (i) £551·25 (ii) 670·05

Simultaneous Equations

An equation can have more than one variable.

Example $x+2y = 5$

Infinitely many pairs of values of x and y satisfy this equation. Given any value of x, find the value of y from the resulting equation

If $x = 1$ $1+2y = 5$
$$2y = 4$$
$$y = 2$$

$x = 1$, $y = 2$ is a pair of solutions which we can write as the ordered pair $(1, 2)$. $(2, \frac{3}{2})$, $(3, 1)$ are also solutions.

Given another equation in x and y with the corresponding solution set of ordered pairs, the intersection of the two solutions sets contains pairs (x, y) which satisfy both equations at the same time.

Example x and y satisfy $x + 2y = 5$ (i)

and $2x - y = 4$ (ii)

(The equations are labelled (i) and (ii) for later reference.) Find the solution set of these simultaneous equations.

Answer   Since the solution sets are infinite it would not be practical to list their elements in order to find those common to both sets. We use a quicker method, manipulating the equations directly

$$x + 2y = 5 \qquad \text{(i)}$$
$$2x - y = 4 \qquad \text{(ii)}$$

Multiply *all* terms of equation (i) by 2

$$2x + 4y = 10 \qquad \text{(iii)}$$

Equations (ii) and (iii) have the same x terms. Subtract these equations

$$
\begin{aligned}
2x - y &= 4 \\
{}^{-}\ 2x + 4y &= 10 \\
\hline
-5y &= -6 \qquad \text{subtract term by term}
\end{aligned}
$$

so $$y = \frac{6}{5}$$

Substitute this value of y into equation (i) (or (ii))

$$x + \frac{12}{5} = 5 \qquad\qquad \text{since } 2y = 2\left(\frac{6}{5}\right) = \frac{12}{5}$$

$$x = 5 - \frac{12}{5}$$

$$x = \frac{5}{1} - \frac{12}{5} = \frac{25 - 12}{5} = \frac{13}{5}$$

The solution set of the **simultaneous equations** (i) and (ii) is $\{(1\tfrac{3}{5},\ \tfrac{6}{5})\}$.

Examples

1. Solve the simultaneous equations

$$2a - 3b = 4 \qquad \text{(i)}$$
$$5a + 2b = 10 \qquad \text{(ii)}$$

Multiply equation (i) by 5 and equation (ii) by 2

$$10a - 15b = 20 \qquad \text{(iii)}$$

$$\underline{10a + 4b = 20} \qquad \text{(iv)}$$

$$-19b = 0 \qquad \text{subtract since the } a \text{ terms are the same}$$

$$b = 0$$

Substitute into equation (i)

$$2a = 4$$

$$a = 2$$

$a = 2, b = 0$ is the solution.

Check: Substitute into equation (ii) $5(2) + 2(0) = 10 + 0 = 10$ which is correct.

2. Solve the equations

$$p + 2q = 7 \qquad \text{(i)}$$

$$3p = 9 \qquad \text{(ii)}$$

This time, equation (ii) gives p directly

$$p = \frac{9}{3}$$

$$p = 3$$

Substitute into (i) $\qquad 3 + 2q = 7$

$$2q = 4$$

$$q = 2$$

The solution is $p = 3, q = 2$.

3. $\qquad\qquad\qquad 5y + 7z = 16 \qquad \text{(i)}$

$$y = 3z - 1 \qquad \text{(ii)}$$

We could rewrite (ii) in the form $y - 3z = -1$ and use the method of the examples above. Alternatively, substitute for y in equation (i)

$$5(3z - 1) + 7z = 16$$

which is an equation in z only. Simplifying

$$15z - 5 + 7z = 16$$

$$22z - 5 = 16$$

$$22z = 21$$

$$z = \frac{21}{22}$$

Substitute in (ii)

$$y = 3\left(\frac{21}{22}\right) - 1$$

$$= \frac{63}{22} - 1$$

$$= \frac{63 - 22}{22} = \frac{41}{22}$$

The solution pair is $y = \frac{41}{22}$, $z = \frac{21}{22}$

Check: Verify that these values satisfy equation (i)

Simultaneous equations can also be solved using graphs (page 163) or matrices (page 343).

Examination questions

1. *Solve the simultaneous equations*

$$2p - q = 6$$
$$2p + 3q = -6$$ [CAM]

2. *Calculate the values of g and h which satisfy the following pair of equations*

$$g - h = 5$$
$$2g - 3h = 13$$ [AEB]

3. *Solve the simultaneous equations*

$$x + y = 101_2$$
$$x - y = 11_2$$

writing your answers in base two.   [SMP]
(Remember to multiply and subtract in *base two*.)

Answers
   1. $p = 1 \cdot 5, q = -3$
   2. $g = 2, h = -3$
   3. $x = 100_2, y = 1_2$

Inequalities

When the equality sign (=) of an equation is replaced by one of the signs

$$> \text{ greater than, } \quad \geqslant \text{ greater than or equal to}$$
$$< \text{ less than, } \qquad \leqslant \text{ less than or equal to}$$

the result is called an **inequality**.

Examples

1. $2 < 4$ **2.** $3 > -1$ **3.** $\frac{1}{2} \leqslant 2 \leqslant 10$

Variables can appear.

4. $x \geqslant 2$. If $x \in \mathbb{N}$ then the solution set is $\{2, 3, 4, \ldots\}$.

5. $-3 < x < 2$. If $x \in \mathbb{Z}$, the solution set is $\{-2, -1, 0, 1\}$.

An inequality is *solved* when its solution set has been found.

Examples

1.
$$x + 3 < 5$$

Treat in the same way as an equation

$$x < 2 \qquad \qquad \text{subtracting 3 from each side}$$

The solution set can be shown as part of the number line by thickening.

The part of the line to the left of 2 is thickened and a circle is placed at the 2 division. Since $x = 2$ is not a part of the solution ($x < 2$) the circle is left open.

2.
$$2x + 4 \geqslant 10$$
$$2x \geqslant 6 \qquad \qquad \text{subtract 4}$$
$$x \geqslant 3 \qquad \qquad \text{divide by 2}$$

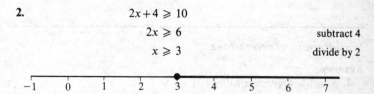

The circle at 3 is filled in to show that $x = 3$ is possible.

Any quantity can be added or subtracted on both sides of an inequality. Any *positive* quantity can multiply or divide on both sides. However, when multiplying or dividing with a *negative* quantity, the inequality sign is reversed

$$2 < 3 \quad \text{but} \quad -2 > -3$$
$$5 < 10 \quad \text{but} \quad -1 > -2$$

Examples

1.
$$-3x < 9$$
$$-x < 3 \qquad \text{divide by 3}$$
$$x > -3 \qquad \text{divide by } -1$$

2.
$$1-x \geqslant 2+x$$
$$1-2 \geqslant x+x \qquad \text{put } x\text{s on right, numbers on left}$$
$$-1 \geqslant 2x$$
$$-\tfrac{1}{2} \geqslant x \qquad \text{divide by } {}^{+}2$$

which can also be written as $x \leqslant -\frac{1}{2}$.

3.
$$\frac{2+3x}{7} < \frac{1-2x}{3}$$
$$3(2+3x) < 7(1-2x) \qquad \text{cross multiply, 3 and 7 are positive}$$
$$6+9x < 7-14x$$
$$14x+9x < 7-6 \qquad \text{add } 14x, \text{ subtract 6}$$
$$23x < 1$$
$$x < \frac{1}{23} \qquad \text{23 is positive}$$

Simultaneous Inequalities

Examples

1. x satisfies *both* inequalities $2x+3 > 7$ (i)

and $\hspace{5cm} 5-x \geqslant 1$ (ii)

Find the solution set (in $\mathbb{R}$).

(i) gives $\qquad$ $2x > 4$

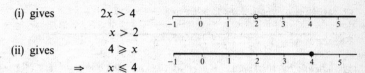

$\qquad\qquad\qquad x > 2$

(ii) gives $\qquad$ $4 \geqslant x$

$\qquad \Rightarrow \qquad x \leqslant 4$

The required solution set is the intersection of these sets. Find this by the overlap on the number lines

The solution set is $2 < x \leqslant 4$.

Note: If the solutions must be in $\mathbb{N}$ then the solution set is $\{3, 4\}$ (not 2).

2. $\qquad\qquad\qquad\qquad a - 3 \leqslant 7 \qquad\qquad\qquad$ (i)

$\qquad\qquad\qquad\qquad\qquad 2a + 1 > 3 \qquad\qquad\qquad$ (ii)

(i) gives $\qquad a \leqslant 10$

(ii) gives $\qquad 2a > 2$

$\qquad\qquad\qquad a > 1$

The overlap is

$\qquad\qquad 1 < a \leqslant 10$

Note: Inequalities such as $a > 2$ and $a < 4$ can be combined together as $2 < a < 4$. However, $x < 1$ or $x > 3$ *cannot* be combined to form $3 < x < 1$.

A chain of inequalities must give a correct statement when the middle link is removed

$\qquad\qquad 2 < a < 4 \Rightarrow 2 < 4$ which is correct

but $\qquad\qquad 3 < x < 1 \Rightarrow 3 < 1$ which is not

Examination questions

1. *Given that* $3 \leqslant 4x + 1 \leqslant 53$, *find*
 (i) the least integer value of x,
 (ii) the greatest integer value of x. $\qquad$ [CAM]

Hint: Split into the two inequalities $3 \leqslant 4x + 1$ and $4x + 1 \leqslant 53$.

2. *Make two copies of the number line*

and indicate by thickening a part of the line, the solution sets of the inequalities.

(i) $2x+1 < -3$ *(ii)* $-14 \leqslant 3x-2$

Hence find the values of x in the set of integers which satisfy both those inequalities simultaneously.   [LON]

Answers

1. (i) 1,   (ii) 13
2. $\{-4, -3\}$

Section 8: Coordinates and Graphs

Axes and Coordinates

Each value of the variable x corresponds to a point on the number line (page 29).

$$x=-2 \quad x=-1 \quad x=0 \quad x=1 \quad x=2 \quad x=3$$

Because the line is described by one variable, we say it is one-dimensional.

A **plane** is a flat surface, like this page. Two variables are needed to specify each point.

Choose a line across the plane as a base line. This is the **x-axis**. Draw a number line through the 0 of the base line and perpendicular to it. This is the **y-axis**, which measures the height above the base line.

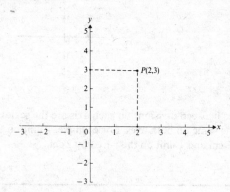

These **coordinate axes** meet at the **origin** 0.

The values of x and y for any point are called its **coordinates** and are written as an ordered pair. The diagram shows the point (2, 3) labelled P.

In this way we can identify the plane with the cartesian product $\mathbb{R} \times \mathbb{R}$. Other cartesian products are represented by subsets of the plane.

Examples

1. If $A = \{-1, 0, 1, 2, 3\}$
and $B = \{1, 2, 3\}$
then $A \times B$ is represented
by the points shown
in the diagram

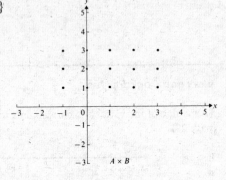

2. If $C = \{x \in \mathbb{R} : 1 \leqslant x \leqslant 2\}$
and $D = \{x \in \mathbb{R} : 3 \leqslant x \leqslant 5\}$
then $C \times D$ is the shaded region
in the diagram

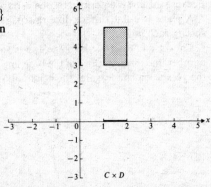

The distances between divisions on each axis are the **scales**. They do not have to be the same on both axes. For example, 1 unit on the x-axis can be given by 1 cm and 1 unit on the y-axis by 2 cm.

Functions and Graphs

Since a function is identified with a set of ordered pairs, a subset of $\mathbb{R} \times \mathbb{R}$

(page 84), then it is represented by a subset of the plane, called the **graph** of the function.

Example The points given by $(0, -3), (1, -1), (2, 1)$ are members of the graph of the function $f(x) = 2x - 3$

when
$$x = 0 \quad f(0) = 2(0) - 3 = -3$$
$$x = 1 \quad f(1) = 2(1) - 3 = -1$$
$$x = 2 \quad f(2) = 2(2) - 3 = \quad 1$$

Plot these points in the plane

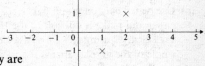

If more points are plotted, they are seen to lie along a straight line.

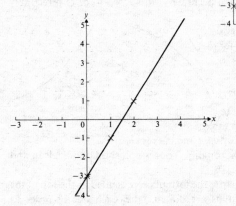

This line is the graph of the function $f(x) = 2x - 3$. This function is linear (see page 107), it has a straight line graph.

You need only plot two or three points of a linear function in order to draw the straight line. However, when drawing graphs of non-linear functions you need to plot several points. These points are then joined with a smooth curve to form the graph.

Note: The variables x and y are commonly used for points in the plane, but *any* two variables could be used. For example, speed–time graphs (page 182). The questions at the end of the section give examples using other variables.

Drawing graphs

Graphs should always be drawn neatly and accurately. Follow the guide-lines below.

(i) You are usually given the formula for the function and a set of values for x. The y values are found by calculation from the formula. Make sure that your calculations are correct – set the values out in a table (see the example below).

(ii) Use pencil *only* on graph paper, ink could easily smear across the paper and make it difficult to use the graph accurately. Draw the axes clearly, using the *correct scales*. Place the axes so that the whole of the graph paper is used – look at the ranges of values of x and y when deciding where to draw the axes.

(iii) Plot points clearly and accurately with a $\times$, $+$, or $\odot$ (preferably a $\times$).

(iv) Use a ruler for straight line graphs, but not for curves. Draw curves from the concave side.

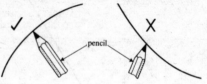

This will enable you to rest your arm on the table.
Draw straight lines *straight* and curves *curvy*!

(v) Rub mistakes out thoroughly. Your graph should look clean and attractive.

(vi) Label the axes, and write the formula represented at the top of the paper. If several graphs are drawn, label each one in order to distinguish them.

Example   Draw the graph of $f : x \mapsto x^2 - 3x + 2$ for $-2 \leqslant x \leqslant 4$. Use scales of 4 cm for 1 unit of x and 2 cm for 1 unit of y. First make a table

x	-2	-1	0	1	2	3	4
x^2	4	1	0	1	4	9	16
$-3x$	6	3	0	-3	-6	-9	-12
2	2	2	2	2	2	2	2
y	12	6	2	0	0	2	6

Include the sign with each term and *add* them all to obtain y. The constant term, 2, is repeated all along the third row. (It is a common error to multiply this by the x values!)

The y values are all positive, draw the x-axis near the bottom of the page. Since x ranges from -2 to 4, the y-axis is drawn a third of the way across the page. Use the correct scales.

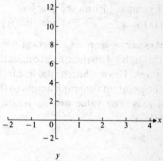

Now plot the points.

Join the points with a smooth curve.

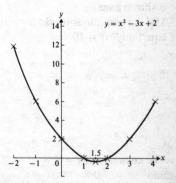

To obtain greater accuracy between the points $(1, 0)$ and $(2, 0)$, the value of y at $x = 1·5$ is calculated

$$f(1·5) = 1·5^2 - 3(1·5) + 2 = -0·25$$

Using graphs

A graph can be used to find further values of the function. This is generally easier than calculation.

Example   From the graph of $f(x) = x^2 - 3x + 2$ above, find $f(1\cdot 7)$.

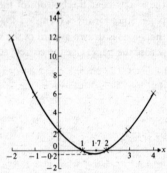

Answer   Drop a vertical line through $1\cdot 7$ on the x-axis to meet the graph. Draw a horizontal line from the point on the graph across to the y-axis. The value on the y-axis is $f(1\cdot 7)$.

When using a graph, show your construction lines: the examiner may only gives marks for *visible* methods.

The value obtained from the graph is $f(1\cdot 7) = -0\cdot 2$.

The accuracy of this method depends on how accurately you have drawn the graph. Further, the larger the scale, the more accurate is the graph.

The graph can also be used to find an x value for a given value of the function.

Example   The graph of the function $f(x) = 2x^2 - 2x + 7$ is shown here.
Use the graph to solve the equation $f(x) = 10$.

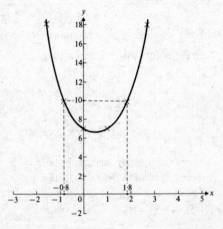

The answers are $x = 1\cdot 8$ and $x = -0\cdot 8$.

Graphs can be used to solve equations of the form
$$f(x) = \text{constant}$$
  (i) Draw the graph of $y = f(x)$.
 (ii) Draw a horizontal line through the given value on the y-axis.
(iii) Read off the x values for the points where this line meets the graph.
 (For equations $f(x) = 0$, the required points are where the graph meets the x-axis.)

Graphs can also be used for equations of the form $f(x) = g(x)$.
  (i) Draw the graphs $y = f(x)$ and $y = g(x)$ on the same axes.
 (ii) Find the points where the graphs meet. These give the x values which solve the equation.

Example
  (i) Draw the graph of $y = x^3/4$ for x between -3 and 3. Use scales of 2 cm for 1 unit of x and 1 cm for 1 unit of y.
 (ii) Use your graph to solve the equation $x^3 = 20$ to 1 decimal place.
(iii) On the same diagram, draw the graph of $y = 2x + 0.75$. Use these graphs to solve the equation $x^3 = 8x + 3$, also to 1 decimal place accuracy.
 (iv) The equation $x^3 = 4x + 2$ can be solved by drawing another line on the diagram. Write down the equation of this line.

Answer (i) Make a table of values

x	-3	-2	-1	0	1	2	3
x^3	-27	-8	-1	0	1	8	27
y	-6.75	-0.5	-0.25	0	0.25	0.5	6.75

(*Divide* the second row by 4 to obtain y.)

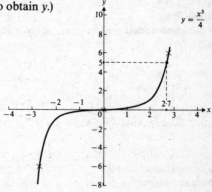

(ii) $$x^3 = 20 \Rightarrow \frac{x^3}{4} = 5$$

$$\Rightarrow y = 5 \qquad \text{since } y = \frac{x^3}{4}$$

Draw the horizontal line through 5 on the y-axis.
This line meets the graph when $x = 2 \cdot 7$.

(iii) $f(x) = 2x + 0 \cdot 75$ is a linear expression. The graph is a straight line – only 3 points need to be plotted.
(Choose values of x far apart for greater accuracy.)

x	-3	0	$+3$
$2x$	-6	0	6
$0 \cdot 75$	$0 \cdot 75$	$0 \cdot 75$	$0 \cdot 75$
y	$-5 \cdot 25$	$0 \cdot 75$	$6 \cdot 75$

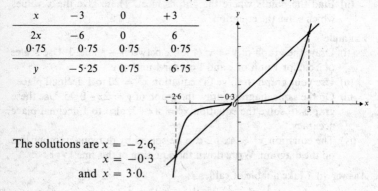

The solutions are $x = -2 \cdot 6$,
$$x = -0 \cdot 3$$
and $x = 3 \cdot 0$.

(iv) $$x^3 = 4x + 2$$

Divide by 4

$$\frac{x^3}{4} = x + 0 \cdot 5$$

Solutions are given by points of intersection of the graphs

$$y = \frac{x^3}{4}$$

and

$$y = x + 0 \cdot 5$$

The required line is $y = x + 0 \cdot 5$.

Maximum and minimum points – greatest and least values

You can use a graph to find greatest and least values of a function for a given range of values of the variable.

Examples

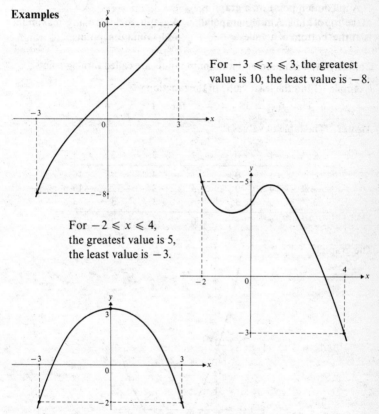

For $-3 \leqslant x \leqslant 3$, the greatest value is 10, the least value is -8.

For $-2 \leqslant x \leqslant 4$, the greatest value is 5, the least value is -3.

For $-3 \leqslant x \leqslant 3$, the greatest value of y is 3, the least value is -2. The range of the function is then $-2 \leqslant f(x) \leqslant 3$ for domain $-3 \leqslant x \leqslant 3$.

In the last example, the least value depends on how wide a range of values of x is taken, but the greatest value is the greatest possible value of the function. It is called a **maximum** value, corresponding to the **maximum point** on the graph.

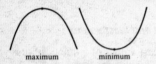

A maximum point on a graph is at the 'top of a hill'. A **minimum point** is at the 'bottom of a valley'.

A graph can have many 'maximum' and 'minimum' points.

Collectively, maximum and minimum points are called **turning points**.

Example   Find the least value of the function

$$f(x) = x^2 - 4x + 3 \quad \text{for } -1 \leqslant x \leqslant 4$$

Answer   The table of values is

x	-1	0	1	2	3	4
x^2	1	0	1	4	9	16
$-4x$	4	0	-4	-8	-12	-16
3	3	3	3	3	3	3
y	8	3	0	-1	0	3

The graph is

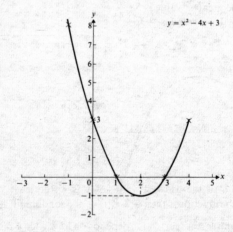

The least value is $y = -1$ (when $x = 2$).

Examination questions

1. *For* $2 \leqslant x \leqslant 10, f: x \mapsto 1 + 3/(x+1)$.

(a) Draw the graph of $y = f(x)$, plotting points for $x = 2, 3, 4, 5, 6, 7, 8, 9, 10$. Use 1 cm for 1 unit.

(b) Use your graph to solve the equation $1 + \dfrac{3}{x+1} = 1 \cdot 8$.

(c) By drawing a straight line on your diagram solve $1 + \dfrac{3}{x+1} = x + 5$.

2. *Taking a scale of 2 cm to represent one unit on the x-axis and 1 cm to represent one unit on the y-axis and using the same axes for both graphs, draw, for $-2 \leqslant x \leqslant 3$ the graphs of the functions*

$$f: x \mapsto x - 2 \text{ and } g: x \mapsto x^2.$$

Copy and complete the statements

$$gf: x \mapsto \ldots, \quad \text{and} \quad f^{-1}: x \mapsto \ldots$$

Using the same scales and axes draw the graphs of the functions

$$gf(x) \quad \text{and} \quad f^{-1}(x).$$

Find from your graphs the values of x for which

(a) $gf(x) = f(x)$, (b) $f^{-1}(x) = g(x)$.   [LON]

3. *A rectangular box has a square base of side x cm, height y cm and constant volume V cm^3. (See page 210.)*

The diagram is the graph of $y = \dfrac{V}{x^2}$ for $2 \leqslant x \leqslant 6$.

(i) Use the diagram to find V.

(ii) By adding a suitable straight line to the graph, or otherwise, find the approximate value of x for which the box is a cube.

(See page 210)

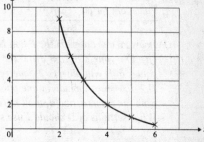

4. *A page from the instruction book with my camera is as follows:*

When the distance setting is at D metres, all objects between F metres and N metres from the camera are in focus. The diagram shows the approximate values of F and N. For example, when D = 5, all objects between 3 and 15 metres from the camera are in focus.

(For the scientifically-minded, the formula for the curves are –

for the F curve

$$y = \frac{7 \cdot 5D}{7 \cdot 5 - D}$$

and for the N curve

$$y = \frac{7 \cdot 5D}{7 \cdot 5 + D}.)$$

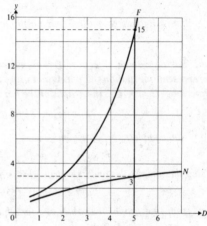

(i) Copy the table below and complete it, using the formula quoted above.

D	1	2	3	4	5
Values of y for the F curve	1·15	2·73			15
Values of y for the N curve	0·88			2·61	3

(ii) Draw on one diagram the F and N curves for values of D from 1 to 5.

(iii) (a) On your diagram draw the line y = 2·5. For what range of values of D will objects 2·5 metres from the camera be in focus?

(b) I wish to include in one photograph a hamster which is 2·5 m from the camera, and a small kitten which is 7·0 m from the camera. What settings of D should I use so that both animals are in focus?

[SMP]

5.

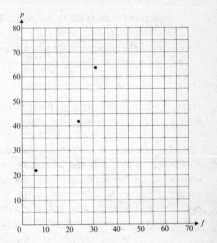

Player	fouls committed f	points scored p
George	16	36
Freddy	8	12
Harry	6	22
Maurice	24	42
Richard	48	72
Stewart	10	22
Thomas	32	64

Fouls committed (f) and points scored (p) by each of 7 players from a basketball squad are given in the table.

The manager calculates for each player a 't' value where t = p/f. The 't' value is a measure of usefulness to the side, players with lower values being less useful.

(i) (a) *Using a scale of 1 cm to 10 units on each axis, copy and complete the plotting of p against f for each player in the squad.*
(b) *Draw the line p = 3f/2, and label it clearly.*

(ii) *The manager drops his 3 least useful players and replaces them with players whose 't' value is better than any others in the squad. He then says that all his players have a 't' value of at least 'k'. Draw the line p = kf, label it clearly and state the value of k.* [SMP]

Hint: You may find it useful to read the section on gradients on page 175.

6. $A = \{x: 0 \leqslant x \leqslant 4\}$, $B = \{y: 0 \leqslant y \leqslant 2\}$,
$C = \{x: 2 \leqslant x \leqslant 5\}$ and $D = \{y: 1 \leqslant y \leqslant 5\}$.
On squared paper, illustrate each of the cartesian products $A \times B$ and $C \times D$ on a single diagram. Use two distinct forms of shading and give a suitable key. Indicate clearly on your diagram the set $(A \times B) \cap (C \times D)$.

[AEB]

7. *Function f is designed for all real values by f: $x \mapsto 3x^2 + 2x - 5$.*
   (i) Calculate $f(2\cdot12)$ and $f(-2\cdot12)$, to 3 sig. fig.
   (ii) Find the values of x for which $f(x) = 0$.
   (iii) Solve the equation $f(x) = f(-x)$.
   (iv) Sketch the graph of $f(x)$.

Note: When sketching a graph, it is not necessary to plot it accurately, only a rough guide to its shape and position is required.

8. *The number, n, of people who attend a school disco is given by $n = ax + b$, where x is the admission charge in pence and a and b are constants. 250 people attend if the admission charge is 30p, but only 190 people attend if the admission charge is raised to 50p. Write down two equations and hence find the values of a and b.*

   The disco produces an income of y pounds where

$$y = \frac{340x - 3x^2}{100}$$

Corresponding values of x and y are given in the table below.

x	0	20	40	60	80	100
y	0	56	88	96	80	40

Using a scale of 1 cm to represent 10 units on each axis, draw the graph of

$$y = \frac{340x - 3x^2}{100}$$

for $0 \leqslant x \leqslant 100$. Use your graph to find the admission charge that would produce the greatest income. The cost of hiring the equipment depends on the admission charge. For $0 \leqslant x \leqslant 40$ the cost is £50, and for $x > 40$ the cost is £70. Draw the lines $y = 50$ and $y = 70$ on your graph. Use your graph to find the admission charges that would just cover the cost of hiring the equipment. [CAM]

Answers
 1. (b) 2·75 (c) −0·21, −4·79
 2. $gf: x \mapsto (x-2)^2$, $f^{-1}: x \mapsto x+2$ (a) 2, 3   (b) −1, 2
 3. (i) 36   (ii) 3·3

Inequalities and Graphs

Graphs can be used for solving inequalities.

Example   If $f(x) = 3x - x^3$, draw the graph of $y = f(x)$ for $-3 \leqslant x \leqslant 3$. From your graph find the range of values of x for which $3x - x^3 \geqslant 1$.

Answer   The graph is

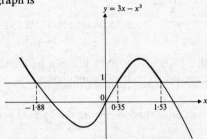

$f(x)$ is greater than 1 when the graph is above the line $y = 1$. This is shown by the thickened line on the graph. The corresponding values of x are $x \leqslant {}^-1 \cdot 88$ and $0 \cdot 35 \leqslant x \leqslant 1 \cdot 53$, correct to two decimal places. (See also linear programming, on page 165.)

Straight-Line Graphs

Linear functions have straight-line graphs, the most general form of a linear function is $f(x) \equiv mx + c$, where m and c are constant numbers. The corresponding graph has equation $y = mx + c$.

Examples

1. $y = 2x - 3$

2. $2x - 4y + 7 = 0$ can be rearranged as $y = \dfrac{1}{2}x + \dfrac{7}{4}$.

3. $y = \dfrac{3x + 5}{7}$ can be written as $y = \dfrac{3}{7}x + \dfrac{5}{7}$.

Example 2 shows that a linear graph may also have an equation of the form $ax + by + c = 0$.

A line parallel to the x-axis has an equation of the form $y = $ constant.
A line parallel to the y-axis has an equation of the form $x = $ constant.

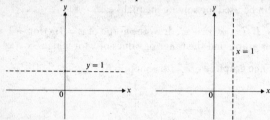

The equation of a particular straight line can be found when the co-ordinates of any two points on the line are known.

Examples

1. Find the equation of the line passing through the points $A(2, 3)$ and $B(^-1, 5)$.

The general equation is $y = mx + c$. Since the line passes through the point $(2, 3)$, when $x = 2$, $y = 3$. Substitute these values into the equation

$$3 = 2m + c \qquad \text{(i)}$$

Similarly for the point $B(^-1, 5)$

$$5 = -m + c \qquad \text{(ii)}$$

a pair of simultaneous equations (page 139).
Subtracting equation (ii) from equation (i)

$$-2 = 3m \qquad\qquad 2m - (^-m) = 3m$$

$$m = -\frac{2}{3}$$

substitute into equation (i)

$$3 = -\frac{4}{3} + c$$

giving

$$c = 3 + \frac{4}{3} = \frac{13}{3}$$

The equation is $y = -\frac{2}{3}x + \frac{13}{3}$ which can be rewritten as

$$3y = -2x + 13 \quad \text{or} \quad 2x + 3y - 13 = 0$$

2. Find the equation of the straight line which cuts the x-axis when $x = 2$ and the y-axis when $y = 7$.

General equation $y = mx + c$. Passes through the points $(2, 0)$ and $(0, 7)$ giving the equation

$$0 = 2m + c \qquad \text{(i)}$$

and

$$7 = 0m + c$$

so

$$c = 7 \qquad\qquad 0 \times m = 0$$

substituting this value of c into equation (i)

$$0 = 2m + 7$$

$$m = -3 \cdot 5$$

This equation is

$$y = -3 \cdot 5x + 7$$

$$2y = -7x + 14$$

$$7x + 2y - 14 = 0$$

Note: c always gives the value of y where the line crosses the y-axis, called the **y intercept**.

3. Find the equation of the line which is parallel to the x axis and passes through the point $(3, 9)$.

The equation is of the form $y = \text{constant}$.
The value of y at the given point is 9,
so that the equation is

$$y = 9$$

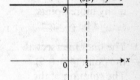

Simultaneous Equations and Graphs

Example Simultaneous equations like

$$2x - 3y = 6 \qquad \text{(i)}$$

$$x + 4y = 8 \qquad \text{(ii)}$$

were solved on page 139. Since each equation represents a straight line graph, the solution can also be found using a graphical method.

A graph represents the set of all ordered pairs (x, y) that satisfy the given equation. The intersection of two graphs represents the ordered pair that satisfies *both* equations. To solve the simultaneous equations, draw the graphs on the same diagram. The coordinates of the point of intersection of the two lines give the values of x and y that satisfy the equations.

Example $2x - 3y = 6$ (i)

$x + 4y = 8$ (ii)

The quickest way to draw the graphs is to find the points where the lines cut the coordinate axes

when $x = 0$ (i) $\Rightarrow -3y = 6$, $y = -2$

when $y = 0$ (i) $\Rightarrow 2x = 6$, $x = 3$

the points $(0, -2)$ and $(3, 0)$ lie on the line.

When $x = 0$ (ii) $\Rightarrow 4y = 8$, $y = 2$

when $y = 0$ (ii) $\Rightarrow x = 8$

the points $(0, 2)$ and $(8, 0)$ lie on the second line.

Note: We can do this because the graphs are straight lines. For more complicated graphs, many more points should be plotted.

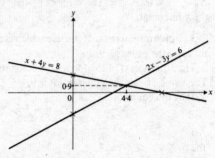

The lines intersect at the point $(4 \cdot 4, 0 \cdot 9)$. The solution of the pair of equations is $x = 4 \cdot 4$, $y = 0 \cdot 9$.

Examination questions

1. *Which pair of equations is represented by the lines p and q?*

(a) $x - y = 4$, $x + y = 2$;

(b) $x + y = 4$, $x + y = 2$;

(c) $y + x = 4$, $y - x = 2$;

(d) $y - x = 4$, $x - y = 2$.

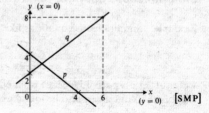

[SMP]

2. *A straight line is defined by* $y = mx + c$ *and passes through the points* $A(0, 7)$ *and* $B(-12, 1)$. *Calculate*

(a) *the value of* c,   (b) *the value of* m,

(c) *the coordinates of the point at which the line crosses the x-axis.*

[AEB]

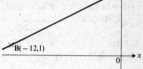

Answers

  1. (c)

  2. (a) 7   (b) 0·5   (c) $(-14, 0)$

Linear Programming

A straight line divides the plane into two regions.

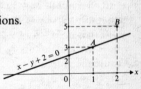

The coordinates of any point on the line satisfy the relation $x - y + 2 = 0$.

The point $A(1, 3)$ is on the line since $1 - 3 + 2 = 0$.

The point $B(2, 5)$ is not on the line since $2 - 5 + 2 = -1 < 0$.

Any point whose coordinates satisfy the inequality $x - y + 2 < 0$ lie above the line.

Those points whose coordinates satisfy the inequality $x - y + 2 > 0$ lie *below* the line.

The region of the plane which lies *above* the line forms the solution set of the inequality $x - y + 2 < 0$.

The **boundary** of this solution set is the straight line with equation $x - y + 2 = 0$.

The best way to determine which side of the line corresponds to < 0 and which side corresponds to > 0 is to try the coordinates of a point known to be on a particular side of the line (drawing the graph would help). When several inequalities must be satisfied, the solution set is the intersection of all the separate solution sets.

Example   Show the region defined by the inequalities $2x + 3y - 1 > 0$, $3x - 4y + 9 \geqslant 0$ and $x \leqslant 3$ on the x–y plane.
List all ordered pairs with integer coordinates that satisfy these inequalities.

Answer   Draw the straight lines that form the boundaries of the regions. Boundaries corresponding to *strict* inequalities ($<0, >0$) are shown as broken lines.

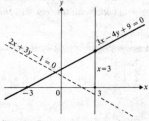

For each inequality, shade the *unwanted* region. Testing $(0, 0)$:

$$2(0) + 3(0) - 1 = -1 < 0$$
$$\therefore (0, 0) \text{ is not in } 2x + 3y - 1 > 0.$$
$$3(0) - 4(0) + 9 = 9 \geqslant 0$$
$$\therefore (0, 0) \text{ is in } 3x - 4y + 9 \geqslant 0.$$

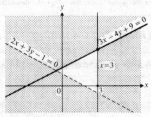

The unshaded region represents the solution set of the problem. The points in this set with integer coordinates are

$$\{(0, 1), (0, 2), (1, 0), (1, 1), (2, 0), (2, 1), (2, 2), (2, 3), (3, -1), (3, 0), (3, 1),$$
$$(3, 2), (3, 3), (3, 4)\}$$

Note: This solution set is a subset of $\mathbb{Z} \times \mathbb{Z}$.

This graphical method for finding a solution set for a set of conditions given in terms of equations and inequalities is called **linear programming**. It is suitable for solving a large range of practical problems, in economics, management sciences, etc. The following example shows the technique applied to a relatively simple problem.

Example   I wish to make up £6 in 10p and 50p pieces. I can use up to 30 ten pence and up to 10 fifty pence coins. I also wish to do this so as to use fewer than 30 coins altogether, at least six of which should be 10p coins.

If x denotes the number of 10p coins and y the number of 50p coins, express these conditions as equations and inequalities. Represent the solution set as a subset of the x–y plane. List the possible values of x and y for the solution set.

Answer   The total cash amount is £6 = 600p

$$10x + 50y = 600$$

which can be simplified as

$$x + 5y = 60 \qquad \text{(i)}$$

I must use at least 6 and no more than 30 ten pence coins

$$6 \leqslant x \leqslant 30 \qquad \text{(ii)}$$

I can use no more than 10 fifty pence coins

$$0 \leqslant y \leqslant 10 \qquad \text{(iii)}$$

The total number of coins cannot exceed or equal 30

$$x + y < 30 \qquad \text{(iv)}$$

Plotting the boundary lines (on graph paper) and shading the unwanted regions

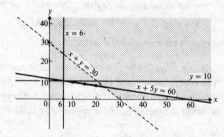

The thickened part of the line $x + 5y = 60$ is the solution set of the conditions. Since x and y must be integers, the possible solutions are

x	y
10	10
15	9
20	8

corresponding to the circled points in the solution set.

Questions 2 and 3 below show that the same methods can be used to solve more complicated problems.

Examination questions

1.

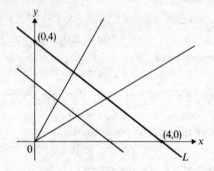

The diagram shows the lines $y = 2x$, $2y = x$, $x + y = 2$ and the line L passing through the points $(4, 0)$ and $(0, 4)$.

(i) Write down the equation of L

(ii) Indicate, on your diagram, the regions defined by the inequalities

$$x + y \leqslant 2, \quad y \geqslant 0 \quad and \quad 2y \leqslant x.$$

Mark the region clearly with the letter R.   [CAM]

2.   *Professor Archie Ology is organizing a 'dig' at a remote site. It will take several days to reach the site and the only form of transport is by camel or by donkey. Let x and y be the number of camels and donkeys, respectively, hired for the expedition. Camels cost £2 each per day to hire, donkeys cost £1 each per day.*

(a) *Given that a maximum of £32 per day can be spent on transport write down an inequality (other than $x \geqslant 0$, $y \geqslant 0$) that must be satisfied.*

Each camel carries either 1 person or 6 packs of supplies. Each donkey can only be used to carry 4 packs.

(b) *Given that the expedition consists of 10 people, write down a second inequality (other than $x \geqslant 0$, $y \geqslant 0$) that also must be satisfied.*

(c) *Write down an expression, in terms of x, for the number of camels available for carrying packs of supplies. If at least 24 packs are needed for the expedition, deduce that $3x + 2y \geqslant 12$.*

Using a scale of 1 cm to represent 2 animals, illustrate the inequalities from (a), (b) and (c) in one diagram on squared paper. Shade the unwanted regions. Find the number of packs that can be taken if the Professor chooses to take one donkey for every two camels.   [AEB]

3. *A small firm which produces radios employs both skilled men and apprentices. Its workforce must not exceed 30 people and it must make at least 360 radios per week to satisfy demand. On average a skilled man can assemble 24 radios, and an apprentice 10 radios per week.*

  (i) (a) If x skilled men and y apprentices are employed by the firm, write down two inequalities, other than x ⩾ 0, y ⩾ 0, that must be satisfied by x and y and show that one of these simplifies to 12x + 5y ⩾ 180.

  (b) Using a scale of 2 cm to 5 people, illustrate these inequalities graphically, shading the unwanted regions.

  (c) Find, from your diagram, the greatest number of apprentices that can be employed, and mark clearly the point corresponding to the solution, labelling it P.

Hint: Find the point in the region with the largest *y* value.

  (ii) (a) Skilled workers and apprentices are paid £100 and £30 a week respectively and new union regulations state that the firm must employ more skilled workers than apprentices. By adding a suitable line to your diagram, find the number of skilled men and apprentices that should be employed to make the amount of money paid out in wages as small as possible, subject to the initial conditions. Mark clearly the point Q corresponding to this solution.

  (b) Calculate the total wage bill in this case.   [SMP]

Answers

  1. (i) $x + y = 4$
  2. (a) $2x + y \leqslant 32$ (b) $x \geqslant 10$ (c) $(x - 10)$, 42
  3. (i)(c) $y = 25$ (ii)(a) $x = 11$, $y = 10$ (b) £1 400

Section 9: Rates of Change

Straight Lines Through the Origin

The equation of a line is of the form $y = mx + c$, but since $y = 0$ when $x = 0$, then $c = 0$. The equation is $y = mx$.

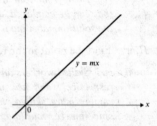

The value of m gives the steepness, or **slope**, of the line. The smaller m is, the less steep is the slope, while for large values of m the line rises rapidly. If m is negative, then the line slopes downwards from left to right.

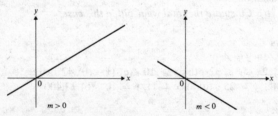

m is also called the **gradient** of the line.

For a given line the slope can be found by choosing a point on the line $P(x_1, y_1)$ say. Then

$$m = \frac{y \text{ coordinate}}{x \text{ coordinate}} = \frac{y_1}{x_1}$$

The same value is found no matter which point P is chosen on the line. This is a very important property of straight lines, the slope is the same at all points.

The slope can also be calculated by taking any two points on the line (not necessarily including the origin) $P(x_1, y_1)$ *and* $Q(x_2, y_2)$. Then

$$m = \frac{y_2 - y_1}{x_2 - x_1}$$

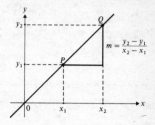

The gradient (slope) is a measure of the relative increase in y and x since

$$\text{slope} = \frac{\text{increase in } y}{\text{increase in } x}$$

for the chosen two points.

The gradient of a straight line which does not pass through the origin is defined in the same way. Choose two points *on the line* and calculate the ratio defined above.

Note that the same value is found for *any* choice of two points. The slope is also called the **rate of change** of y with x.

The equation $y = mx + c$

We have already seen that c is the value of the y intercept of the line (page 163). m is the gradient of the line. If the gradient of a line is known, and the coordinates of one point on the line are also known, then the equation can be found.

Example A line has gradient -2 and passes through $A(3, 7)$. Find the equation of this line.

Answer $\qquad\qquad\qquad\qquad y = mx + c$

$m = \text{gradient} = -2 \qquad \therefore \; y = -2x + c$

substitute $\quad x = 3, \quad y = 7$

$$7 = -6 + c$$
$$c = 13$$

The equation is $\qquad\qquad y = -2x + 13$

Lines which have the same gradient are **parallel** and do not meet.

Examples

1. $y = 2x - 3$ and $y = 2x + 7$ are parallel

2. $2x + 3y = 5$ has gradient $-\frac{2}{3}$

                                                                                        (since $y = -\frac{2}{3}x + \frac{5}{3}$)

                                     $2x + 3y = 10$ has gradient $-\frac{2}{3}$

3. $y = 6x - 5$

                                        $2y = 12x + 7$ both have gradient 6.

Proportionality

The equation $y = mx$ of a straight line through O can also be expressed by the phrase

                                    y is **proportional** to x

or y **varies directly** with x

This is written in symbols as $y \propto x$. m, the slope, is called the **constant of proportionality** and can be found once a pair of values of x and y is given.

Example   If y is proportional to x and $y = 3$ when $x = 1$, find a relation between x and y.

Answer $y \propto x$

                                    $\Rightarrow y = kx$ for some constant k

put $x = 1$, $y = 3$ $\Rightarrow 3 = k$

The relation is $y = 3x$

The function may depend on other powers of the variable:

Examples

$V \propto r^2$, V is proportional to the square of r, $V = kr^2$

$A \propto b^3$, A varies directly as the cube of b, $A = kb^3$

$y \propto x^4$, y is proportional to the fourth power of x, $y = kx^4$

$p \propto \sqrt{q}$, p varies as the square root of q, $p = k \cdot q^{1/2}$

$$y \propto \frac{1}{x}, \quad y \text{ is } inversely \text{ proportional to } x, \quad y = \frac{k}{x}$$

$$x \propto \frac{1}{t^2}, \quad x \text{ varies inversely as the square of } t, \quad x = \frac{k}{t^2}$$

The constant of proportionality k can be found when a pair of values of the function and variable is given.

Example V varies inversely as the square of t, and $V = 2$ when $t = 3$. Find the value of V when $t = 2$.

Answer

$$V \propto \frac{1}{t^2}$$

$$V = \frac{k}{t^2}$$

$V = 2, \quad t = 3 \qquad \Rightarrow 2 = \frac{k}{9}$$

$$k = 18$$

$$\Rightarrow V = \frac{18}{t^2}$$

put $t = 2$ $\qquad \Rightarrow V = \frac{18}{4}$

$$V = 4{\cdot}5 \quad \text{when } t = 2$$

The graphs of those functions which vary *directly* with the variable all pass through the origin $(0, 0)$

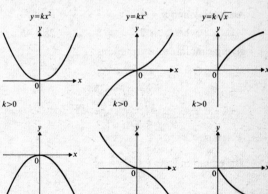

Since a function like $f(x) = 1/x$ is not defined for $x = 0$, then the graph cannot go through $(0, 0)$. Its graph has the shape shown

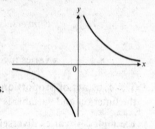

A function may depend on several variables.

Example $$F = \frac{G M_1 M_2}{r^2}$$

has variables M_1, M_2 and r while G is a constant. (F gives the attractive force between two bodies of masses M_1 and M_2 a distance r apart.) We say that F varies **jointly**, directly with M_1 and M_2 and inversely as the square of r. G is the constant of proportionality.

A function may be in several parts, each proportional to a different power.

Example A function y of x has two terms. One term is proportional to x while the other is proportional to the square of x.

$$\text{The first term} \propto x \Rightarrow ax \quad a = \text{constant}$$

$$\text{The second term} \propto x^2 \Rightarrow bx^2 \quad b = \textit{another} \text{ constant}$$

The combined function $y = ax + bx^2$ has *two* unknown constants. We need to know *two* pairs of values of x and y in order to find a and b.

Example The function of the last example contains the ordered pairs $(1, 3)$ and $(2, 8)$. Find the equation for y in terms of x

Answer when $x = 1$, $y = 3 \therefore 3 = a + b$ (i)

   when $x = 2$, $y = 8 \therefore 8 = 2a + 4b$ (ii)

giving simultaneous equations

$$6 = 2a + 2b \quad \text{(iii)} \qquad\qquad \text{multiply (i) by 2}$$

$$2 = 2b \qquad\qquad \text{subtract (ii)} - \text{(iii)}$$

$$b = 1$$

$$3 = a + 1 \qquad\qquad \text{substitute into (i)}$$

$$2 = a$$

The equation is $y = 2x + x^2$

Exponential Functions

The examples above were functions depending on powers of the variable. An **exponential** function has the *variable as a power*.

Examples $y = 2^x$, $y = 3(4^{x+1})$, $y = 3^{1-x}$ are all exponential functions.

The graph of $y = 2^x$ can be drawn by calculating pairs of values of x and y

x	-2	-1	0	1	2	3
y	0·25	0·5	1·0	2·0	4·0	8·0

$$\left(2^{-2} = \frac{1}{2^2} = \frac{1}{4} = 0.25, \text{ etc., see page 35.}\right)$$

Plotting these points and drawing the graph

This function increases very rapidly with x. The associated function $y = 2^{-x}$ has graph

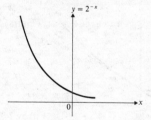

and *decreases* very rapidly with x. Functions which have this behaviour are said to show **exponential growth** and **exponential decay** respectively. An example of exponential decay is the rate at which a radioactive substance emits particles of radiation.

Gradients

Graphs give a good indication of how quickly a function is changing in terms of the variable. However, it is easy to be misled when comparing graphs, particularly when different scales are used. On page 171, the slope of a straight line was defined. This provides a *numerical* measure of the speed with which a function changes. For a straight line this quantity is independent of the choice of two points used for the calculation. For other graphs this is not so.

Definition: For any two points on any graph, define the *average* rate of change between the two points as

$$\frac{\text{difference in } y\text{-coordinates}}{\text{difference in } x\text{-coordinates}} = \frac{y_2 - y_1}{x_2 - x_1}$$

with similar definitions when other variables are used.

This gives the gradient of the straight line joining the two points. The value of this quantity will in general depend very much on the particular points chosen.

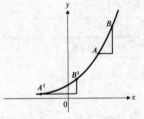

Now imagine the two points moving nearer to each other along the curve. As they become just one point, the line joining them becomes the tangent at that point. A **tangent** to a given curve at a given point is a line which just touches the curve at that point.

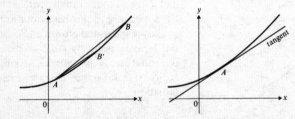

Definition: The gradient (or rate of change) of a function at a given point on the graph is the gradient of the tangent at that point.

Since a tangent is a straight line, its gradient can be easily found.

Summary – measuring gradients from graphs

1. Straight line graphs

Example   Measure the gradient of the line in the diagram

Choose points *A* and *B* on the line,
as *far apart as possible*.
The gradient is then

$$\frac{5-2}{8-1} = \frac{3}{7}$$

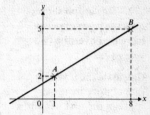

The points *A* and *B* are taken far apart to reduce the percentage error in the calculation. For example, a one decimal place accuracy in the measurement of a large quantity has a smaller percentage error than a one decimal place accuracy in the measurement of a small quantity.

   2. Curving graph. Draw a tangent at the given point and calculate the gradient as in 1.

Example   Find the gradient of
the function $y = x^2 - 1$
when $x = 2$.

Answer   Draw the graph, and
a tangent at the point
where $x = 2$.

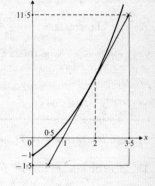

The gradient is 4.

Note: An accurate answer can only
be found when the graphs and
tangents are drawn carefully.

Examples
   1. The graph shows how the volume of a metal block changes with temperature. Calculate the rate of change of volume with temperature when the temperature is 20 °C.

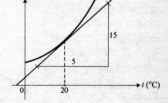

Draw the tangent at $T = 20$.
The gradient is then $^{15}\!/_5 = 3$.
The rate of change is 3 cm³/°C.

2. This graph shows how the price of petrol increased over the two years 1982–3.

Calculate the *average* rate of price increase
  (a) in the first 6 months
  (b) over the two year period

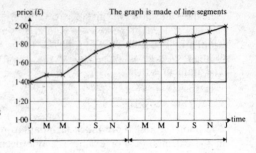

Answer

(a) rate of increase $= \dfrac{y_2 - y_1}{x_2 - x_1}$

$\dfrac{1\cdot 60 - 1\cdot 40}{6} = 0\cdot 03$ £/month in first 6 months

(b) rate of increase $= \dfrac{2\cdot 00 - 1\cdot 40}{24}$ £/month

$= 0\cdot 025$ £/month, over the two years

Speed, Distance and Time

The ideas of 'rates of change' are commonly applied to speed and distance.

$$\textbf{average speed} = \frac{\textbf{distance travelled}}{\textbf{time taken}}$$

so that speed = rate of change of distance with time. If distance s is plotted against time t, the result is a **distance–time graph**. The speed is found by calculating the gradient. Speed is usually measured in m/s (m s^{-1}), km/h (km h^{-1}) or miles per hour.

Example

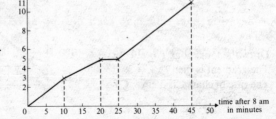

The diagram shows the distance travelled by a cyclist on his way to work. He sets off from home at 8 a.m. and arrives at work at 8.45. The distance from his home to work is 11 km.

Each straight line segment of the graph corresponds to the cyclist travelling at constant speed.

The speeds are

(a) from 8 to 8.10

$$\text{speed} = \frac{3}{10} \text{ km/min}$$

$$= \frac{3 \times 60}{10} \text{ km/h}$$

$$= \frac{180}{10} \text{ km/h}$$

$$= 18 \text{ km/h}$$

(b) from 8.10 to 8.20

$$\text{speed} = \frac{2}{10} \text{ km/min}$$

$$= \frac{2 \times 60}{10} \text{ km/h}$$

$$= 12 \text{ km/h}$$

(c) from 8.20 to 8.25   speed = 0   he has stopped

(d) from 8.25 to 8.45

$$\text{speed} = \frac{6}{20} \text{ km/min}$$

$$= \frac{6 \times 60}{20} \text{ km/h}$$

$$= 18 \text{ km/h}$$

Note: To change km/min to km/h, multiply by 60 since 60 minutes = 1 hour.

The average speed for the whole journey is

$$\frac{11}{45} \text{ km/min} = \frac{11 \times 60}{45} \text{ km/h} = 14 \cdot 67 \text{ km/h}$$

Note: If the gradient of a distance–time graph is negative then the motion is *towards* the initial point.

Example The diagram shows the distance of a particle from the origin. For the first 10 seconds, it moves away from 0 with speed 0·6 m/s. For the next 15 seconds it moves towards 0 with speed 0·4 m/s.

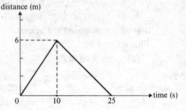

When the *direction* of motion is also taken into account, we refer to the **velocity** rather than speed. In the last examples, the *speeds* were 0·6 m/s and 0·4 m/s while the *velocities* were +0·6 m/s and −0·4 m/s.

Two or more distance–time graphs can be drawn on the same diagram.

Example The graphs in the diagram represent the journeys of two motorists travelling from Oxford to Banbury.

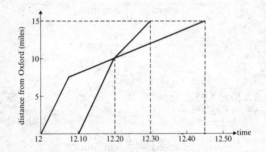

One motorist leaves Oxford at 12.00 and arrives at Banbury, 15 miles away, at 12.45. A second motorist leaves Oxford at 12.10 and arrives at Banbury at 12.30.

The two graphs intersect at a point corresponding to a distance of 10 miles from Oxford and a time of 12.20. The second car overtakes the first at 12.20, 10 miles from Oxford.

Note: Since the gradients for both journeys are positive, we can see that both cars travel away from Oxford. A graph of negative gradients would show a journey *towards* Oxford.

Summary

From a distance–time graph you can find

1. The distance travelled.

Example

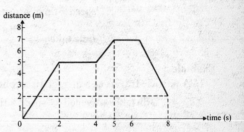

distance travelled on outward journey = $5 + 0 + 2 + 0$ m

$\qquad\qquad\qquad\qquad\qquad\qquad\quad = 7$ m

distance travelled on return journey $\quad = 6$ m

total distance travelled $\qquad\qquad\quad = 13$ m

2. (Average) speeds, from the gradients of the graph.

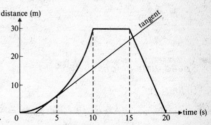

Example The speed at $t = 5$ s is found by drawing a tangent, whose gradient is found to be $^{30}/_{20} = 1\cdot5$. The speed is $1\cdot5$ m/s.

The speed from 10 s to 15 s is zero

the speed from 15 s to 20 s is $\dfrac{30}{5}$ $\qquad = 6$ m/s, towards 0

the average speed for the whole journey $= \dfrac{\text{total distance travelled}}{\text{total time taken}}$

$\qquad\qquad\qquad\qquad\qquad\qquad\quad = \dfrac{30 + 0 + 30}{20}$ m/s

$\qquad\qquad\qquad\qquad\qquad\qquad\quad = \dfrac{60}{20}$ m/s

$\qquad\qquad\qquad\qquad\qquad\qquad\quad = 3$ m/s

When speed is *constant* $$\text{speed} = \frac{\text{distance}}{\text{time}}$$

which can be rearranged as

$$\text{speed} \times \text{time} = \text{distance}$$

and $$\text{time taken} = \frac{\text{distance}}{\text{speed}}$$

Example

1. A particle travels at 5 m/s for 10 seconds.

$$\text{distance travelled} = \text{speed} \times \text{time} = 5 \times 10 \text{ m}$$
$$= 50 \text{ m}$$

2. A second particle travels 10 m at a speed of 3 m/s

$$\text{time taken} = \frac{\text{distance}}{\text{speed}} = \frac{10}{3} = 3 \cdot 3 \text{ s}$$

Note: The units must match, if speed is in m/s then distance should be in m and time in s.

Speed–time graphs

Definition:

$$\textbf{Average acceleration} = \frac{\textbf{change in velocity}}{\textbf{time taken}}$$

measured in m/s (m s^{-2}), km/h^2 (km h^{-2}) etc.

Acceleration is the rate of change of velocity, and is measured by the gradient of a speed–time graph.

Example The diagram shows the speed–time graph for a cyclist travelling along a straight road.

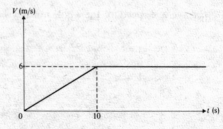

The acceleration over the first 10 seconds is $^6/_{10} = 0\cdot6$ m/s^2.
The acceleration over the next 20 seconds is zero, since the velocity is not changing.

Calculation of distance travelled

The graph shows the speed of a particle t seconds after leaving a fixed point. Since the gradient is zero (graph horizontal) the velocity is constant.

Using the formula

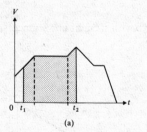

$$\text{distance travelled} = \text{speed} \times \text{time taken}$$

then

$$\text{distance travelled in 10 seconds} = 8 \times 10 = 80 \text{ m}$$

This is equal to the area of the rectangle $OABC$. The equality of area below the graph and the distance travelled is true no matter what shape the graph is.

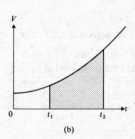

(a)   (b)

The distance travelled between times t_1 and t_2 is equal to the area beneath the graph between $t = t_1$ and $t = t_2$.

(a) When the graph is composed of straight line segments, the area can be split into triangles and rectangles whose areas can be found from the formulae

$$\text{Area of rectangle} = \text{base} \times \text{height}$$

$$\text{Area of triangle} = \frac{1}{2} \times \text{base} \times \text{height} \qquad \text{(see page 208)}$$

(b) When the graph is a curve, the area must be estimated either by

(i) Counting squares
on the graph paper.

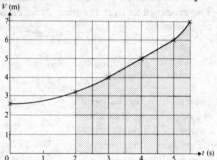

There are 30 whole squares. The remaining 7 squares are incomplete. Counting each incomplete square as ½ gives a further 3·5.

The area is equivalent to approximately 33·5 squares. Each square represents $0·5 \times 1$ m (from the given scales) and so the shaded area represents approximately $0·5 \times 33·5 = 16·75$ m.

The distance travelled is approximately 16·75 m.

This form of estimation can lead to large errors. The calculation is more accurate for larger numbers of squares.

(ii) Approximating to the curve with straight line segments.

The area is split into
3 trapezia (see page 209)
with areas

$$\frac{1}{2} \times (3·2+4) \times 1 = 3·6$$

$$\frac{1}{2} \times (4+5·5) \times 1·5 = 7·1$$

$$\frac{1}{2} \times (5·5+7) \times 1 = 6·25$$

total area $= 16·95$

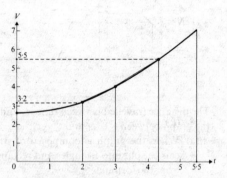

This method is called the **trapezoidal rule** for estimating areas under graphs.

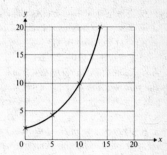

Examination questions

1. *Estimate the gradient of the graph when x = 10.*

[SMP]

2. *The table shows values of x and y consistent with* $y = kx^n$, *where n is a negative integer and k is a constant*

x	1	2
y	4	1

Find the value of (i) k,   (ii) n.

[SMP]

3. *The graph shows the bank balance for a small company, given at the end of each month over a complete year. There were two consecutive months in which the balance increased by the same amount.*

The months were
(a) February and March,
(b) March and April,
(c) August and September,
(d) November and December.

[SMP]

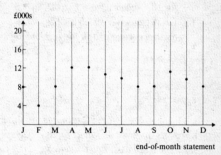

end-of-month statement

4. *If y varies inversely as the cube of* $(x+1)$ *and k is the constant of proportionality, then*

$$A \quad y = kx^3 + 1 \quad B \quad y = k(x+1)^3 \quad C \quad y = \frac{k}{x^3 + 1} \quad D \quad y = \frac{k}{(x+1)^3}$$

$$E \quad y = \frac{1}{(x+1)^3} + k$$

[LON]

5. *The line y = mx cuts the curve*
y = 4x − x² as shown in the diagram.
What is the value of m?
  A ⅓   B 1   C 2   D 3
E It cannot be determined from
the information given.

[LON]

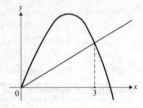

6. *Which one of the following equations could*
be represented by the sketch graph below?

$$A \;\; y = \frac{1}{x} \quad B \;\; y = \frac{1}{x^2} \quad C \;\; y = \frac{1}{x^3}$$
$$D \;\; y = 2^x \quad E \;\; y = 1^x$$

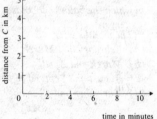

[LON]

7. *A car travelled the 5 km from C to D in 10 minutes. The car travelled*
at 60 km/h for the first 3 minutes, then stopped for 2 minutes and finally
completed its journey at a uniform speed.

  (i) Find the average speed, in km/h,
      for the journey from C to D.
 (ii) On the given axes, draw the
      distance–time graph for the journey.

8. *A car travels for 30 minutes at an average speed of 50 km/h and*
then travels another 45 km at an average speed of 60 km/h. Calculate
  (i) the total distance travelled,   (ii) the total time taken,
 (iii) the average speed for the whole journey.   [AEB]

9. *The distance, d metres, travelled by a skier down a slope at St Lorenz*
at various times, t seconds, after beginning his descent of the slope is given
in the table.

t	0	2	4	6	8
d	0	11	28	51	80

Using a scale of 2 cm to represent 1 unit on the t-axis (across the squared paper) and 2 cm to represent 10 units on the d-axis, plot the ordered pairs (t, d) given by the table and join them with a smooth curve.

Use your graph to estimate

(i) the average speed of the skier during the first 3 s of his descent,

(ii) the speed of the skier 3 s after beginning his descent.

The relation between d and t is of the form $d = at + bt^2$ where a and b are constants.

Use the ordered pairs (2, 11) and (4, 28) to calculate the values of a and b. Hence calculate the length of the slope, correct to the nearest metre, if the skier reaches the bottom after 11 s. [AEB]

10.

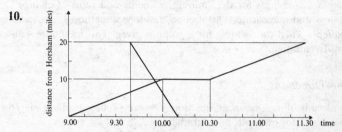

From Horsham to Worthing is 20 miles along the A24. The diagram shows the distance–time graphs of a cyclist travelling from Horsham to Worthing and of a car travelling in the opposite direction. From the diagram find

(i) the time when the car passes the cyclist;

(ii) the average speed of the cyclist over the whole journey;

(iii) the latest time at which the car could leave Worthing and, travelling at the same speed, pass the cyclist while he is stationary. [SMP]

Answers

1. 2
2. (i) 4 (ii) −2
3. (a)
4. D
5. B
6. B
7. (i) 30 km/h
8. (i) 70 km (ii) 1¼ hours (iii) 56 km/h
9. (i) 6·25 m/s (ii) $a = 4$, $b = ¾$, 135 m
10. (i) 9·56 (ii) 8 mph (iii) 10·15

Section 10: Differentiation and Integration

Differentiation and Rates of Change

Graphical methods for determining gradients and rates of change can be slow and inaccurate. This section develops a method for *calculating* gradients when the formula for a graph is given. This method is known as **differentiation**.

Linear functions

As already noted, a linear function $y = mx + c$ has gradient m. Thus $y = 3x - 2$, for example, has a gradient of 3.

Quadratic functions

The simplest quadratic function is $y = x^2$, which has the graph

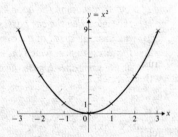

To find the gradient at a point $P(x, y)$ on the curve, we should draw a tangent at P. Since tangents are very difficult to draw accurately, suppose that we actually have a line PQ, intersecting the curve again at a nearby point Q. Since Q is near P, it should have x coordinate $x + \delta$ where δ is small. As P and Q are on the curve $y = x^2$, then they have coordinates $P(x, x^2)$ and $Q(x + \delta, (x + \delta)^2)$. We can calculate the gradient of PQ from the formula

$$\text{gradient} = \frac{y_2 - y_1}{x_2 - x_1} = \frac{(x+\delta)^2 - x^2}{(x+\delta) - x}$$

$$= \frac{x^2 + 2x\delta + \delta^2 - x^2}{x + \delta - x} \quad \text{from squaring formula (page 111)}$$

$$= \frac{2x\delta + \delta^2}{\delta}$$

$$= \frac{\delta(2x + \delta)}{\delta} \quad \text{factorizing the top}$$

$$= 2x + \delta \quad \text{dividing out factor}$$

Suppose that we are able to draw the line PQ so that it becomes closer to the required tangent at P. This corresponds to the **error term** δ decreasing in magnitude.

Eventually, when the tangent has been drawn exactly the error term δ has reduced to zero. Putting $\delta = 0$ in the formula for the gradient we are left with

$$\text{gradient} = 2x$$

The result is

the gradient of the function $y = x^2$ at the point $P(x, y)$ is $2x$

When the x coordinate is given, we can evaluate the gradient.

Example Find the gradient of $y = x^2$ when $x = 3$.

Answer The gradient is given by $2x$. Put $x = 3$ to give the gradient 6.

Because the gradient depends on the value of x, it is a function. We denote it by the symbol

$$\frac{dy}{dx}$$

(which is meant to remind us that a gradient is a ratio).
Another notation used is $D_x y$ and $f'(x)$.

Other functions

The method used to derive the gradient functions of $f(x) = x^2$ could be used for other functions, but would become long and tedious. The results are listed in the following table.

Function $y = f(x)$	1	x	x^2	x^3	x^n
Gradient function $\dfrac{dy}{dx}$	0	1	$2x$	$3x^2$	nx^{n-1}

We say that y has been differentiated to give $\dfrac{dy}{dx}$.

The last entry is the general result that if

$$y = x^n \qquad\qquad f(x) = x^n$$

then

$$\frac{dy}{dx} = nx^{n-1} \qquad\qquad f'(x) = nx^{n-1}$$

where n is *any* power.

You may *quote* these results *without* proof whenever they are required. The power n of the general result can also be negative or a fraction.

Examples

1. If $y = x^5$, $\dfrac{dy}{dx} = 5x^4$

2. If $f(x) = x^{\frac{1}{2}}$, $f'(x) = \frac{1}{2}x^{-\frac{1}{2}}$

since $x^{\frac{1}{2}} = \sqrt{x}$, then we have, if $f(x) = \sqrt{x}$, $f'(x) = \dfrac{1}{2\sqrt{x}}$

3. If $f(x) = \dfrac{1}{x} \Rightarrow f(x) = x^{-1}$

$$\Rightarrow f'(x) = (-1)x^{-2}$$

$$= -\frac{1}{x^2} \qquad\qquad x^{-2} = \frac{1}{x^2}$$

4. If $f: x \mapsto x^{1\cdot2}$ then $f': x \mapsto 1\cdot2\, x^{0\cdot2}$

5. If $y = x^7$, find the gradient when $x = 2$.

Answer $\qquad\qquad\qquad\qquad \dfrac{dy}{dx} = 7x^6$

Put $x = 2$ $\qquad\qquad$ gradient $= 7(2^6) = 7 \times 64 = 448$

To differentiate polynomials (functions with several terms) use this method for each term.

Example $f(x) = 3x^3 - 2x^2 + 5x - 3$. Find the gradient when $x = 1$.

Answer
$$f(x) = 3(x^3) - 2(x^2) + 5(x) - 3(1)$$
$$f'(x) = 3(3x^2) - 2(2x) + 5(1) - 3(0)$$
$$f'(x) = 9x^2 - 4x + 5$$

put $x = 1$ $\qquad f'(1) = 9 - 4 + 5 = 10$

The gradient is 10.

Notes: 1. The numerical factors in each term are unaffected by the differentiation, but multiply the results.
2. The constant term always gives 0 when differentiated.

Functions of other variables follow the same method.

Examples

1. $\quad V = 3r^2, \quad \dfrac{dV}{dr} = 6r$ $\qquad$ differentiate V with respect to r

2. $\quad x = 4t^2 - 2t + 1$

$\quad \dfrac{dx}{dt} = 8t - 2$ $\qquad$ differentiate x with respect to t

Acceleration, speed, distance and time

Since speed = rate of change of distance with time, then denoting speed by v, distance by x and time by t

$$v = \frac{dx}{dt}$$

Similarly, as acceleration = rate of change of velocity

$$a = \frac{dv}{dt}$$

Example A particle moves along the x-axis so that its distance, in metres, from O at time t is given by $x = t^2 + 3t + 1$.
(a) Find the velocity when $t = 3$.

(b) Find the distance from O when $t = 0$.

(c) Find the distance travelled in the first 3 seconds.

(d) Find the acceleration when $t = 3$.

Answer

(a) $v = \dfrac{dx}{dt} = 2t + 3$

$\qquad\qquad = 6 + 3$ when $t = 3$

$\qquad\qquad = 9$ m/s

(b) when $t = 0$, $x = 0 + 0 + 1 = 1$ m

(c) when $t = 3$, $x = 9 + 9 + 1 = 19$ m

Since v is positive for $t > 0$, the particle moves in one direction only.

$\qquad \therefore$ distance travelled $\qquad = 19 - 1$

$\qquad\qquad\qquad\qquad\qquad = 18$ m   it does *not* start at O

(d) $a = \dfrac{dv}{dt} = 2$ which is the same at all values of t

$\dfrac{dy}{dx}$ can be used to find the points on a curve where the gradient takes given values.

Example   Find the points on the curve $f(x) = x^3 - 3x^2 + x$ where the gradient is 1.

Answer   Gradient function $= f'(x) = 3x^2 - 6x + 1 = 1$

$\qquad\qquad\qquad\qquad\qquad\qquad \Rightarrow 3x^2 - 6x = 0$

$\qquad\qquad\qquad\qquad\qquad\qquad \Rightarrow x^2 - 2x = 0$

$\qquad\qquad\qquad\qquad\qquad\qquad \Rightarrow x(x - 2) = 0$

$\qquad\qquad\qquad\qquad\qquad\qquad\qquad \Rightarrow x = 0 \;\; \text{or} \;\; x - 2 = 0$

$\qquad\qquad\qquad\qquad\qquad\qquad\qquad\qquad\qquad x = 2$

when $x = 0$, $y = f(0) = 0^3 - 3(0^2) + 0 = 0$

when $x = 2$, $y = f(2) = 2^3 - 3(2^2) + 2 = 8 - 12 + 2 = -2$

The points where the gradient is 1 are $(0, 0)$ and $(2, -2)$.

Since the gradient of the tangent to the curve is the same as the gradient of the curve, we can find the equation of the tangent at a given point.

Example   Find the equation of the tangent to the curve
$$y = 3x^2 - 4x + 1 \quad \text{at the point } (2, 5)$$

Answer   gradient $= \dfrac{dy}{dx} = 6x - 4$

when $x = 2$, $\qquad \dfrac{dy}{dx} = 12 - 4 = 8$

So the tangent has gradient 8. It is a straight line and so has equation $y = mx + c$.

$$m = \text{gradient} = 8 \Rightarrow y = 8x + c$$
$$(2, 5) \text{ is on this line} \Rightarrow 5 = 8(2) + c$$
$$5 = 16 + c$$
$$c = -11$$

The equation of the tangent is

$$y = 8x - 11$$

Turning Points – Maxima and Minima

Maxima and minima
were defined on
page 165

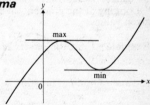

The diagram illustrates that the tangents at turning points are parallel to the x-axis, and so have zero gradient.

For a turning point, $\dfrac{dy}{dx} = 0$

Example   Find the coordinates of any turning points on the graph of
$$y = x^3 - 3x^2 + 1$$

Answer $\dfrac{dy}{dx} = 3x^2 - 6x = 0 \qquad\qquad$ for a turning point

$$\Rightarrow x^2 - 2x = 0$$

$$\Rightarrow x(x-2) = 0$$
$$\Rightarrow x = 0 \quad \text{or} \quad x = 2$$
$$y = 1 \qquad y = -3 \qquad \text{putting } x \text{ values into } f(x)$$

The required turning points are $(0, 1)$ and $(2, -3)$

We should also be able to distinguish between a maximum and a minimum. It is *not* always true that a maximum is greater than a minimum value, as the following graphs show

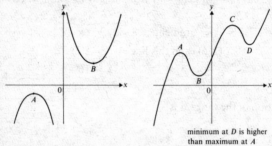

minimum at D is higher
than maximum at A

We require a method which does not depend on detailed knowledge of the graph.

Looking at the gradient on either side of a turning point

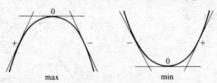

we can see that at a maximum point, the gradient changes from positive to negative as x increases. At a minimum point, the gradient changes from negative to positive.

It is also possible to have a point with zero gradient which is neither a maximum nor a minimum point.

These are called **points of inflexion.**

Example Find any maximum or minimum points for the function $f(x) = x + 4/x$, distinguishing between them.

Answer
$$f'(x) = 1 - \frac{4}{x^2} \qquad \text{from table on page 190}$$

$$= 0 \qquad \text{for a turning point}$$

$$\Rightarrow 1 = \frac{4}{x^2}$$

$$\Rightarrow x^2 = 4$$

$$\Rightarrow x = -2 \quad \text{or} \quad x = 2$$

Now construct tables

x	$-2\cdot1$	-2	$-1\cdot9$
$f'(x)$	$0\cdot09$	0	$-0\cdot11$
	$+$	0	$-$

x	$1\cdot9$	2	$2\cdot1$
$f'(x)$	$-0\cdot11$	0	$0\cdot09$
	$-$	0	$+$

taking values of x near to -2 and 2. Make sure that these x values *increase* from left to right.

About $x = -2$, the gradient goes from $+$ to $-$, a maximum

About $x = +2$, the gradient goes from $-$ to $+$, a minimum

$$f(-2) = -2 + \frac{4}{-2} = -2 - 2 = -4$$

$$f(2) = 2 + \frac{4}{2} = 4$$

so $(-2, -4)$ is a maximum, $(2, 4)$ is a minimum.

Examination questions

1. *Differentiate $3x^4 - 2x^2 + 15$ with respect to x.*

2.
   (a) *Show that the point with coordinates (3, 4) lies on the curve with equation $y = x^3 - 3x^2 + 4$. Calculate the gradient of the curve at this point.*
   (b) *A hydrogen atom consists of an electron and a proton. In appropriate units, the energy E of the atom is given by*

$$E = \frac{1}{x^2} - \frac{k}{x} \quad (x \neq 0)$$

where k is a non-zero constant and x is the (variable) distance between the electron and the proton.

Show that E has a turning point when x = 2/k.

For this value of x, determine the energy of the atom in terms of the constant k. Show that this energy is negative. [AEB]

3.

(a) *A function f is defined for all values of x by*

$$f: x \mapsto x^3 - 3x^2 - 9x + 1.$$

Write down the expression for $f'(x)$ and evaluate $f'(-1)$. Hence deduce the equation of the tangent to the curve $y = f(x)$ at the point where $x = -1$.

(b) *At present, a certain motor company employs 50 workers who each assembles 100 cars per month. Because of increasing demand, the company wishes to employ extra workers. Experience has shown however, that for every extra worker employed, the number of cars assembled by each worker is reduced by one per month.*
Let the company employ x extra workers.

(i) *Write down expressions, in terms of x, for the new number of workers and for the new number of cars assembled per month by each worker. Hence find an expression for the total number of cars assembled per month in the form $a + bx + cx^2$.*

(ii) *Determine the maximum number of cars that can be assembled per month under these conditions.* [AEB]

4. *A ball was thrown vertically upwards and, after t seconds its height, h metres, above the ground was given by*

$$h = 33 + 4t - 5t^2.$$

(a) *Calculate the height from which the ball was thrown.*
(b) *Find the speed with which it was thrown.*
(c) *Find the time when the speed became zero.*
(d) *Calculate the greatest height above the ground reached by the ball.*
(e) *Find how many seconds elapsed from the time the ball was thrown until it reached ground level.* [LON]

5. *A closed cylindrical can of base radius r cm is made from sheet metal. The surface area of the can is* $A = 2\pi r^2 + \dfrac{800}{r}$ *where π is the constant 3·14 (to 2 significant figures). Find* $\dfrac{dA}{dr}$ *and hence find the value of r for which A is a minimum.* [LON part]

Answers
  1. $12x^3 - 4x$
  2. (a) 9 (b) $\dfrac{dE}{dx} = -\dfrac{2}{x^3} + \dfrac{k}{x^2}$. $E = -\dfrac{k^2}{4}$
  3. (a) $f'(x) = 3x^2 - 6x - 9, f'(-1) = 0$. Tangent $y = 6$
     (b)(i) $(50 + x), (100 - x), 5\,000 + 50x - x^2$ (ii) $5\,625$
  4. (a) 33 m (b) 4 m/s (c) 0·4 sec (d) 33·8 m (e) 3 sec
  5. 15·9

Integration

Differentiation is a relation between functions. The following mapping diagram illustrates the relation

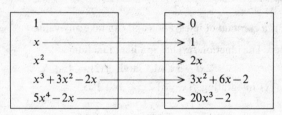

functions   *gradient functions*

The inverse mapping is called **integration**. For example, integrating $2x$ gives x^2.

Notation: 'Integrate the function $f(x)$ with respect to x' is written
$$\int f(x)\,dx$$
(*With respect to x means that the variable is x.*)

Examples

1.
$$\int (x^2 - 2x + 1)\,dx = \frac{x^3}{3} - x^2 + x$$

because differentiating $\dfrac{x^3}{3} - x^2 + x$ gives $x^2 - 2x + 1$.

2.
$$\int -\frac{1}{x^2}\,dx = \frac{1}{x}$$

In general
$$\int x^n\,dx = \frac{x^{n+1}}{n+1}$$

The constant of integration

If $f(x) = x^2 + 2x + 1$ then $f'(x) = 2x + 2$

If $g(x) = x^2 + 2x + 3$ then $g'(x) = 2x + 2$, also.

Two functions which differ only by a constant term have the same gradient function, because differentiation of a constant produces zero (page 191).

Because of this, integration does *not* produce a unique answer. Integration is a one-many map.

Example
$$\int x^3\,dx = \frac{x^4}{4} + c$$

where c is a **constant of integration** and can take any value.

Example   The function $f(x)$ has gradient function
$$2x^2 - 3x + 1, \quad \text{and} \quad f(2) = 4$$

To find $f(x)$, integrating, $f(x) = \int 2x^2 - 3x + 1\,dx$
$$= \frac{2x^3}{3} - \frac{3x^2}{2} + x + c$$

(using the formula above)

But $f(2) = 4$, so
$$\frac{2(2^3)}{3} - \frac{3(2^2)}{2} + 2 + c = 4$$

$$\frac{16}{3} - 6 + 2 + c = 4$$

$$c = 4 - 2 + 6 - \frac{16}{3}$$

$$= 8 - \frac{16}{3} = \frac{24 - 16}{3} = \frac{8}{3}$$

$$\therefore \qquad f(x) = \frac{2x^3}{3} - \frac{3x^2}{2} + x + \frac{8}{3}$$

In order to find the integral completely, we needed the extra information $f(2) = 4$.

The connection between distance, velocity and acceleration was shown on page 191 to be

$$x \xrightarrow{\text{differentiate}} v \xrightarrow{\text{differentiate}} a$$

where x = distance, v = velocity and a = acceleration.

Integration allows us to reverse this diagram

$$x \xleftarrow[\text{integrate}]{} v \xleftarrow[\text{integrate}]{} a$$

Example   A particle moves along the x-axis. Its velocity at time t is given by

$$v = 3t - 2$$

(a) Find the position of the particle at $t = 3$
   given that $x = 0$ when $t = 0$
(b) Find the acceleration when $t = 2$.

Answer
(a) Integrate v to find x

$$x = \int (3t - 2)\, dt = \frac{3t^2}{2} - 2t + c \qquad\qquad c = \text{constant}$$

$$x = 0 \text{ when } t = 0 \qquad 0 = 0 - 0 + c \quad \therefore c = 0$$

so $\qquad x = \dfrac{3t^2}{2} - 2t$

When $t = 3$ $\qquad x = \dfrac{3 \times 3^2}{2} - 2 \times 3 = \dfrac{27}{2} - 6 = \dfrac{15}{2}$

(b) To find acceleration, differentiate v

$$a = \frac{dv}{dt} = 3$$

Integration and Area

Integration can be used to calculate the area between the x-axis and a curve $y = f(x)$, for x in a given range.

If $a \leqslant x \leqslant b$, the area shown in the diagram below is given by

$$\int_a^b f(x)\,dx$$

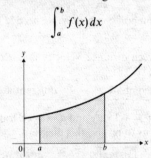

This is called a **definite integral** with **limits** a and b.

When the function has been integrated, substitute the top value $x = b$ and then the bottom value $x = a$ into the resulting formula. Finally subtract the $x = a$ value from the $x = b$ value ('top' – 'bottom').

Note: On page 183, distance travelled was calculated by evaluating the area under the velocity graph. This follows since distance is found by integrating velocity.

Examples

1. Evaluate
$$\int_1^3 x^3\,dx$$

integrating
$$\left[\frac{x^4}{4}\right]_1^3 \qquad \text{no constant of integration necessary}$$

Substituting $x = 3$ and $x = 1$

$$\frac{3^4}{4} - \frac{1^4}{4} = \frac{81}{4} - \frac{1}{4} = \frac{80}{4} = 20$$

Note the use of square brackets with limits $\left[\quad\right]_1^3$

2. Find the area under
the curve $y = x^2 + 1$
between $x = 1$ and $x = 5$.

$$\text{Area} = \int_1^5 (x^2 + 1)\, dx = \left[\frac{x^3}{3} + x\right]_1^5$$

$$= \left(\frac{5^3}{3} + 5\right) - \left(\frac{1^3}{3} + 1\right)$$

$$= \frac{125}{3} + 5 - \frac{1}{3} - 1$$

$$= \frac{124}{3} + 4 = \frac{124}{3} + \frac{12}{3}$$

$$= \frac{136}{3}$$

Note: The integral gives the area underneath the curve when the graph is *above* the x-axis. Integrating a function which is negative gives a negative result. The area is then found by discarding the minus sign.

3. The function $f(x)$ has gradient function $f'(x) = 1 + x^2$ and $f(0) = 1$. Find $f(x)$ in terms of x. Evaluate $f'(3)$, and obtain the approximate increase in $f(x)$ as x increases from 3 to 3·01. Estimate $f(3·01)$.

Answer $f'(x) = 1 + x^2$

integrating $f(x) = \dfrac{x^3}{3} + x + c$

given $f(0) = 0 + 0 + c = 1$ $\therefore c = 1$

so $f(x) = \dfrac{x^3}{3} + x + 1$

Also $f'(3) = 1 + 3^2 = 10$

From the diagram

$$f(3·01) \approx f(3) + QR = 13 + QR$$

From triangle PQR, $\dfrac{QR}{PR} = \text{gradient at } P$

$$QR = \text{gradient at } P \times PR$$

$$QR = f'(3) \times 0\cdot01$$
$$= 10 \times 0\cdot01$$
$$= 0\cdot1$$

So $f(3\cdot01) \approx 13 + 0\cdot1 = 13\cdot1$

4. $f(x) = x^2 + 3x + 2$.   Evaluate $\displaystyle\int_{-3}^{0} f(x)\,dx$.

Answer

$$\int_{-3}^{0} (x^2 + 3x + 2)\,dx = \left[\frac{x^3}{3} + \frac{3x^2}{2} + 2x \right]_{-3}^{0}$$

$$= (0 + 0 + 0) - \left(-\frac{27}{3} + \frac{27}{2} - 6 \right)$$

$$= 0 + (9 - 13\cdot5 + 6)$$

$$= 1\cdot5$$

Note: This result is *not* the area between the curve and the *x*-axis. The graph shows that some of the curve is below the *x*-axis, and so will contribute a negative amount to the integral.

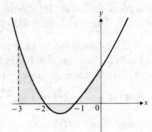

Examination questions

1. *A particle moves along an x-axis so that at $t = 0$ (sec) it is at 0, with speed 4 ms^{-1}. At t secs the acceleration is $(3t + 1)$ ms^{-2}.*
  (i) Find the velocity, v, in terms of t.
  (ii) Find v when $t = 1$ and $t = 3$.
  (iii) Sketch the graph of v against t for $0 \leqslant t \leqslant 4$.
  (iv) Calculate the distance travelled in the first 3 seconds.

2. *The gradient of a function f is given by $f'(x) = 5 - \dfrac{10}{x^2}$ for all values of x except $x = 0$.*

(i) *Find the values of x of which the graph has turning points.*

(ii) *Given that $f(1) = 14$ find $f(x)$ in terms of x.*

(iii) *Write down the value of $f'(10)$ and* hence *obtain the approximate increase in the value of $f(x)$ as x increases from 10 to 10·001. Hence deduce an estimate for $f(10·001)$.*

(No credit will be given for a direct evaluation of $f(10·001)$.) [AEB]

3. *A function f is defined by $f: x \mapsto 3x - x^2$ for all values of x.*

(i) *Calculate the coordinates of the points where the graph of $y = f(x)$ cuts the x-axis. Make a quick free-hand sketch of the graph.*

(ii) *Evaluate $\int_0^3 f(x)\,dx$.*

(iii) *With reference to the graph of $y = f(x)$, explain briefly why it is possible to have a value of b (where $b < 5$) for which*

$$\int_0^b f(x)\,dx = 0.$$

Find this value of b.

(iv) *By considering the symmetry of the graph of $y = f(x)$ over the interval $-2 \leqslant x \leqslant 5$, find the value of a for which*

$$\int_a^3 f(x)\,dx = 0.$$ [AEB]

4. *A function f is defined by*

$$f: x \mapsto x + \frac{12}{x} \quad for \quad 1 \leqslant x \leqslant 8.$$

(a) *On squared paper, using a scale of 1 cm to represent 1 unit draw the graph of $y = f(x)$, plotting values of y for $x = 1, 2, 3, 4, 5, 6, 8$.*

(b) *If $f(x) = 9$, show that $x^2 = 9x - 12$. Hence use your graph to estimate the values of x for which $x^2 = 9x - 12$.*

(c) *Using the trapezoidal rule with intervals of 1 unit, estimate the value of $\int_1^4 f(x)\,dx$, i.e. divide the area under the curve into 3 trapezia and calculate their areas. State whether your approximation is an over or under estimate giving a brief reason for your answer.* [AEB]

(See page 184.)

Answers

   1. (i) $v = \frac{3}{2}t^2 + t + 4$ (ii) $13\frac{1}{2}$, $41\frac{1}{2}$ (iv) 30 m

   2. (i) $\pm\sqrt{2}$ (ii) $5x + \dfrac{10}{x} - 1$ (iii) 4·9, 0·0049, 50·0049

   3. (i) 0, 3   (ii) 4·5   (iii) 4·5

   4. (b) 1·63, 7·37   (c) 25 square units, overestimate

Section 11: Two- and Three-Dimensional Problems

Coordinates and Three Dimensions

Three coordinates are required to specify the position of a point in space.

Take a horizontal $x-y$ plane. Every point in this plane has two coordinates, x and y. A point in space also has a third coordinate, the height above the base plane, z.

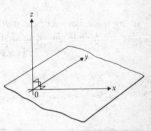

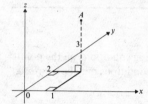

The Ox, Oy, Oz axes meet at right angles at the origin O. In this way, each point is represented by an **ordered triple** of coordinates. The diagram shows the point $A(1, 2, 3)$.

A point in the $x-y$ plane has zero z coordinate, so the equation of this plane is $z = 0$. The equation $z = \text{constant}$ represents a horizontal plane (i.e. parallel to the $x-y$ plane). Similarly $x = \text{constant}$ is a plane parallel to the $y-z$ plane and $y = \text{constant}$ is parallel to the $x-z$ plane.

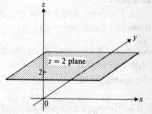

A plane not parallel to any of these has the general equation

$$ax + by + cz + d = 0$$

where a, b, c and d are constants. (Compare with the equation of a line, $ax + by + c = 0$, in two dimensions.)

Two planes which are not parallel meet in a line

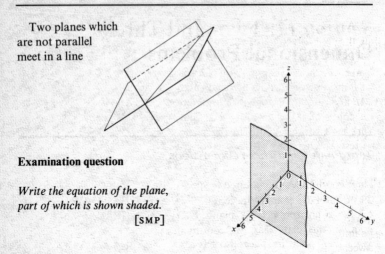

Examination question

Write the equation of the plane, part of which is shown shaded.

[SMP]

Loci in Two Dimensions

Subsets of the plane can be defined by imposing conditions on the points (such as the inequalities of page 165). Other conditions may be expressed geometrically.

Examples

1. Describe the set of points which are a constant distance of 2 cm from the fixed point $C(1, 3)$.

Answer   Any point P on the circle centre C radius 2 cm satisfies the given condition.

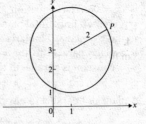

All of the required points must lie on this circle, which is called the **locus** of P.

A locus of points is a subset of the plane satisfying a given set of constraints. (A graph is a particular type of locus.)

2. A point *P* is subject to the condition that it should be *equidistant* from two fixed points *A* and *B*. That is $PA = PB$

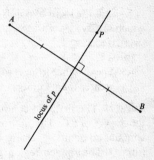

Answer From the diagram you can see that *P* must lie on the line perpendicular to *AB* and passing through its mid-point. You could find this line by 'trial and error', take various points in the plane and test whether they satisfy the condition (see also page 224).

3. A point *P* satisfies the condition that the *sum* of the distances from *P* to two fixed points *A* and *B* is constant. Describe the locus of *P*.

Answer You can construct the locus in the following way. Fasten two pins into a board on which paper has been placed. Tie a piece of string between these pins, the string being longer than the separation of the pins. Place the point of a pencil against the string and pull taut.

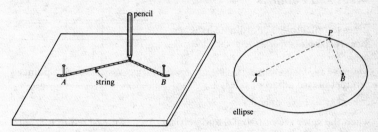

ellipse

By moving the pencil, while keeping the string taut, a curve is sketched. Repeat with the pencil on the other side of the string. The resulting curve is an *ellipse*.

4. A point *P* moves so as always to be a perpendicular distance of 2 cm from a given line *L*. Describe the locus of *P*.

Answer

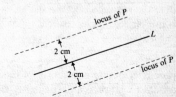

The locus is the two lines parallel to *L* and either side of *L*.

5. Find the locus of points $P(x, y)$ which satisfy

(a) $0 \leqslant x \leqslant 4$
(b) $0 \leqslant y \leqslant 4$
(c) The distance from P to 0 is greater than 4 units.

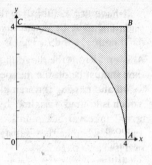

Answer   The first two conditions define the 'box' $OABC$. The quarter-circle AC contains all points which are 4 units away from O. The shaded region gives points which are further than 4 units from O.

Loci can also be defined in terms of other geometrical properties of lines and circles (see page 258).

Areas and Volumes

Lines parallel to the coordinate axes form **rectangles**.

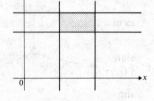

The area of the rectangle is the product of two adjacent sides

area = base × height

when the sides are horizontal and vertical. Area is measured in m², cm² etc. The **perimeter** of the rectangle is the sum of the lengths of the four sides.

Rectangles are examples of **quadrilaterals**, which are shapes formed by the intersections of four lines. These lines are not necessarily parallel.

Triangles are formed by cutting along a diagonal of a quadrilateral,

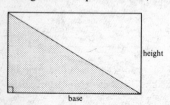

height

base

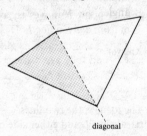

diagonal

and have three sides. If a rectangle is split in this way, the triangle is **right-angled**, with area $= \frac{1}{2} \times$ base $\times$ height

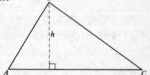

The same formula can be used to calculate the area of a triangle which is not right-angled

Choose one of the sides, AC for example, as base. The perpendicular distance from B to AC is the height of the triangle (this line is called an **altitude**). Suppose that the base AC is split into lengths x and y. Two right-angled triangles are formed, with areas

$$\frac{1}{2}xh \quad \text{and} \quad \frac{1}{2}yh$$

The total area is then

$$\frac{1}{2}xh + \frac{1}{2}yh = \frac{1}{2}(x+y)h$$
$$= \frac{1}{2} \times AC \times h$$

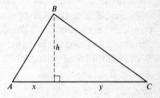

Area of a triangle $= \frac{1}{2} \times$ **base** $\times$ **height**

The area of a general quadrilateral can usually be found by splitting it into triangles and rectangles whose areas can be easily calculated.

Example
A **trapezium** has two parallel sides

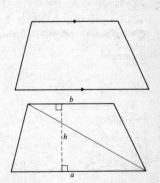

its area is found by splitting it into a rectangle and two right-angled triangles, or alternatively into two triangles.

If the parallel sides have lengths a and b, and they are distance h apart, the area is $\frac{1}{2}(a+b)h$.

Notice that if two triangles are formed by points on the same pair of parallel lines, then they have the same height. (For more about quadrilaterals, see page 226.)

Three-dimensional figures

A rectangular box is formed when six
rectangles are joined at right angles

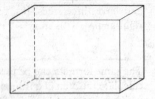

the volume is given by the product of three adjacent sides, or equivalently

$$\text{volume} = \text{length} \times \text{width} \times \text{height}$$
$$= \text{base area} \times \text{height}$$

The surface area of the box is the sum of the areas of the faces which
form the box.

A box is a particular case of a **prism** which is a solid object with a
constant cross-section. That is, if it is cut in a plane parallel to the base,
the shape formed is the same no matter at what height the cut is made.
Some examples of prisms are

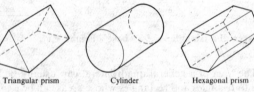

Triangular prism   Cylinder   Hexagonal prism

The volume of
a prism is given
by the formula   **volume = cross-sectional area × length.**

Take a prism and choose a point on the top face. Join the vertices of
the base to this point to form a **pyramid**.

Examples

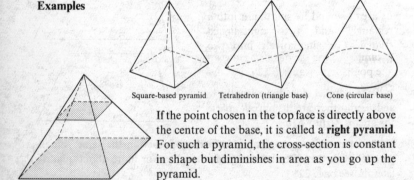

Square-based pyramid   Tetrahedron (triangle base)   Cone (circular base)

If the point chosen in the top face is directly above
the centre of the base, it is called a **right pyramid**.
For such a pyramid, the cross-section is constant
in shape but diminishes in area as you go up the
pyramid.

The volume of a pyramid is $\frac{1}{3} \times$ **base area** $\times$ **height**

Pythagoras' Theorem

The sides of a right-angled triangle are related by this theorem, one of the best known of geometry. It states that, for the right-angled triangle

$$\mathbf{a}^2 = \mathbf{b}^2 + \mathbf{c}^2$$

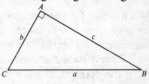

or, 'the square on the hypotenuse is equal to the sum of the squares on the other two sides'. (The hypotenuse is the side opposite the right angle.) We can prove it in the following way

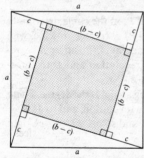

The large square is formed by fitting together four identical right-angled triangles with sides of length a, b and c.

(*Exercise*: Show that this quadrilateral is right-angled; see page 226.)

These triangles each have area $\frac{1}{2}bc$ and the small square in the centre has area $(b-c)^2$.

so, $a^2 = 4 \times \frac{1}{2}bc + (b-c)^2$

$a^2 = 2bc + (b^2 - 2bc + c^2)$ (page 111)

$a^2 = b^2 + c^2$

This result can be used for calculating distances.

Example   Find the distance between the points $A(1, 4)$ and $B(2, 9)$.

Answer

The sides AC and BC of the triangle are $9-4 = 5$ and $2-1 = 1$.   From the theorem

$$AB^2 = 5^2 + 1^2 = 25 + 1 = 26$$

so $AB = \sqrt{26}$

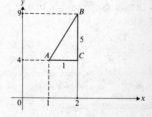

Section 12: Angles and Figures

Circular Measure

We have so far been concerned with linear measurements – distances which can be represented by marks on a number line. We now consider angular measurements.

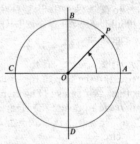

In the diagram, OP is a rotating pointer fixed at O. OA and OB are fixed perpendicular lines.

Supposing that P starts at A, each position of P on the circle determines an angle AOP (also written as $\angle AOP$ or $\widehat{AOP}$). P rotates anticlockwise through one complete **revolution** to arrive back at A. Position B corresponds to a quarter revolution, C to a half revolution and D to three-quarters of a revolution.

The most commonly used unit for measuring angles is the **degree**. There are 360 degrees (written as 360°) in a complete revolution, and so 180° = half a revolution, 90° = a quarter revolution, and so on. 90° = one right angle.

A scale can be marked off on the circle. An angle between 0° and 90° is **acute**, between 90° and 180° it is **obtuse** and between 180° and 360° it is **reflex**. Angles greater than 360° correspond to the point P travelling round the circle more than once. A negative angle corresponds to the pointer travelling clockwise from A.

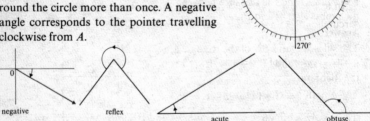

The size of the angle does not depend on the lengths of the lines which form it:

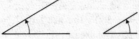

both represent the same angle.

Degrees are further divided into 60 **minutes**, which are then divided into 60 **seconds** (which is a base 60 number system, see page 51). An angle could then be of the form $50°21'\ 30''$. This can be expressed solely in degrees as $50° + 21/60° + 30/3600° = 50\cdot358°$ (to 3 decimal places).

Circles

A circle has a **centre**, which is a fixed point, and a **radius**, which is a fixed length. The circle forms the locus of points which are all the same fixed distance away from the fixed point.

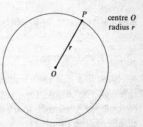

The distance around the perimeter of the circle is called its **circumference**. The width of the circle, across the centre, is called its **diameter** (so that the diameter is twice the radius).

It can be found, by measurement, that the ratio of the circumference of the circle to its diameter is always the same no matter what the size of the circle. This ratio is called π (**pi**, the Greek letter p) and is equal to $3\cdot1416$ to 4 decimal places. π is an irrational number, and so cannot be written down exactly as a decimal. The approximation $^{22}/_7$ is also often used, and was known to the ancient Greeks.

In terms of π

circumference of the circle $= 2\pi r$ (diameter × pi)

and

area of the circle $= \pi r^2$

Two radii of a circle form an angle, and cut off a **sector** of the circle

The sector is bounded by the radii OA and OB and the curved **arc** AB.

It can be shown that the length of the arc, and the area of the sector are both proportional to the size of the angle. So arc length $= c\theta$ and area $= k\theta$, where θ is the angle and c and k are the constants of proportionality (see page 172). When $\theta = 360°$, the arc length = circumference = $2\pi r$, and the area is the same as the area of the circle = πr^2.

so
$$2\pi r = 360c \quad \text{and} \quad \pi r^2 = 360k$$

$$c = \frac{\pi r}{180} \qquad k = \frac{\pi r^2}{360}$$

so arc length
$$= \frac{\pi r \theta}{180}$$

and area
$$= \frac{\pi r^2 \theta}{360}$$

Angles are often represented by Greek letters, θ, ϕ, α, β.

Chords and segments

A **chord** is a line that joins two points on the circle. If the chord passes through the centre, then it is a diameter. A chord divides the circle into two pieces: the larger part of the circumference is the **major arc** and the smaller is the **minor arc**.
The interior of the circle is then divided into a major **segment** and a minor segment

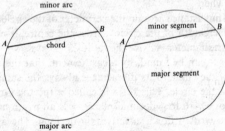

The area of a segment can be found by splitting a sector into the segment and a triangle, and finding the difference between these areas.

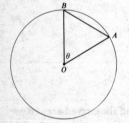

The lines *AO* and *BO* form the sector, the angle between them is called the angle *subtended* by the arc or chord at the centre.

Solids

A prism with circular cross-section (see page 210) is a **cylinder**. Since the cross-sectional area is then πr^2, **the volume of the cylinder is $\pi r^2 l$** where l is the length.

The surface area can be found by 'unwrapping' the cylinder. Opening out to form a rectangle with sides $2\pi r$ and l the area is $2\pi rl$. The end pieces both have areas of πr^2. The total area of a closed cylinder is $2\pi rl + 2\pi r^2 = 2\pi r(r+l)$.

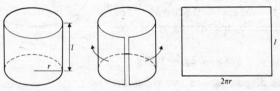

A **cone** is formed when the sides slope to a point. The **volume is $\frac{1}{3}\pi r^2 h$**, where h is the vertical height. The curved surface area is πrl, where l is the **slant height**. If the base radius and vertical height are known, then the slant height can be found from Pythagoras' theorem.

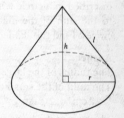

In three dimensions, the locus of points which are all the same distance from a fixed point is a **sphere** (ball shape). A sphere has a centre and radius.

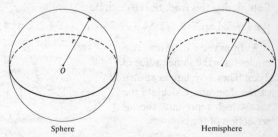

Sphere   Hemisphere

The **volume of a sphere** is given by $\frac{4}{3}\pi r^3$, and the **surface area** is $4\pi r^2$.

A **hemisphere** is half a sphere, and so the formulae for volume and *curved* surface area should be halved.

Examples

1. A metal coin has diameter 20 mm and thickness 2 mm. The density of the metal used is $17 \cdot 2 \, \text{g/cm}^3$. Find the volume of metal in the coin, and the mass of metal used.

Answer   The coin is a cylinder of base radius $20 \div 2 \, \text{mm} = 10 \, \text{mm} = 1 \, \text{cm}$ and height $2 \, \text{mm} = 0 \cdot 2 \, \text{cm}$ (converting all lengths to cm). The volume is $\pi r^2 l = 3 \cdot 142 \times 1^2 \times 0 \cdot 2 \, \text{cm}^3 = 0 \cdot 628 \, \text{cm}^3$.   The mass is found by multiplying by the density

$$\text{mass} = 0 \cdot 628 \times 17 \cdot 2 \, \text{g} = 10 \cdot 8 \, \text{g}$$

2. The diagram shows two equal circles inscribed in a circle whose diameter is equal to the sum of the diameters of the smaller circles. Find the shaded area

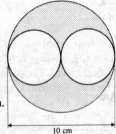

Answer

The radius of the large circle is $10 \div 2 \, \text{cm} = 5 \, \text{cm}$. The radii of the small circles are then $5 \div 2 \, \text{cm} = 2 \cdot 5 \, \text{cm}$.

The area of the large circle is $\pi(5)^2 = 25 \, \pi \text{cm}^2 = 78 \cdot 54 \, \text{cm}^2$.

The area of a smaller circle is $\pi(2 \cdot 5)^2 = \pi \times 6 \cdot 25 = 19 \cdot 63 \, \text{cm}^2$

The two small circles have a combined area of $2 \times 19 \cdot 63 = 39 \cdot 26 \, \text{cm}^2$

Subtracting this from the large circle

the shaded area is $(78 \cdot 54 - 39 \cdot 26) \, \text{cm}^2 = 39 \cdot 28 \, \text{cm}^2$.

3. In a Venn diagram, two circles have the same radius of 2 cm. They overlap as shown in the diagram. Calculate the area which represents the intersection of the two sets.

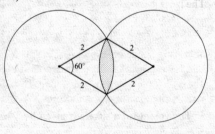

Answer
The area is twice that of the segment shown
here:

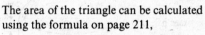

$$\text{area of sector } OAB = \frac{60}{360}\pi 2^2 = \frac{1}{6} \times 3 \cdot 142 \times 4$$

$$= 2 \cdot 094 \, \text{cm}^2$$

The area of the triangle can be calculated
using the formula on page 211,

$$\text{area of triangle} = 1 \cdot 732 \, \text{cm}^2$$

Subtracting gives $0 \cdot 362 \, \text{cm}^2$ as the area of the segment. Doubling gives
the area of the overlap as $0 \cdot 724 \, \text{cm}^2$.

4. Find the length of the arc
of the sector shown.

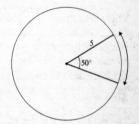

Answer   Arc length $= \dfrac{50}{180} \times \pi \times 5 = 4 \cdot 36 \, \text{cm}$

5. Four angles form a complete revolution and are in the ratio
$1 : 2 : 3 : 4$. Find the largest angle.

Answer

Divide $360°$ in the ratios $1 : 2 : 3 : 4$
(see page 48).

$1 + 2 + 3 + 4 = 10, \quad 360 \div 10 = 36$
The largest angle is $4 \times 36° = 144°$.

6. A cone is formed so that its base and apex
touch the inside of a sphere of radius 5 cm. If
the base radius of the cone is r cm, and the
height is h cm, find r in terms of h. Write down
an expression for the volume of the cone in
terms of h only.

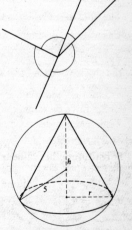

Use differentiation to find the greatest possible volume of the cone. Calculate the volume left when the cone of maximum volume is cut out from the sphere (use $\pi = 3\cdot1416$).

Answer

Using Pythagoras' theorem in triangle OBC

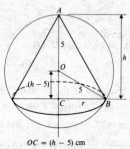

$OC = (h - 5)$ cm

$$5^2 = (h-5)^2 + r^2$$
$$r^2 = 25 - (h-5)^2$$
$$= 25 - (h^2 - 10h + 25)$$
$$= 25 - h^2 + 10h - 25 \qquad \text{(see page 88)}$$
$$r^2 = 10h - h^2$$
$$r = \sqrt{10h - h^2}$$

Volume of cone $= \dfrac{1}{3}\pi r^2 h = \dfrac{1}{3}\pi(10h - h^2)h$

$$= \dfrac{1}{3} \times \pi \times (10h^2 - h^3)$$

$$= \dfrac{10\pi h^2}{3} - \dfrac{\pi h^3}{3}$$

To find the maximum value, differentiate and set equal to zero (page 193)

$$\dfrac{20\pi h}{3} - \pi h^2 = 0$$

$$\therefore h\left(\dfrac{20\pi}{3} - \pi h\right) = 0$$

$$\therefore \dfrac{20\pi}{3} - \pi h = 0 \qquad \text{since } h \text{ cannot be 0}$$

$$\pi h = \dfrac{20\pi}{3}$$

$$h = \dfrac{20}{3}$$

Substituting this value into the expression for volume

$$\text{volume} = \tfrac{1}{3}\pi\left(10 \times \dfrac{400}{9} - \dfrac{8\,000}{27}\right) \text{cm}^3$$

$$= \frac{1}{3}\pi\left(\frac{4\,000}{9} - \frac{8\,000}{27}\right)$$

$$= \frac{4\,000\pi}{81} \text{ cm}^3$$

The volume of the sphere is

$$\frac{4}{3}\pi r^3 = \frac{4\pi}{3} \times \frac{8\,000}{27}$$

$$= \frac{32\,000\pi}{81} \text{ cm}^3$$

The volume left when the cone is removed is

$$\left(\frac{32\,000\pi}{81} - \frac{4\,000\pi}{81}\right) = \frac{28\,000\pi}{81}$$

$$= 1\,086 \text{ cm}^3$$

Examination questions

1. *The radius of the chain wheel of a bicycle is 9 cm. Given that the portion of the chain in contact with the wheel is of length 33 cm and taking π to be 22/7, calculate the angle subtended at the centre of the wheel by this portion of chain.* [LON]

2. *The length, in cm, of the arc PQ of the circle centre O and radius r is*

$A\ \dfrac{\pi r\alpha}{180}$ $B\ \dfrac{\pi r\alpha}{360}$ $C\ \dfrac{\pi r^2\alpha}{180}$ $D\ \dfrac{\pi r^2\alpha}{360}$

E none of these   [LON]

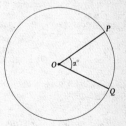

3.

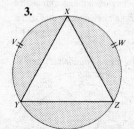

In the figure, arc XY = arc XZ. The circle has radius 2 cm. Calculate the shaded area to 2 decimal places.

4. *The area, in cm², of a circle with diameter 19 cm is approximately*

A 60   B 120   C 300   D 1 200   [AEB]

5. *A cylindrical drinking mug, internal diameter 7 cm, stands on a horizontal table and contains milk to a depth of 6 cm. Taking π to be ²²/₇, calculate   (a) the total surface area of the mug in contact with the milk, (b) the mass of milk in the mug if 1 litre of milk has a mass of 1·3 kg.*

[AEB]

6. *Two concentric circles (i.e. having the same centre) have radii 1 cm and 8 cm. Taking π to be ²²/₇, calculate   (i) the difference in the lengths of the circumferences,   (ii) the area between the circles.*   [CAM]

7. *Given that the area of a circle is 100 cm², calculate, correct to 3 significant figures,   (i) the area of a sector of the circle of angle 60°, (ii) the radius of the circle, taking π to be 3·142.*   [CAM]

8. *A square is inscribed in a circle of radius 5 cm.*

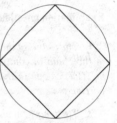

   (i) Taking π to be 3·14, find the area of the circle.
   (ii) Find the area of the square.   [CAM]

9.

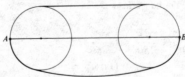

Two pulleys of radius 2·00 m and with centres 4·5 m apart are driven by a belt as shown. Calculate the shorter length of belt between A and B to the nearest cm. (Take π to be 3·14).   [SMP]

10. *The area of the inside surface of a shallow circular dish with a narrow lip surround as shown is*

$A = 2\pi rh + \pi r^2$.
A is given as 62·8 cm² and h is 0·5 cm.

(i) Using $\pi = 3\cdot14$, *find the value of* $r + r^2$,

(ii) By writing $r + r^2$ *as* $r(r+1)$, *or otherwise, find the radius of the dish.*

[SMP]

11. *The area of the shaded semicircle is* $18\ cm^2$.
Find the area of the square $WXYZ$.   [SMP]

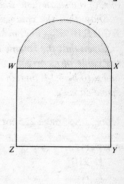

12.

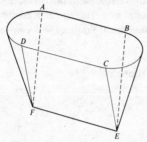

The diagram shows a vessel used for filtering coffee. $ABEF$ *and* $DCEF$
are rectangles with $EF = 6\cdot0\ cm$ *and* $AF = DF = 13\cdot0\ cm$, *while each end
is half a cone with base radius* $5\cdot0\ cm$ *and slant height* $13\cdot0\ cm$.

(i) Find the height of $ABCD$ *above* EF *when* $ABCD$ *is horizontal.*

(ii) Calculate the volume of the vessel. (Take π *to be* $3\cdot14$.)*   [SMP]

13. *The diagram shows three semicircles of
radii 1, 2, 3 units. The areas of the two small
semicircles are* A *and* B. *If the area of the
shaded region is* C, *then*

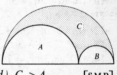

(a) $C = A + B$ *(b)* $C < A$ *(c)* $C = A$ *(d)* $C > A$ [SMP]

14. *Figure (a) shows a
space capsule which consists
of a portion of cone whose
parallel plane ends are circles
of radii 2 metres and* r *metres
joined to a hemisphere of
radius 2 metres. In figure (b)
$ACDEB$ is the cross-section*

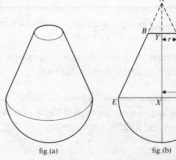

fig. (a)   fig. (b)

of the complete cone of which the portion *BCDE* is the cross-section of the upper portion of the capsule. Given that the height *AX* of the complete cone is 6 metres, find, by using similar triangles, the height *AY*, in terms of *r*, of the small cone whose cross-section is *ABC*.

Show that the volume of the portion of the cone whose cross-section is *BCDE* is $(\pi 8 - \pi r^3)\, m^3$.

Given that the volume is equal to the volume of the hemisphere, calculate the value of *r* correct to 2 decimal places. Taking the value of *r* to be 1·4 and π to be 3·14, find, in m^3 to 3 significant figures, the volume of the whole space capsule.

[LON]

Note: See page 225 for similar triangles.

Answers

1. 210°
2. A
3. 7·37 cm²
4. C
5. (a) 170 cm²   (b) 0·3 kg
6. (i) 44 cm   (ii) 198 cm²
7. (i) 16·7 cm²   (ii) 5·64 cm
8. (i) 78·5 cm²   (ii) 50 cm²
9. 10·78 m
10. (i) 20   (ii) 4 cm
11. 45·8 cm²
12. (i) 12 cm   (ii) 1 380·5 cm³
13. (c)
14. $AY = 3r, r = 1{\cdot}39\ m, 33{\cdot}2\ m^3$

Lines and Polygons

Two intersecting lines form four angles, which are equal in pairs as shown

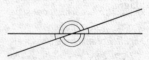

Parallel lines do not intersect. Two lines are indicated as parallel by putting arrows on them. If a third line is drawn across a pair of parallel lines, several angles are formed.

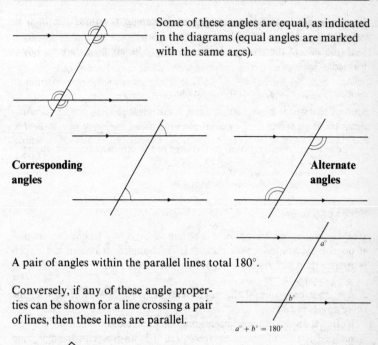

Some of these angles are equal, as indicated in the diagrams (equal angles are marked with the same arcs).

Corresponding angles

Alternate angles

A pair of angles within the parallel lines total 180°.

Conversely, if any of these angle properties can be shown for a line crossing a pair of lines, then these lines are parallel.

$a° + b° = 180°$

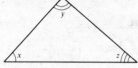

Triangles: Three lines, no two of which are parallel, form a triangle. Three **interior** angles are formed.

Fit three identical triangles together as in the following diagram

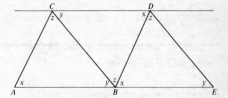

AB is parallel to CD (written as $AB/\!/CD$) (alternate angles $\angle ABC$ and $\angle BCD$). Also $CD/\!/BE$ (alternate angles $\angle BDC$ and $\angle DBE$). This means that ABE is a straight line and so $x° + y° + z° = 180°$.

The interior angles of a triangle add up to 180°

It is sufficient to know two angles of a triangle, the third can then be calculated.

If one side of the triangle is extended (**produced**), an **exterior** angle is formed

Since $\quad\quad x° + e° = 180°$ $\quad\quad$ straight line

and $\quad\quad x° + y° + z° = 180°$ $\quad\quad$ sum of interior angles

then $\quad\quad\quad\quad e° = y° + z°.$

The exterior angle is equal to the sum of the opposite interior angles.

Types of triangle

If all the angles of a triangle are less than 90°, it is said to be **acute-angled**. If one of the angles is 90°, then it is **right-angled**. If one of the angles is greater than 90°, then it is an **obtuse-angled** triangle.

Note: that only one of the angles can be $>90°$, since the sum of the three angles is 180°.

If all of the sides of the triangle are of different lengths, then the triangle is **scalene**. If two of the sides are equal, it is an **isosceles** triangle, and if all three sides are equal, it is **equilateral**.

Two of the angles of an isosceles triangle are equal, they are often called the **base angles** of the triangle.

A proof is demonstrated by the following diagrams

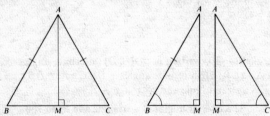

Drop a line from A perpendicular to the base BC. The triangle is then split into two smaller right-angled triangles. Since the isosceles triangle is left–right symmetric (so that it does not matter whether we look at it from in front or behind, it is the same shape), then the two right-angled triangles must be identical. In particular the angles $\angle ABM$ and $\angle ACM$ must be the same, as stated above. (An O-level examiner would require a more 'formal' proof. As an exercise, prove this result using congruent triangles (see below).) It follows that the angles of an equilateral triangle must all be equal to $\dfrac{180°}{3} = 60°$. When two triangles are identical (the same shape and size), we say that they are **congruent**. If one figure is an enlargement of the other, they are said to be **similar**. All the sides of one figure are multiplied by the same factor to obtain the sides of the other figure.

To show that two triangles are similar, it is enough to show that a pair of angles in one triangle is the same as a pair of angles in the second triangle.

To show that two triangles are congruent, it is enough to show *one* of the following:

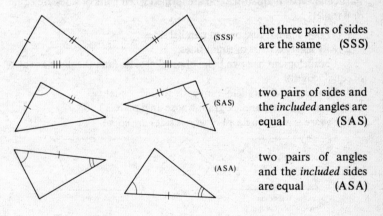

the three pairs of sides are the same (SSS)

two pairs of sides and the *included* angles are equal (SAS)

two pairs of angles and the *included* sides are equal (ASA)

For a right-angled triangle it is sufficient to show that the hypotenuses are equal and also one pair of corresponding sides (the right-angled hypotenuse side – RHS). The third side in each triangle can be calculated from Pythagoras' theorem (page 211), so this is a special case of SSS.

In the proof that the base angles of an isosceles triangle are equal, we made use of a line from a vertex to the base which meets the base at right angles. Such a line is called an **altitude** of the triangle. It measures the height of the triangle. An altitude can be drawn from any of the three vertices. A line from the vertex to the mid-point of the opposite side is called a **median** of the triangle. A line could also be drawn which cuts the angle into equal halves, called an **angle bisector**. When the triangle is isosceles (and only then), these three lines are identical.

Quadrilaterals

A quadrilateral is formed by four inter-secting straight lines. Since a quadri-lateral can be split into two triangles, then the sum of the interior angles must be $2 \times 180° = 360°$.

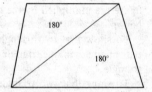

Particular types of quadrilateral are formed when pairs of sides are equal or parallel.

1. **Trapezium** has one pair of parallel sides.
2. **Kite** has two pairs of equal sides.
3. **Parallelogram** has two pairs of parallel sides (and the pairs are also of equal length).
4. **Rhombus** is a parallelogram with all sides equal.
5. **Rectangle** is a parallelogram whose angles are all 90°.
6. **Square** is a rectangle all of whose sides are equal.

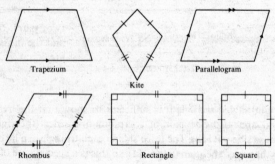

Trapezium Kite Parallelogram

Rhombus Rectangle Square

Note: that if T is the set of trapezia, P the set of parallelograms, $R = \{\text{rectangles}\}$, $S = \{\text{squares}\}$, and $Rh = \{\text{Rhombi}\}$, then $S \subset R \subset P \subset T$ and $R \cap Rh = S$ (see example on page 72).

Quadrilaterals can be characterized in terms of the properties of their diagonals, as shown by the following table.

Diagonal properties of quadrilaterals

	Diagonals bisect each other	Diagonals bisect the angles of the quadrilateral	Diagonals meet at 90°	Diagonals equal in length
Trapezium	—	—	—	—
Parallelogram	yes	—	—	—
Rhombus	yes	yes	yes	—
Rectangle	yes	—	—	yes
Square	yes	yes	yes	yes
Kite	one	one pair	yes	—

A dash (—) indicates that the property does not necessarily hold.

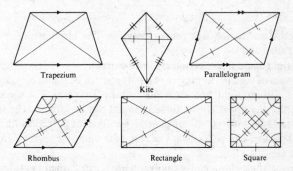

Trapezium

Kite

Parallelogram

Rhombus

Rectangle

Square

The area of a quadrilateral can be found by splitting it into triangles. Other useful formulae are

Area of a parallelogram = base × perpendicular height

Area of a rectangle = product of two adjacent sides

Area of square = square of the side

Area of rhombus = ½ × product of diagonals

Area of trapezium = ½ × sum of parallel sides × distance between them

Polygons

Triangles and quadrilaterals are examples of **polygons**. A polygon is a figure made up from straight line segments.

Number of sides	5	6	7	8	9	10
Name	pentagon	hexagon	heptagon	octagon	nonagon	decagon

When all of the sides and angles of a polygon are equal, then it is said to be **regular**.

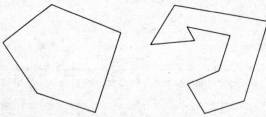

The figure on the left is a **convex** polygon. The interior angles are all smaller than 180°.

The right-hand figure is **concave** or **re-entrant.**

The sum of the interior angles of a polygon can be found by joining the vertices with straight line segments to form triangles. For the convex polygon of the figure above, three triangles can be formed. The interior angles total $3 \times 180° = 540°$. In general, for a convex polygon with n sides, $(n-2)$ triangles can be formed. The sum of the interior angles is $(n-2) \times 180°$ or $(2n-4) \times 90°$.

Exterior angles for a convex polygon are formed when the sides of the polygon are produced. These angles total 360°, no matter how many sides the polygon has. To see this, imagine the polygon shrinking until the produced sides seem to radiate from a point. The exterior angles then form a complete revolution.

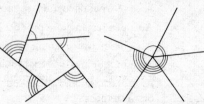

When the polygon is regular, all of the exterior angles are equal, and so each is $360°/n$. The interior angle can be found by subtracting the exterior angle from $180°$. Thus, for a regular pentagon, the exterior angle is $360°/5 = 72°$. The interior angle is $180° - 72° = 108°$.

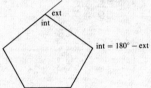

Examples

1. $ABCD$ is a parallelogram. M is the mid-point of AD. If the area of the parallelogram is $12\,\text{cm}^2$, find the area of the triangle ABM.

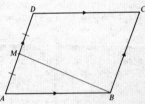

Answer   The height of the triangle is half that of the parallelogram, and they have the same base. So the area of the triangle is a quarter that of the parallelogram, $3\,\text{cm}^2$.

2. Determine whether the triangles ABC and PQR below are congruent.

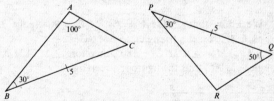

Answer   Angle $C = 180° - 100° - 30° = 50° =$ angle Q.   Angle $B = 30° =$ angle P and the sides BC and PQ are both $5\,\text{cm}$. The triangles are congruent (ASA).

3.

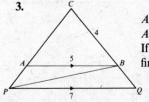

AB is parallel to PQ. Prove that the triangles ABC and PQC are similar.
If $AB = 5\,\text{cm}$, $BC = 4\,\text{cm}$ and $PQ = 7\,\text{cm}$, find the length of BQ.

Answer $\angle CAB = \angle CPQ$ (corresponding angles) and $\angle PCQ$ is the same as $\angle ACB$. The two triangles are similar.

The ratio $AB/PQ = 5/7$ is the same as the ratio BC/CQ since the triangles are similar, so

$$\frac{CB}{CQ} = \frac{5}{7}$$

$$CQ = \frac{7CB}{5}$$

$$= \frac{7 \times 4}{5} = \frac{28}{5} = 5 \cdot 6 \, \text{cm}$$

Hence $BQ = (5 \cdot 6 - 4) \, \text{cm} = 1 \cdot 6 \, \text{cm}$.

4. An isosceles triangle is split by an altitude and the two halves arranged as in the diagram. Show that the resulting figure is a rectangle.

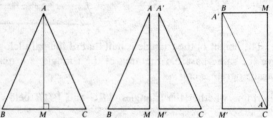

Answer We know that $\angle BMA = \angle A'M'C = 90°$ (page 224). Also $MBA = M'CA'$ (isosceles triangle), so $BM//CM'$.

Hence $\angle M'AM + \angle A'M'C = 180°$, therefore $\angle M'AM$ is also $90°$. All the angles are $90°$, thus the figure is a rectangle.

5.
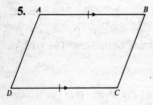

Two sides of the quadrilateral $ABCD$ are equal and parallel. Show that $ABCD$ is a parallelogram.

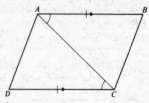

Answer   Draw diagonal AC

$\angle BAC = \angle DCA$ (alternate angles). Hence $\triangle$s ABC and ACD are congruent (SAS). Hence $\angle DAC = \angle BCA$ which proves that $AD//BC$ (alternate angles).

6. The diagram shows a regular octagon. Calculate (a) $\angle HAF$ (b) $\angle DAF$

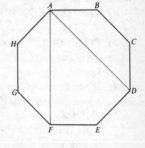

Answer   The exterior angle $= {}^{360}\!/_8 = 45°$ so the interior angles are all
$180° - 45° = 135°$.

(a) $AFGH$ is a quadrilateral. Two of the angles are each $135°$, totalling $270°$. The remaining two (equal) angles total $360° - 270° = 90°$, and so each is $45°$.
$\angle HAF = 45°$.

(b) By the same reasoning, $\angle BAD = 45°$ and so
$$\angle DAF = 135° - 45° - 45°$$
$$= 45°$$

7. Calculate angle x in the diagram.

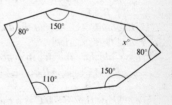

Answer   The sum of the interior angles of a six-sided polygon is
$$(6-2) \times 180° = 4 \times 180° = 720°$$
The sum of the given angles is $150° + 80° + 110° + 150° + 80° + x°$
$$= 570° + x°$$
$$\therefore \quad x° = (720 - 570)° = 150°$$

Examination questions

1. *PQRS is a parallelogram. Diagonals PR and QS intersect at X. Y lies on SR such that $SY:YR = 1:3$. Calculate*
$$\frac{area \, \triangle SYX}{area \, PQRS}.$$

2. *The side of the square PQRS is of length m +n. Points W, X, Y, Z are taken on the sides PQ, QR, RS, SP respectively such that PW = QX = RY = SZ = m.*

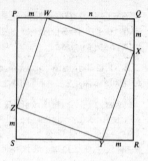

(a) *Prove that △QXW is congruent to △RYX*

(b) *Prove that ∠WXY is a right angle.*

(c) *Give reasons why WXYZ is a square.*

(d) *Write down, in terms of m and n, the areas of square PQRS and of △PWZ.*

> *By considering the areas of the squares and the triangles, verify that WX² = m² + n².*

(e) *Given that WY = 4m, calculate the value of the ratio m:n.*

[LON]

3. *ABCDE is a regular pentagon.*

(a) *Write down the size in degrees of ∠BAE.*

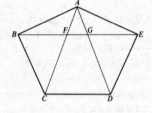

The diagonals AC, AD cut the diagonal BE at F and G respectively.

(b) *Calculate the size in degrees of ∠BAC, ∠ABE, ∠CBF and ∠CFB.*

(c) *Show that BGDC is a rhombus.*

(d) *Taking each side of the pentagon to be of length one cm, find the length in cm of FC.*

(e) *Taking AF to be of length x cm, find, in terms of x, the length, in cm, of FG.*

(f) *Show that △AFG is similar to △ACD and hence that AF.CD = AC.FG.*

(g) *By substituting the lengths in terms of x in the equation, form and simplify an equation in x but do not solve it.* [LON]

4. *In △XYZ, XY = 9 cm, PQ is parallel to YZ and the area of △XPQ is ⁴/₉ of the area of △XYZ. The length of XP is*

A 2 cm   B 3 cm   C 4 cm
D 6 cm   E none of these.

[LON]

(See also next section.)

5. Line segments *OA, OB, OC, OD, OE* form angles such that $\angle AOB = 2\angle AOE$, $\angle AOE = \angle DOE = \angle COD$, $\angle BOC = {}^3\!/_2 \angle AOB$. $\angle AOB =$

   A 45° *B* 90° *C* 48° *D* 96°

6. The area in cm^2 of the trapezium *PQRS* is

   A 36 *B* 45 *C* 48 *D* 72

             [AEB]

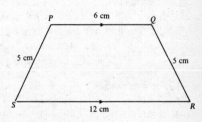

Hint: Drop perpendiculars from *P* and *Q* to *SR.*

7. *DC‖AB. BCE, ACF* are straight lines. Given that $\angle BAC = 43°$ and $\angle DCE = 54°$, calculate

(a) g, (b) h.

             [AEB]

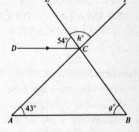

8.

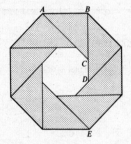

In triangle *ABC*, *AB = BC =* 2 cm and $\angle ABC = 90°$. Eight such congruent triangles are combined to make the shaded area shown in the diagram. Calculate

  (i) the shaded area *(ii)* CD *(iii)* BE.   [CAM]

9. Which triangles are similar to $\triangle PRS$?
(a) PRT and PQR (b) PQR and RTS
(c) RTS and PRT (d) None of these
[AEB]

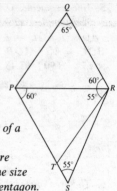

10. Given that $ABCDE$ is a regular
pentagon, calculate the size of the angle
EBD.

11. (a) Calculate the size of each interior angle of a
        regular polygon with 9 sides.
     (b) The five exterior angles of a pentagon are
        $y°$, $2y°$, $3y°$, $4y°$ and $5y°$. Calculate the size
        of the smallest exterior angle of the pentagon.
[AEB]

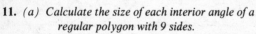

12. $ABCD...L$ is a regular polygon with
12 sides. Calculate the size of angle ABD.
[SMP]

13. In the diagram, $\angle DAB = 20°$ and
$AD = AB = CD$. Find the values of r and s.
[SMP]

Answers
1. $\frac{1}{16}$
2. (e) $1 : \sqrt{7}$
3. (a) $108°$ (b) $36°, 36°, 72°, 72°$ (d) 1 cm   (e) x^2 cm
   (g) $x^2 + x - 1 = 0$
4. D
5. B
6. A
7. (a) $54°$ (b) $83°$
8. (i) 16 cm^2 (ii) $2(\sqrt{2}-1)$ cm   (iii) $2(\sqrt{2}+1)$ cm
9. (a)
10. $36°$
11. (a) $140°$ (b) $24°$
12. $135°$
13. $r = 80°, s = 60°$

Section 13: Geometry and Transformations

Similar Shapes

Maps and models

The linear dimensions in similar figures are all scaled by the same factor.

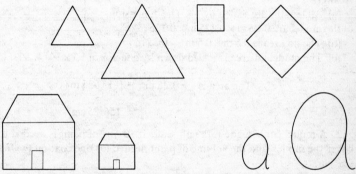

A scale model is similar to the object it copies, a diagram showing an **elevation** of a side of a building is similar to the shape of the side of the building. A pattern of roads marked on a map is similar to the pattern of the roads themselves.

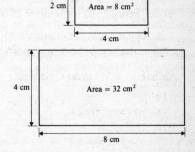

The height and length of the small rectangle are both doubled to give the dimensions of the larger rectangle. The *linear scale factor* is 2.

Since an area involves linear dimensions in two directions, then the scale factor for areas is the *square* of the linear scale factor. The area of the larger rectangle is $2^2 = 4$ times that of the smaller. Similarly, volumes are scaled by the *cube* of the linear factor.

Examples

1. A quarter size scale model is made of a box measuring $1\,m \times 0\cdot5\,m \times \times 0\cdot5\,m$, as shown in the diagram. Find

  (a) the dimensions of the model,
  (b) the area of the lid of the box and
  (c) the area of the corresponding lid on the model.

Answer

  (a) All lengths are scaled by $\frac{1}{4}$. The dimensions of the model are $0\cdot25\,m \times 0\cdot125\,m \times 0\cdot125\,m$.

  (b) The lid area is $0\cdot5\,m \times 0\cdot5\,m = 0\cdot25\,m^2$

  (c) The model lid area is scaled down by a factor of $\frac{1}{4} \times \frac{1}{4} = \frac{1}{16}$

$$\text{The area is } \frac{1}{6} \times 0\cdot25\,m^2 = 0\cdot15\,625\,m^2$$

$$= 156\cdot25\,cm^2$$

2. A model car is made to $\frac{1}{50}$th scale. If $10\,cm^3$ of paint is needed to cover the model, find the volume of paint needed for one coat on the full size car.

Answer
$$\text{Linear scale factor} = \frac{1}{50}$$

$$\text{Area scale factor} = \frac{1}{50} \times \frac{1}{50}$$

The surface area on the car is $50 \times 50 = 2\,500$ times as large as that on the model, hence $2\,500 \times 10\,cm^3 = 25\,000\,cm^3$ of paint is needed.

3. A cylindrical can of diameter $10\,cm$ holds $0\cdot5$ litre of water. A similar can has diameter $15\,cm$, how much water does it hold?

Answer
$$\text{Linear scale factor} = \frac{15}{10} = 1\cdot5$$

$$\text{Volume scale factor} = 1\cdot5^3 = 3\cdot375$$

$$\therefore \text{Capacity} = 3\cdot375 \times 0\cdot5 \text{ litres}$$

$$= 1\cdot6875 \text{ litres}$$

4. A map has a scale of $1:200\,000$. Find the distance corresponding to $2\cdot5\,\text{cm}$ on the map. An area on the map is measured to be $15\,\text{cm}^2$. What area does this represent?

Answer   Linear scale factor $= \dfrac{1}{200\,000}$

Scaling up $2\cdot5 \times 200\,000\,\text{cm} = 2\cdot5 \times 2\,\text{km}$

$$= 5\,\text{km}$$

Area scaling factor $= \left(\dfrac{1}{200\,000}\right)^2$

Scaling up $15 \times 200\,000 \times 200\,000\,\text{cm}^2 = \dfrac{15 \times 4 \times 10^{10}}{10^2 \times 10^2 \times 10^3 \times 10^3}\,\text{km}^2$

$$= 60\,\text{km}^2$$

Examination questions

1. *Calculate the distance in metres between two towns A and B which are represented on a map of scale 1 : 50 000 by two points 3 cm apart.*   [CAM]

2. *The capacity of a railway wagon is $10\,m^3$ and a scale model of it has a capacity of $0\cdot01\,m^3$. How many times as long as the model is the wagon?*
(a) 1 000   (b) 100   (c) 31·6   (d) 10   [SMP]

3. *Using a scale of 1 cm to 500 m, draw a scale diagram of a triangle A B C with the following measurements.*

AB = 6 000 m,   AC = 5 000 m   and   ∠ BAC = 71°.

By measurement from your diagram find, in metres, the distance BC. [SMP]

4. *A nest of tables is shown in side elevation. Each of the larger two is an exact enlargement in 3 dimensions of the smallest. The table tops are rectangular with the largest 60 cm long and of area 2520 cm². Calculate*
(i) the length of the middle sized table;
(ii) the area of the top of the smallest table, correct to the nearest cm².

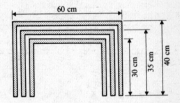

[SMP]

5. *A television screen may be considered as a rectangle. Its 'size' is the length of a diagonal, correct to the nearest cm. All screens are the same shape.   (a) Calculate the 'size' of screen A which is 52 cm wide and 40 cm in length.*

(b) Calculate to the nearest cm the width of screen B whose 'size' is 45 cm.   [SMP]

6. *Tins of baked beans have labels which cover the whole of the curved surface. The area of the label on one tin is 300 cm². A similar tin contains twice the amount. The area of its label is, correct to 3 significant figures*

(a) 300 cm²,   (b) 600 cm²,   (c) 1 200 cm²,   (d) None of these [SMP]

Answers

1. 1 500 m
2. (d)
3. 6 440
4. (i) 52·5 cm   (ii) 1 418 cm²
5. (a) 66 cm   (b) 36 cm
6. (d)

Three Dimensions – Polyhedra

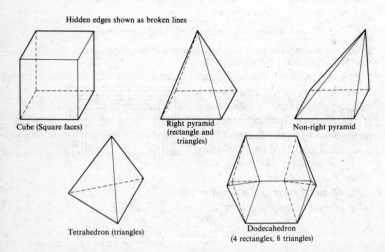

Hidden edges shown as broken lines

Cube (Square faces)

Right pyramid (rectangle and triangles)

Non-right pyramid

Tetrahedron (triangles)

Dodecahedron (4 rectangles, 8 triangles)

A solid formed by fitting polygons together is called a **polyhedron**. The polygons form its faces.

In a *right* pyramid, the top vertex is directly above the centre of the base. Just as polygons can be fitted together to form more complicated figures, polyhedra can be fitted together. Two pyramids on square bases can be joined to make an octahedron.

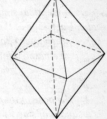

The methods for calculating lengths and angles in two dimensions can also be used for three-dimensional problems.

Example   Find the length of the diagonal AG in the cube of side 5 cm shown in the diagram.

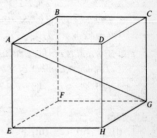

Answer   Triangle AEG is right-angled, so we can use Pythagoras' theorem. Draw a frontal view of this triangle.

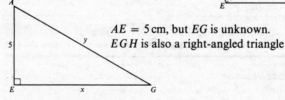

$AE = 5$ cm, but EG is unknown.
EGH is also a right-angled triangle

From Pythagoras' theorem

$$x^2 = 5^2 + 5^2$$
$$= 25 + 25$$
$$= 50$$

From Pythagoras' theorem in $\triangle AEG$

$$y^2 = x^2 + 5^2$$
$$= 50 + 25$$
$$= 75$$

$$\therefore AG = y = \sqrt{75}\text{ cm}$$
$$= \sqrt{3 \times 25}\text{ cm} = \sqrt{3}\sqrt{25}\text{ cm} = 5\sqrt{3}\text{ cm}$$

Examination questions

1. *27 identical small unpainted cubes are fitted together to make a large cube. Each face of the large cube is then painted. State the number of small cubes which have exactly*

   (i) one painted face,   (ii) two painted faces,   (iii) 3 painted faces.

[CAM]

2. *The base of the right pyramid shown is a square of side 2m and the height PQ is 1m.*

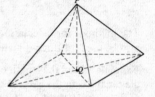

   (i) The length of each sloping edge is

   (a) $\sqrt{2}m$,   (b) $\sqrt{3}m$,
   (c) $2m$,   (d) $2\sqrt{2}m$.

   (ii) Pyramids of this size and shape are joined together, to make a cube. The least number of pyramids used is

   (a) 2,   (b) 4,   (c) 6,   (d) 8.

[SMP]

Answers

   1. (i) 6   (ii) 12   (iii) 8
   2. (i) (b)   (ii) (c)

Patterns – Tessellations

Civilizations from earliest times have used geometric patterns in artistic and decorative work. One particular form is patterns made from tiles. A tiling pattern is called a **tessellation**.

Examples

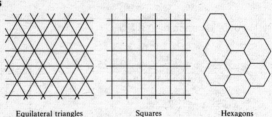

Equilateral triangles   Squares   Hexagons

These are the only tessellations that can be formed from *regular* polygons all of one type. To be able to tessellate with a regular polygon, the interior angle must be a factor of 360°. The least value is 60° (3 sides). The only factors of 360° which are less than 180 and greater than or equal to 60 are 60, 72, 90 and 120.

An equilaterial triangle has angle 60°, a square has angle 90° and a hexagon has angle 120°. No regular polygon has interior angle 72° (since the exterior angle would then be 108°, which would correspond to $\dfrac{360}{108} = 3\dfrac{1}{3}$ sides which is not possible).

Tessellations can also be formed by combining different regular polygons.

Examples

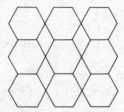 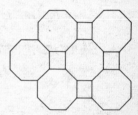

Hexagons and rhombi   Octagons and squares

Nets – Making Polyhedra

Polyhedra can be formed by folding suitable patterns of polygons, called **nets**. A net of a cube is Folding as indicated produces a cube.

Examples

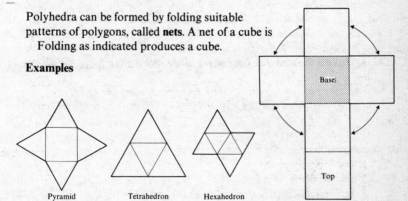

Pyramid   Tetrahedron   Hexahedron

Examination questions

1.

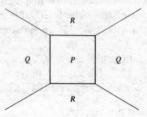

The diagram shows part of a tessellation formed with three types of regular polygon, P, Q and R. If P is a square and Q is a hexagon, then the number of sides of R is

(a) 8, (b) 10, (c) 12, (d) 15. [SMP]

2. Which of the following is a net for a regular octahedron?

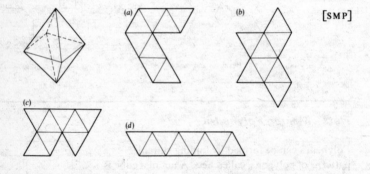

[SMP]

3. You can be sure that you can tessellate with a given polygon if all you know about it is that

(a) all its angles are equal, (b) its opposite sides are equal,

(c) its angle sum is a factor of 360°, (d) it has a centre of symmetry.

[SMP]

Answers

1. (c)
2. (b)
3. (c) (Find counter examples for (a), (b) and (d).)

Transformations and Symmetry

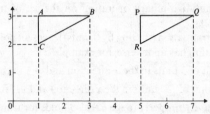

The triangles ABC and PQR are congruent (page 225) and have the same orientation with respect to the axes. If $\triangle ABC$ is moved, without turning, 4 units in the x direction, it will cover triangle PQR exactly. $\triangle PQR$ is the **image** of $\triangle ABC$ under the **translation** of 4 units in the x direction.

A **plane transformation** is a one–one or many–one mapping of the plane to itself. A translation is a particular kind of transformation, which shifts all points of the plane by a given amount in a given direction.

If a transformation T maps the plane to itself, the image of a plane figure can be found by considering the images of its vertices.

For the translation above, $T(A) = P$, $T(B) = Q$ and $T(C) = R$. Denoting triangle ABC by $\triangle$, then triangle PQR is $T(\triangle)$.

Transformations can be combined by composition (page 80). Let T_1 be a translation of 2 units in the positive x-direction, and T_2 be a shift of 3 units in the y-direction. $T_1 \circ T_2$ or $T_1 T_2$ means 'do T_2 first and then T_1'. The image of a figure can be found in two stages.

Denoting the shaded square by $\square$, $T_2(\square)$ is its image under T_2. Let $\square' = T_2(\square)$. Also let $\square'' = T_1(\square')$. Then $T_1 T_2(\square) = \square''$. The combined transformation is also a translation, shown by the broken arrow in the diagram. It is a shift of 2 units in the x-direction and 3 units in the y-direction.

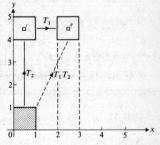

The 'size' of the translation, the distance moved, can be found using Pythagoras' theorem

$$d^2 = 2^2 + 3^2 = 13$$
$$d = \sqrt{13}$$

The translation $T_1 \circ T_2$ is found to be the same as $T_2 \circ T_1$. Composition is a closed commutative binary operation on the set of translations (see pages 57 and 62).

The **identity translation** (shifting by 0 units) leaves all points unchanged.
Each translation has an inverse, for example

if T is a shift of 3 units in the x direction and -1 in the y direction

then T^{-1} is a shift of -3 units in the x direction and $+1$ in the y direction

(The associativity property (page 62) also holds for translations.

Exercise:
If $T_1 = $ shift 2 units in x direction
                          $T_2 = $ shift 3 units in y direction
and $T_3 = $ shift 1 unit of x and -2 units of y
show that $T_1 \circ (T_2 \circ T_3) = (T_1 \circ T_2) \circ T_3$
by considering the effects on the square of the last example.

Note: When two translations are combined, you add the respective x and y shifts. The associativity then follows from the associativity of addition of numbers.

The set of translations forms a commutative group (page 62) under composition.

A translation can be specified by two **components** (in the x and y directions). A translation of 2 units in the x-direction and 3 units in the y-direction is **specified** by the **column vector** $\begin{pmatrix} 2 \\ 3 \end{pmatrix}$ (see page 328). The inverse translation is given by $\begin{pmatrix} -2 \\ -3 \end{pmatrix}$.

A translation can also be specified by a distance and a direction; for example, 3 km in direction north-east (see bearings, page 291).

Other transformations

Reflections

1. In a given line

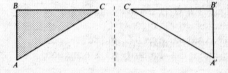

△ *A′ B′ C′* is the image of △ *A B C* under reflection in the broken line, which is called the **axis** of the reflection. The image you see in a mirror is this type of reflection. A reflection is specified by giving the axis.

2. In a given point

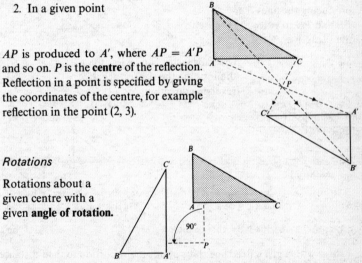

AP is produced to *A′*, where *AP* = *A′P* and so on. *P* is the **centre** of the reflection. Reflection in a point is specified by giving the coordinates of the centre, for example reflection in the point (2, 3).

Rotations

Rotations about a given centre with a given **angle of rotation.**

The diagram shows a rotation of 90° anticlockwise (positive angle) about the point *P*. A rotation is specified by its centre and the angle of rotation. For example 90° anticlockwise about *P*(1, 3).

These transformations are **isometric**, they leave distances and areas unchanged – in fact these particular transformations do not alter the shape or size of the object figure.

Not all transformations do this.

Enlargement

Example

Triangle $A'B'C'$ is an enlargement, with scale factor 2, of $\triangle ABC$. $A'B'C'$ is similar to ABC, and so enlargement is a **similarity transformation**.

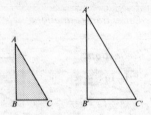

An enlargement is specified by giving the centre and scale factor.

Example   An enlargement with scale factor 2 about the point $P(2,0)$.

The image is found by producing the lines PA, PB and PO to twice their lengths.

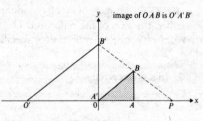

The scale factor can be less than 1 (diminishing the size) or negative (reversing direction)

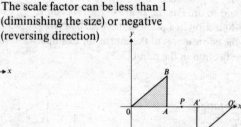

scale factor $\frac{1}{2}$

scale factor -1

Shear

A shear with a given fixed line shifts points in proportion to their distance from the fixed line, parallel to the fixed line.

The diagram shows a shear, which shifts in the direction of the x-axis. The amount of the shift is twice the distance of a point from the x-axis, so that the shear has a **factor** of 2.

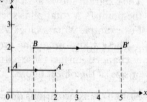

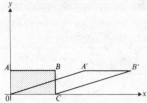

The image of a rectangle is a parallelogram, with the same base and height.

The *area* of the figure is not changed by a shear.

Invariants

A point, line or figure left unchanged by a transformation is said to be **invariant** under the transformation.

The fixed line of a shear is an invariant of the shear – all points on the line are mapped to themselves.

To specify a shear it is sufficient to give the invariant line and the image of one point not on this line. For example, a shear with invariant line $y = 0$ such that $(0, 1) \mapsto (1\frac{1}{2}, 1)$.

Examples

1. An infinite horizontal line is invariant under a translation in the x direction.

2. We can generalize to patterns. The tessellation shown

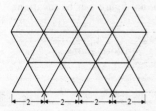

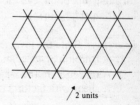

/ 2 units

is invariant under a translation of 2 units in the x direction. It is also invariant under other translations

3. The centre of a rotation is invariant under the rotation. A square is invariant under rotations of 90° about its centre. If the rotation is performed 4 times, the square is restored to its original orientation. We say that it has **four-fold rotation symmetry**, or **symmetry of order 4.**

4. A circle is invariant under any rotation about its centre.

5. The following shapes are invariant under the reflections with axes indicated as broken lines

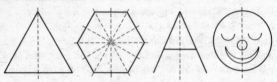

The axis is called an **axis** (or **line**) **of symmetry**.
A figure is **symmetric** about its axes of symmetry.

6. The following shapes are invariant under reflections in the given points

They illustrate **point symmetry**. Point symmetry is equivalent to symmetry under a half-turn **rotation**.

7. The fixed line of a shear is invariant.

8. The centre of an enlargement is invariant, as is any line passing through this point. No closed two-dimensional figure can be invariant under an enlargement.

Exercise: State the inverses of the following transformations
1. A rotation of 45° about the origin.
2. A reflection in the x-axis.
3. A shear with factor 3 in the direction of the y-axis.

A transformation can be defined by giving the image of a general point (x, y), in the same way that a function can be defined by a formula.

Examples
1. $T: (x, y) \mapsto (x + 2, y + 3)$ is a translation.
2. $T: (x, y) \mapsto (-x, y)$ is reflection in the y-axis.
3. $T: (x, y) \mapsto (-y, x)$ is rotation of 90° about 0.
4. $T: (x, y) \mapsto (x, 0)$ maps all points onto the x-axis. This transformation is a many–many map and so has no inverse.

Example

The triangle ABC has vertices $A(1,0)$, $B(1,1)$ and $C(2,0)$. Draw this triangle on graph paper. Find the image of $\triangle ABC$ under

(a) a reflection in the line $x = 3$,

(b) a rotation of $180°$ anticlockwise about 0,

(c) a shear with invariant line the x-axis and such that $(1,1) \mapsto (4,1)$,

(d) a reflection R in the line $x = 1$ followed by a translation T, of 1 unit in the x direction and 2 units in the y direction,

and show them on your diagram.

Answer

(a) The image of $(1,0)$ is $(5,0)$, the image of $(1,1)$ is $(5,1)$ and the image of $(2,0)$ is $(4,0)$.

(b)

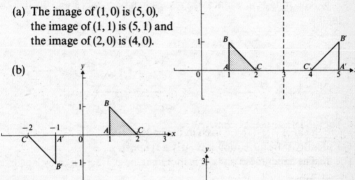

(c) Under this shear

$$\left.\begin{array}{l}(1,0) \mapsto (1,0) \\ (1,1) \mapsto (4,1) \\ (2,0) \mapsto (2,0)\end{array}\right\} \;(x,y) \mapsto (x+3y, y)$$

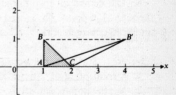

(d)

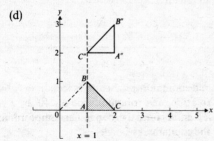

The image of $\triangle ABC$ under TR is $\triangle A''B''C''$ (TR means R followed by T).

Symmetry groups

A figure is invariant under its **symmetry transformations**. For example, the equilateral triangle shown has symmetry transformations

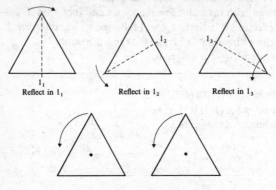

where the lines l_1, l_2, l_3 are fixed in the page.

The identity transformation is clearly a symmetry.

The images under these transformations can be characterized by labelling the vertices.

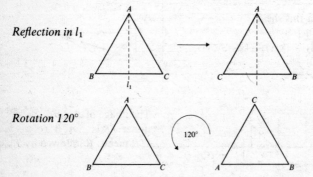

Denote reflection in l_1 by T_1, reflection in l_2 by T_2 and reflection in l_3 by T_3. Also, rotation through 120° by R_1 and rotation through 240° by R_2. I is the identity. I, T_1, T_2, T_3, R_1 and R_2 form a group under composition, called the **symmetry group** of the equilateral triangle.

We can form the group operation table by forming products $T_1 T_2$, $T_1 R_1$, etc.

Note: This group is *not* commutative, so that $T_1 T_2$ and $T_2 T_1$ should be worked out carefully.

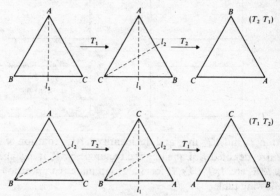

It can be seen that $T_2 T_1 = R_2$ (rotate 240°)

and $T_1 T_2 = R_1$ (rotate 120°)

Exercise: Find all other products of pairs of transformations. You will see that composition *is* a closed operation since two symmetry transformations result in another symmetry.

The operation table is

		First transformation				
∘	I	T_1	T_2	T_3	R_1	R_2
I	I	T_1	T_2	T_3	R_1	R_2
T_1	T_1	I	R_1	R_2	T_2	T_3
T_2	T_2	R_2	I	R_1	T_3	T_1
T_3	T_3	R_1	R_2	I	T_1	T_2
R_1	R_1	T_3	T_1	T_2	R_2	I
R_2	R_2	T_2	T_3	T_1	I	R_1

Second transformation (row labels: I, T_1, T_2, T_3, R_1, R_2)

Remember that the *order* of the transformations in a product is important.

From the table, $T_2 \circ T_1 = R_2$

Note: that I, R_1, R_2 also form a group.

Other shapes have symmetry groups.

Examples   The symmetries of a rectangle are

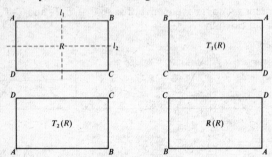

reflection T_1 in l_1, T_2 in l_2 and the identity I. Also rotation of $180°$ about the centre, denoted R. Labelling the rectangle by R, it has images $T_1(R)$, $T_2(R)$, $R(R)$ etc. I, T_1, T_2, R form a group under composition which has the following table

		First			
	$\circ$	I	R	T_1	T_2
	I	I	R	T_1	T_2
	R	R	I	T_2	T_1
Second	T_1	T_1	T_2	I	R
	T_2	T_2	T_1	R	I

This group *is* commutative.

A square has many more symmetries

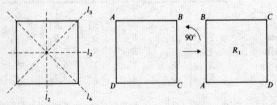

four reflections and three rotations ($90°$, $180°$, $270°$).

Three dimensions

Solid figures can also be symmetric.

Reflection in a plane:

The right square pyramid has
plane symmetry.

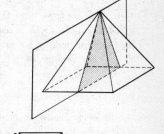

A cube has nine planes of symmetry

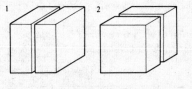

and so on

The following solid has rotational symmetry of order 3

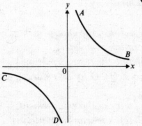

Examination questions

1.

The diagram is part of the graph of $y = x^n$.
   (i) State a possible value for n.
   (ii) Describe completely the transformation which maps arc AB onto
      arc CD.   [CAM]

   2. The translation T maps the point (1, 2) onto the point (2, 5). Under
T the line $y = 2x$ is mapped onto the line $y = mx + c$. Find   (i) the value
of m,   (ii) the value of c.   [CAM]

3. *O is the origin, A is the point (0,8) and B is the point (0,4). Under an anti-clockwise rotation, A is mapped onto O and B is mapped onto a point on the x-axis.*

Find   (i) the angle of rotation,

(ii) the coordinates of the centre of rotation.   [CAM]

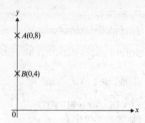

4.

(a) Under an enlargement of scale factor 2, the point (3, 1) is mapped onto the point (6, 2). State the coordinates of the centre of enlargement.

(b) Under an anti-clockwise rotation of 90° with centre (2, 0), the point (6, 0) is mapped onto the point (h, k). Find h and k.   [CAM]

5. *OABC is a square of side 4 cm. Q is the midpoint of BC and P is the point on AB such that PB = 1 cm. AB produced meets OQ produced at R.*

(i) Find the length of BR.

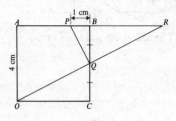

△PBQ is mapped onto △QCO by an enlargement, centre P, followed by a rotation about P, and finally by a transformation V.

(ii) State the scale factor of the enlargement.

(iii) Describe the rotation completely.

(iv) Describe completely the transformation V.

△OAR is mapped onto △QCO by an enlargement centre O, followed by a transformation W.

(v) State the scale factor of the enlargement.

(vi) Describe completely the transformation W.   [CAM]

6. *A rotation maps P(1,0) to P′(0,1) and Q(0,1) to Q′(1,2). State the coordinates of the centre and find the angle of rotation.*

7.

(a) From the word   **E X A C T**

write down all the letters that have
(i) a vertical line symmetry,
(ii) a horizontal line symmetry,
(iii) point symmetry.

(b) Draw all the lines of symmetry
for this square in the plane of
the paper.

[AEB]

8. If a quadrilateral has point symmetry but not line symmetry, then it is a
A Parallelogram   B Rectangle   C Kite   D Cyclic quadrilateral.
[AEB]

9. Complete the figure below so that it has rotational symmetry.

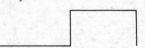

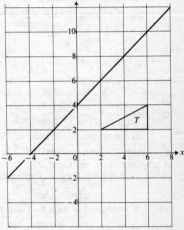

10. The diagram on the right shows a triangle T together with the line $y = x + 4$.

The transformations R and S are rotations through $180°$ about the points $(0, 0)$ and $(-3, 3)$ respectively. Using a scale of 1 cm to represent 1 unit, copy Fig. 1 on squared paper and on your diagram draw and label $R(T)$ and $SR(T)$, the image of T under R followed by S.

M_1, M_2 and M_3 are reflections in the lines m_1, m_2 and m_3 respectively, such that $M_3 M_1(T) = M_1 M_3(T) = SR(T)$.

Given that m_1 is the line $y = x + 4$, find, draw and label $M_1(T)$ and $M_3(T)$ on your diagram.

Write down the equation of each of the lines m_2 and m_3 respectively. The transformation S may be defined by S: $(x, y) \rightarrow (-x - 6, -y + 6)$. Define each of the transformations R and SR in a similar way.   [AEB]

11. (The whole of this question should be answered on squared paper or graph paper.)

(i) *E, F are enlargements with scale factors 1·5 and 2 respectively. Say what you can about the transformation FE.*

(ii) *E,F are now chosen to have centres (0, 0) and (12, 0) respectively. T is the triangle with vertices P(6, 0), Q(6, 4), R(4, 4).*

(a) *Using scales of 1 cm to a unit, draw axes to show 0 ⩽ x ⩽ 12 and 0 ⩽ y ⩽ 12.*
On this diagram show T, E(T) and FE(T), labelling all the vertices (use P′, Q′, R′; P″, Q″, R″).

(b) *Give a complete description of FE.*

(c) *State the coordinates of P′, F(P′) and EF(P′) and give a complete description of EF.*

(d) *Comment on the way in which E and F combine.*   [SMP]

12. *ABCDEF is a regular hexagon of side 3 cm.*

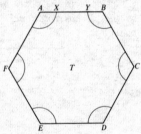

(i) *State (a) the order of rotational symmetry,*

(b) the size of the interior angle at A.

(ii) *Sectors of radius 1 cm with centres at the vertices are removed from the hexagon to leave the shape T.*

Calculate   (a) the total area of the six sectors removed.

(b) the area of T. [The area of an equilateral triangle of side a is 0·433a².]

(iii) *A pillar is 4 m high and has a cross section similar to T with XY equal to 5 cm. Calculate its volume in cubic metres.*   [SMP]

13. *An enlargement E has centre (3, 0). The point Q is the image of the point P(9, 2) under E.*

(i) *State the scale factor of E if Q is the point (15, 4).*

(ii) *Find the coordinate of Q if the scale factor of E is − ½.*   [SMP]

14.

(i) *The diagram shows a regular pentagon P. On the answer sheet, draw all the lines of symmetry that lie in the plane of the paper.*

(ii) *An irregular pentagon Q has q lines of symmetry in its own plane. State the two possible values of q.* [SMP]

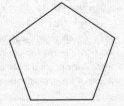

15. *In this question use a scale of 2 cm to represent 1 unit on each axis, taking values of x from −1 to +7 and values of y from −5 to +5. Draw on graph paper △ABC, where A, B, C are respectively the points (2, 2), (6, 2) and (6, 4).*

The transformation E is an enlargement about the point (4, 0) with scale factor −½ The transformation R is a rotation through 180° about the point (3, 0).

Construct the images of △ABC under the transformations E, R, ER and RE marking your diagram carefully to distinguish the 4 images. Describe in words the single transformation T such that TRE = ER. [LON part]

Answers

1. (i) −1 for example   (ii) reflection in $y = -x$
2. (i) 2   (ii) 1
3. (i) 90°   (ii) (4, 4)
4. (a) (0, 0)   (b) (2, 4)
5. (i) 4 cm   (ii) 2   (iii) 90° clockwise about P
   (iv) translation 1 ∥ to AB, 2 ∥ to BC (v) ½
   (vi) rotation of 180° about the mid-point of QO
7. (i) X, A, T,   (ii) X, E, C   (iii) X
8. A
10. m_2: $y = x + 10$ m_3: $y = x - 2$. R: $(x, y) \mapsto (-x, -y)$,
    SR: $(x, y) \mapsto (x - 6, y - 6)$
12. (i) (a) 6   (b) 120°   (ii) (a) 6·28 cm²   (b) 17·1 cm²
    (iii) 0·17 m³
13. (i) 2   (ii) (0, −1)
14. (ii) 0, 1

Circle Geometry

The circle is important as a geometrical figure. It is defined as the locus of points equidistant from a fixed point. It is symmetric about *any* diameter. Various geometrical properties of circles are collected together in this section.

If the end points of an arc are joined to a third point on the circumference, then an angle is formed.

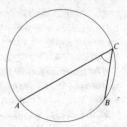

The angle *ACB* is called the angle subtended by arc *AB* at *C*.

Property 1:   The angle *ACB* is the same no matter where *C* is taken on
the major arc *AB*, i.e. angles in the same segment are equal. Similarly,
all the angles subtended on the minor arc are equal.

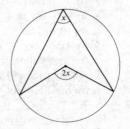

Property 2:   The angle subtended by an arc
at the centre is twice the angle subtended at
the circumference.

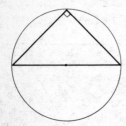

Property 3:   This is a consequence of Property
2. When the chord is a diameter, then the angle
at the centre is 180°. The angle at the circumference is 90°, i.e. the angle in a semicircle is a
right angle.

Property 4 – Intersecting chord theorem:

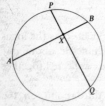

When the two chords *AB* and *PQ* intersect at *X*,
then $AX.XB = PX.XQ$ (whether *X* is inside
or outside the circle). This follows from the fact
that $\triangle$s *APX* and *QBX* are similar.

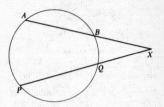

Property 5 – Tangent-secant theorem: Consider the figure above which shows two secants meeting at *X* outside the circle. Imagine secant *PQX* dropping until it *touches* the circle. *P* and *Q* are now the same point, the point of contact. The line is now a tangent to the circle at *P*. Then $AX \cdot BX = PX^2$.

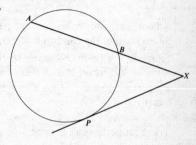

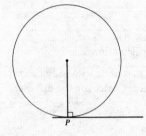

Property 6: The tangent to a circle at *P* is perpendicular to the radius which meets the circumference at *P*.

Property 7 – Alternate segment theorem: *TX* is a tangent to the circle at *T*. *ST* is a chord, subtending an angle *SRT* at *R* in the opposite segment. The angles $\angle SRT$ and $\angle STX$ are equal.

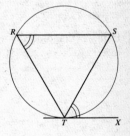

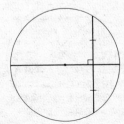

Property 8: A diameter bisects a chord at right angles.

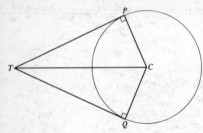

Property 9: From a point T outside the circle, two tangents can be drawn, meeting the circle at P and Q. The triangles PTC and QTC are congruent. In particular $PT = QT$.

Any of these properties can also be used to define a circle, since no other figure satisfies the conditions.

Example   A point P moves so that angle $APB = 90°$, where A and B are fixed. From Property 3, P must lie on a circle with diameter AB.

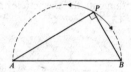

These properties can also be used in distance calculations.

Example   A tangent is drawn from a point T to a circle with radius 5 cm and centre C. If the length of this tangent is 12 cm, calculate the distance CT.

Answer

$\angle TPC = 90°$

Using Pythagoras' theorem

$$CT^2 = 12^2 + 5^2$$
$$= 144 + 25$$
$$= 169$$
$$\therefore CT = \sqrt{169} = 13 \text{ cm}$$

A quadrilateral inscribed in a circle is called a **cyclic quadrilateral**.

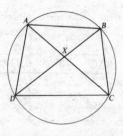

   The diagonals AC and BD meet at X. It follows from the intersecting chord theorem that a quadrilateral is cyclic if and only if $AX.XC = BX.XD$.

Another property is that opposite angles of a cyclic quadrilateral add up to 180°, i.e. they are **supplementary**.

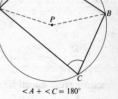

Proof:

$\angle DPB = 2\angle C$ Property 2

reflex $\angle DPB = 2\angle A$ i.e. $360° - \angle DPB$

But these two angles add up to 360°

So $2\angle A + 2\angle C = 360°$

           $\therefore \angle A + \angle C = 180°$

$<A + <C = 180°$

Examples

1.

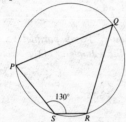

Angle $PQR = 180° - 130° = 50°$

2. AB is a diameter and is 10 cm long. AC is a chord 4 cm long. Find the length of chord BC.

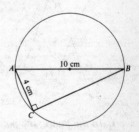

Answer $\angle ACB = 90°$ (angle in a semicircle), so we can use Pythagoras' theorem

3. Find angle ABC.

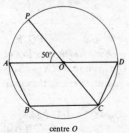

centre O

$$AB^2 = AC^2 + BC^2$$
$$10^2 = 4^2 + BC^2$$
$$100 = 16 + BC^2$$
$$BC^2 = 100 - 16 = 84$$
$$BC = \sqrt{84} \text{ cm}$$
$$= \sqrt{4 \times 21} \text{ cm}$$
$$\therefore BC = 2\sqrt{21} \text{ cm}$$

Answer $\angle AOC = 180° - 50° = 130°$, which is the angle subtended by arc AC at the centre. From Property 2, the angle subtended at D on the circumference is $130°/2 = 65°$

$ABCD$ is a cyclic quadrilateral, so

$$\angle ABC = 180° - \angle ADC$$
$$= 180° - 65°$$
$$= 115°$$

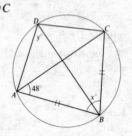

Examination questions

1. *The cyclic quadrilateral ABCD has $AB = BC$ and the angle $BAC = 48°$.*

Calculate (i) x,   (ii) y.   [AEB]

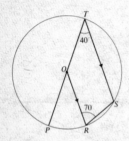

2. *In the figure, TS is parallel to OR. Prove that POT is a diameter of the circle.*

3. *In the figure, the points A, B and C are on the circumference of the circle, centre O. The angle $AOC = 140°$ and AO is parallel to BC. Calculate the values of*
(a) d,   (b) e.   [AEB]

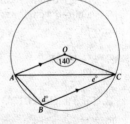

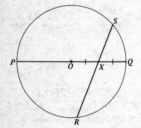

4. *O is the centre of the circle, PQ is a diameter and SR is a chord which cuts PQ at X so that $OX = XQ$. Given that $RX = 8$ cm and $XS = 6$ cm, the radius, in cm, of the circle is*

A 4 B 8 $C\sqrt{48}$ D $2\sqrt[3]{24}$
E 12   [LON]

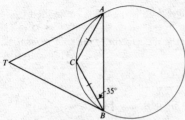

5. *Tangents TA and TB touch a circle at A and B. The point C, on the minor arc AB, is such that CA = CB. Given that $A\hat{B}C = 35°$, calculate*

(i) $A\hat{C}B$, (ii) $A\hat{T}B$. [CAM]

6. *In the diagram, AB is a diameter of the circle and TA is the tangent at A.*
$T\hat{A}D = 2x°$ *and* $C\hat{A}B = x°$
Find, in terms of x,
(i) $A\hat{D}C$, (ii) $D\hat{B}C$. [CAM]

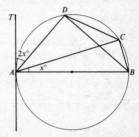

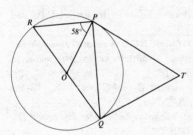

7. *TP and TQ are tangents to a circle centre O, touching it at P and Q. QOR is a diameter and $R\hat{P}O = 58°$.*

Showing your reasons clearly, calculate
(i) $P\hat{O}R$, (ii) $P\hat{Q}O$,
(iii) $P\hat{T}Q$ [CAM]

8.

In the diagram (which is not drawn to scale) the circle C_2 is the image of the circle C_1 under an enlargement E, centre O. A and B are the centres of C_1 and C_2 respectively, and the circles touch at T, so that OATB is a straight line. The straight line OPQ touches C_1 at P and C_2 at Q.
$OP = 4\,cm$, $AP = 3\,cm$, $BQ = x\,cm$.
(i) Find the length of OA.
(ii) Express OB in terms of x in the following ways:
(a) by considering the images of OA and PA under E;

(b) by considering OA, AT and TB.
Hence form an equation for x.
Solve this equation, and state the scale factor of the enlargement E.
(iii) Calculate PQ.   [SMP]

9. *AB and CD are chords of the circle*
centre O. AB cuts CD at X and AC = CX.
Calculate   (i) the angle A   (ii) the angle B.
                                                [SMP]

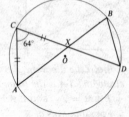

10. *A, B, C lie on a circle, centre O.*
Triangle ABC is isosceles. Triangle DCB is
obtained from ABC by a half turn. Angle
BOC = 2α°

(i) What relation exists between AC and
BD?

(ii) Triangle BCD is rotated through 2α°
about O anticlockwise. The image is
B′C′D′.

(a) Show this on a sketch and identify B′ and C′.
(b) Describe the symmetry of B′CC′D′.
(c) State, with reasons, the size of the angle between BD and B′D′.
(d) What is the size of angle D′B′C?
(e) Deduce the size of angle BAC.   [SMP]

Answers

1. (i) 84°   (ii) 48°

3. (a) 110°   (b) 20°

4. B

5. (i) 110°   (ii) 40°

6. (i) 90° + x°   (ii) 90° − 3x°

7. (i) 64°   (ii) 32°   (iii) 64°

8. (i) 5 cm   (ii) (a) $\dfrac{5x}{3}$ (b) 8 + x. Scale factor 4   (iii) 12 cm

9. (i) 58°   (ii) 64°

10. (i) AC = BD   (ii) (c) α°   (d) 180° − 2α°   (e) α°

Section 14: Trigonometry

Sine, Cosine and Tangent

The angles of a triangle are invariant under an enlargement, since the shape does not change. Let OAB be a right-angled triangle and $OA'B'$ be the image under an enlargement about O with scale factor 2.

Under the enlargement,

$$OB \to OB' = 2OB$$

and

$$AB \to A'B' = 2AB.$$

So

$$\frac{A'B'}{OB'} = \frac{2AB}{2OB} = \frac{AB}{OB}.$$

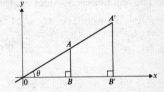

The ratio of height to base for this triangle is invariant under an enlargement. It does however depend on the angle θ and so we define the *tangent* of the angle θ

$$\tan \theta = \frac{AB}{OB} = \text{gradient of line } OA.$$

Similarly we define the ratios sine and cosine by

$$\sin \theta = \frac{AB}{OA} \text{ and } \cos \theta = \frac{OB}{OA}$$

(sin, cos and tan are used as shortened forms for sine, cosine and tangent).

Summary: Given an angle which is between 0° and 90°, a right-angled triangle can be constructed with this angle. Label the side opposite the angle *opposite*, the side opposite the right angle is called the *hypotenuse*, the remaining side is the *adjacent* side.

It follows from the definitions above that

$$\sin \theta = \frac{\text{opposite}}{\text{hypotenuse}}, \quad \cos \theta = \frac{\text{adjacent}}{\text{hypotenuse}}, \quad \tan \theta = \frac{\text{opposite}}{\text{adjacent}}$$

(You can remember this as S O H, C A H, T O A.)

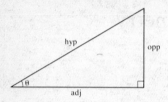

Note: that the triangle *must* be right-angled.

For a particular angle, the triangle can be constructed and the ratios measured.

Example   Find sine, cosine and tangent of 50° by measurement.

Draw a triangle, on graph paper, with base 10 cm. Measure a right angle and an angle of 50° with a protractor.

The remaining two sides are then measured, and found to be

$PR = 15.6$ cm and $RQ = 11.9$ cm (to 1 decimal place).

So
$$\sin 50° = \frac{11.9}{15.6} = 0.763$$

$$\cos 50° = \frac{10}{15.6} = 0.641$$

and
$$\tan 50° = \frac{11.9}{10} = 1.19$$

Notice that
$$\tan \theta = \frac{\sin \theta}{\cos \theta}$$

Multiplier methods

It follows from the definitions of the trigonometric ratios that, for a hypotenuse of length R, the other sides of the triangle are $R \cos \theta$ and $R \sin \theta$.

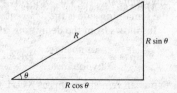

$\cos \theta$ is known as the **central multiplier** and $\sin \theta$ as the **sideways multiplier**.

Example   Find $\cos\theta$ for the triangle

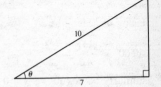

Answer $R = 10$ and $R\cos\theta = 7$

$\therefore \quad 10\cos\theta = 7$

$\therefore \quad \cos\theta = 0{\cdot}7$

In the same way, if the base of the triangle is x, the height is $x\tan\theta$.

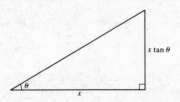

Example

$$3 = 8\tan\theta$$

$$\therefore \quad \tan\theta = \tfrac{3}{8} = 0{\cdot}375$$

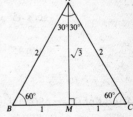

This method for finding the ratios depends on drawing an accurate diagram, and would be very tedious to do for many angles. For some angles, the ratios can be *calculated*.

Angles of 30° and 60°

ABC is an equilateral triangle of side 2 units.
The interior angles are all 60° (see page 224).
AM is a perpendicular from A to the side BC.

AM bisects the angle at A and also the side BC (since ABC is isosceles).
So $\angle BAM = 30$ and $BM = 1$ unit. Side AM of the right-angled triangle AMB can be calculated using Pythagoras' theorem.

$$AB^2 = AM^2 + BM^2$$

$$2^2 = 1^2 + BM^2$$

$$4 = 1 + BM^2$$

$$BM^2 = 3$$

so $$BM = \sqrt{3}$$

Using these lengths,

$$\sin 60° = \frac{AM}{AB} = \frac{\sqrt{3}}{2}$$

similarly $\cos 60° = \dfrac{1}{2} = 0\cdot 5$ and $\tan 60° = \dfrac{\sqrt{3}}{1} = \sqrt{3}$

and for the 30° angle

$$\sin 30° = \frac{1}{2}, \quad \cos 30° = \frac{\sqrt{3}}{2}, \quad \tan 30° = \frac{1}{\sqrt{3}}$$

Angles of 45°

ABC is a right-angled isosceles triangle, so that the base angles are each 45°. The perpendicular sides are each 1 unit, the hypotenuse is calculated from Pythagoras' theorem to be $\sqrt{2}$ units.

Reading off from the diagram

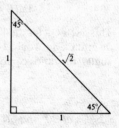

$$\sin 45° = \frac{1}{\sqrt{2}} = \frac{\sqrt{2}}{2}$$

$$\cos 45° = \frac{1}{\sqrt{2}} = \frac{\sqrt{2}}{2}$$

$$\tan 45° = 1$$

Angles of 0° and 90°

No triangle can be drawn with an angle of 0°; however, we can have a triangle with a very small angle.

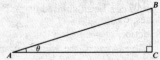

$\sin \theta = \dfrac{BC}{AB}$, and as θ decreases, side BC decreases to 0. So $\sin 0° = 0$.

Also, as θ decreases, the two sides AB and AC become equal.

$$\cos \theta = \frac{AC}{AB} \rightarrow 1, \text{ and so } \cos 0° = 1$$

Dividing

$$\tan 0° = \frac{\sin 0°}{\cos 0°} = \frac{0}{1} = 0$$

As the angle BAC above shrinks to zero, the angle ABC approaches 90°.

$$\sin \angle ABC = \frac{AC}{AB} \rightarrow 1 \text{ as } \theta \text{ decreases}$$

$$\cos \angle ABC = \frac{BC}{AB} \rightarrow 0$$

$$\sin 90° = 1 \text{ and } \cos 90° = 0$$

Since

$$\tan \theta = \frac{\sin \theta}{\cos \theta}$$

and

$$\cos 90° = 0, \textbf{ tan is undefined at 90°.}$$

Summary

	sin	cos	tan
0°	0	1	0
30°	$\frac{1}{2}$	$\frac{\sqrt{3}}{2}$	$\frac{1}{\sqrt{3}}$
45°	$\frac{1}{\sqrt{2}}$	$\frac{1}{\sqrt{2}}$	1
60°	$\frac{\sqrt{3}}{2}$	$\frac{1}{2}$	$\sqrt{3}$
90°	1	0	∞

It is useful to memorize this table.

The ratios for a general angle cannot be found in this way. Tables of sines, cosines and tangents can be used, although it is easier to use the function buttons on a calculator (see page 381).

Given one of the trigonometric ratios for an angle, you can calculate the other two.

Example   If $\sin x = 0\cdot4$, find $\cos x$ and $\tan x$.

Answer $\sin x = 0 \cdot 4 = \dfrac{4}{10}$.

Draw a right-angled triangle
containing an angle x.

Since $$\text{sine} = \frac{\text{opposite}}{\text{hypotenuse}}$$

the opposite side can be taken to be 4 units and the hypotenuse to be
10 units. The adjacent side can be calculated using Pythagoras' theorem,
and is found to be $\sqrt{84} = 9 \cdot 165$ (to 3 d.p.). Reading off from the diagram

$$\cos x = \frac{9 \cdot 165}{10} = 0 \cdot 9165$$

$$\tan x = \frac{4}{9 \cdot 165} = 0 \cdot 436$$

See also Pythagoras' theorem, page 274.

Angles of any size

So far we have only defined the trigonometric ratios for acute angles.
Angles can have any magnitude, and can even be negative. The definitions
of sine, cosine and tangent should cover these cases.

Recall that angles are defined by a rotating pointer (page 212).

For P in any position, the perpendicular from P
to the x-axis, PN, can be drawn.
If θ is an acute angle, then it is
contained in the right-angled
triangle ONP. From this triangle

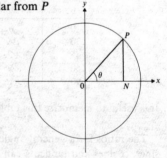

$$\sin \theta = \frac{PN}{OP}, \quad \cos \theta = \frac{ON}{OP}$$

The length of the pointer does
not affect the angle; choose
$OP = 1$ for convenience. ON is
just the x coordinate of P while
PN is the y coordinate. So

$$\left.\begin{array}{l} \sin \theta = y \text{ coordinate of } P \\ \cos \theta = x \text{ coordinate of } P \end{array}\right\} \text{ if } OP = 1$$

We take these as the *definitions* of sine and cosine for any *angle*. We can then define tan θ by the property

$$\tan \theta = \frac{\sin \theta}{\cos \theta}$$

Auxiliary angles

Tables of trigonometric functions only give values for acute angles (although most calculators will allow for a larger range of values). We can still use tables for other angles in the following way.

The circle is divided into four **quadrants**

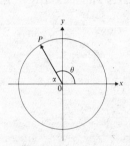
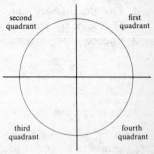

The point P of the figure has coordinates ($\cos \theta, \sin \theta$). If P is in the second quadrant these are ($-\cos \alpha, \sin \alpha$) where $\alpha° = 180° - \theta°$ is the *auxiliary angle*. α is acute and so tables can be used to calculate $\sin \alpha$, $\cos \alpha$ and $\tan \alpha$.

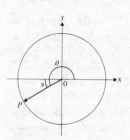

For P in the third quadrant, $\alpha° = \theta° - 180°$ and P has coordinates ($-\cos \alpha, -\sin \alpha$).

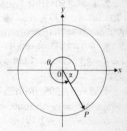

For P in the fourth quadrant, $\alpha° = 360° - \theta°$ and P has coordinates ($\cos \alpha, -\sin \alpha$).

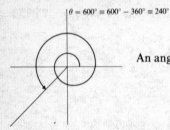

$\theta = 600° \equiv 600° - 360° \equiv 240°$

An angle larger than 360° is equivalent to some angle between 0° and 360°.

Negative angles correspond to a clockwise rotation.

Summary

1. Find the auxiliary *acute* angle α that *OP* makes with the *x-axis*.
2. Find sin α, cos α and tan α (tables or calculator, say).
3. Choose + or − according to the diagram below.

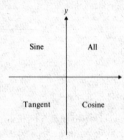

The letter in each quadrant tells you which ratios are *positive*.

Examples

1. $\theta = 120°$ (second quadrant). $\alpha = 180° - 120° = 60°$. sin 120° = sin 60° = $\sqrt{3}/2$, cos 120° = −cos 60° = ½, tan 120° = −tan 60° = $-\sqrt{3}$.

2. $\theta = 250°$ (third quadrant). $\alpha = 250° - 180° = 70°$, sin 250° = −sin 70° = −0·9397, cos 250° = −cos 70° = −0·3420, tan 250° = tan 70° = 2·7475 (calculator or tables).

3. $\theta = 280°$ (fourth quadrant). $\alpha = 360° - 280° = 80°$. sin 280° = −sin 80° = −0·9848, cos 280° = cos 80° = 0·1736, tan 280° = −tan 80° = −5·6713.

4. $\theta = -50°$ (fourth quadrant, *clockwise*). $\alpha = 50°$. sin (−50°) = −sin 50° = −0·7660, cos (−50°) = cos 50° = 0·6428, tan (−50°) = −tan 50° = −1·1918.

We can also find angles with given ratios.

Examples

1. Find the value of θ in the range $90° < \theta < 270°$ such that $\tan \theta = -\tan 50°$

Answer   The sign of $\tan \theta$ is $-$, so that θ must be in the second quadrant.
The auxiliary angle is $50°$.

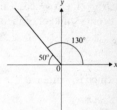

θ is $130°$.

2. Find the acute angle x such that $\cos 2x = -\cos 40°$. The auxiliary angle is $40°$, the minus sign indicates that $2x$ is either in the second or third quadrants.

From the diagram,
either $2x = 140$ or $2x = 320$

so $x = 70$ or $x = 160$

$x°$ is an acute angle,

so $x° = 70°$.

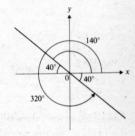

3. Show that $\sin 60°$ and $\cos 750°$ are equal.

Answer

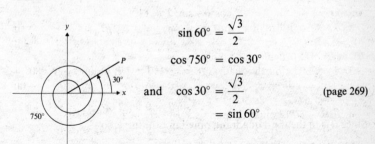

$$\sin 60° = \frac{\sqrt{3}}{2}$$

$$\cos 750° = \cos 30°$$

and $\cos 30° = \dfrac{\sqrt{3}}{2}$ (page 269)

$$= \sin 60°$$

Pythagoras' Theorem

$OP = 1$, $ON = \cos\theta$ and $PN = \sin\theta$.
From Pythagoras' theorem

$$ON^2 + PN^2 = 1^2$$
$$(\cos\theta)^2 + (\sin\theta)^2 = 1$$

which is written as

$$\cos^2\theta + \sin^2\theta = 1$$

(Notice that $\cos^2\theta$ means $(\cos\theta)^2$.) This relation can be used, for example, to find $\cos\theta$ when $\sin\theta$ is given.

Example If $\sin\theta = 0\cdot3$

$$\cos^2\theta + \sin^2\theta = 1$$
$$\cos^2\theta = 1 - \sin^2\theta$$
$$= 1 - (0\cdot3)^2$$
$$= 1 - 0\cdot09$$
$$\therefore \cos^2\theta = 0\cdot91$$

and so

$$\cos\theta = \pm\sqrt{0\cdot91}$$
$$\cos\theta = 0\cdot9539 \text{ or } \cos\theta = -0\cdot9539$$

Notice that two values of $\cos\theta$ are possible. If you know which quadrant θ is in then you can say whether the $+$ or $-$ should be used.

Example If $\cos\theta = -0\cdot25$ and θ is in the third quadrant, find $\sin\theta$ and $\tan\theta$.

Answer

$$\cos^2\theta + \sin^2\theta = 1$$

so

$$\sin^2\theta = 1 - \cos^2\theta$$
$$= 1 - (-0\cdot25)^2$$
$$= 1 - 0\cdot0625$$
$$= 0\cdot9375$$
$$\therefore \sin\theta = 0\cdot9682 \text{ or } \sin\theta = -0\cdot9682$$

Since θ is in the third quadrant, only tan is positive, so

$$\sin\theta = -0\cdot9682$$

Using the values of $\sin \theta$ and $\cos \theta$

$$\tan \theta = \frac{\sin \theta}{\cos \theta} = \frac{-0.9682}{-0.25} = 3.873$$

We have now defined $\sin \theta$, and $\cos \theta$ for any real number. They each have domain $\mathbb{R}$. The domain of $\tan \theta$ is $\{\theta \in \mathbb{R} : \theta \neq \pm 90°, \pm 270°, \pm 450°, \ldots\}$. Notice that $\tan \theta$ is undefined for any multiple of $90°$, since these values of θ have zero cosine.

ON and PN must both be less than 1, and so the ranges of $\sin \theta$ and $\cos \theta$ are

$$-1 \leqslant \sin \theta \leqslant 1$$

and

$$-1 \leqslant \cos \theta \leqslant 1$$

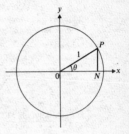

Tan θ can take any value, since it measures the gradient of OP. The range of $\tan \theta$ is $\mathbb{R}$.

Graphs of the Trigonometric Functions

The graph of $y = \sin x$ can be drawn by plotting points represented by the ordered pairs $(x°, \sin x°)$. Take values of x from -90 to 450, in steps of 30.

x	-90	-60	-30	0	30	60	90	120	150	180
$\sin x$	-1	-0.866	-0.5	0	0.5	0.866	1	0.866	0.5	0

x	210	240	270	300	330	360	390	420	450
$\sin x$	-0.5	-0.866	-1	-0.866	-0.5	0	0.5	0.866	1

Evaluating sines with a calculator, or using tables with the methods above, the resulting graph is shown overleaf. The graph **oscillates** between -1 and $+1$. It is called a periodic function because the same basic pattern is repeated endlessly. The graphs of $\cos x$ and $\tan x$ can be drawn in a similar way.

Tan $x°$ is not defined for $x° = -90°$ or $x° = 90°$, so the graph has been drawn for $-90° < x° < 90°$.

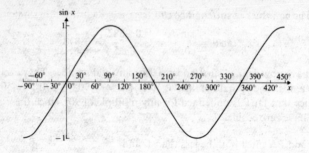

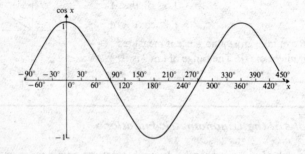

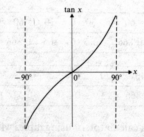

The trigonometric functions can be composed with other functions.

Examples

1. $f(x) = \sin x$ and $g(x) = 2x+3$, both defined for all real numbers.

$$gf(x) = g(\sin x) = 2(\sin x)+3$$

We can draw the graph of gf.

x	0°	30°	60°	90°	120°	150°	180°	210°	240°	270°	300°	330°	360°
$\sin x$	0	0·5	0·866	1·0	0·866	0·5	0	−0·5	−0·866	−1·0	−0·866	−0·5	0
$2\sin x$	0	1·0	1·732	2·0	1·732	1·0	0	−1·0	−1·732	−2·0	−1·732	−1·0	0
$2\sin x +3$	3·0	4·0	4·732	5·0	4·732	4·0	3	2·0	1·268	1·0	1·268	2·0	3·0

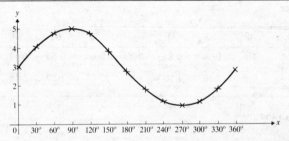

2. Which of the graphs shows the function $f(\theta) = 3\cos 2\theta$?

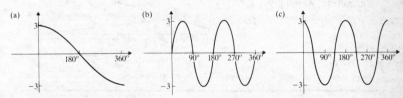

Answer Take points on each of the graphs and test the values of the coordinates in the formula.

(a) The graph cuts the θ-axis at $\theta = 180°$, in other words $f(180) = 0$.
Now $f(180) = 3\cos(360) = 3 \times 1$ since $\cos 360 = 1$

$$= 3 \neq 0$$

This is not the correct graph.

(b) The graph goes through the origin so $f(0) = 0$.
But $f(0) = 3\cos 0 = 3 \times 1 = 3 \neq 0$. This is not the graph.

The correct answer must be (c). To check, notice the graph cuts the θ-axis at $\theta = 45°$. $f(45°) = 3 \times \cos 90° = 3 \times 0 = 0$.

3. $f: x \mapsto \cos x°$ for $0 \leqslant x \leqslant 90$

and $g: x \mapsto \dfrac{x}{30} + \dfrac{1}{2}$ for $0 \leqslant x \leqslant 90$

Draw the graphs of f and g, taking values of $x = 0, 20, 30, 40, 50, 60, 80$ and 90. Taking $1\,\text{cm}$ for $10\,\text{units}$ on the x-axis and $1\,\text{cm}$ for $1\,\text{unit}$ on the y-axis. Using your graph find a solution of the equation

$$\cos x = \frac{x}{30} + \frac{1}{2}$$

Answer

x	0	20	30	40	50	60	80	90
$\cos x°$	1	0·94	0·87	0·77	0·64	0·50	0·17	0·0
$\dfrac{x}{30} + \dfrac{1}{2}$	0·5	1·16	1·50	1·83	2·17	2·50	3·16	3·5

The graphs are

The solution of the equation
corresponds to the point of
intersection, which gives $x = 14$.

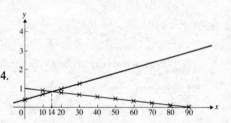

The Inverse Trigonometric Functions

See page 97 for an account of inverse functions.

Given an angle, you can find its sine. A number between -1 and 1 can be expressed as the sine of an angle.

Example   If $\sin x° = 0·5$ then $x = 30$ is a possible value of x. This can be written as

$$30 = \sin^{-1} 0·5$$

where $\sin^{-1}$ is the inverse sine function.

$\sin^{-1}x$ is interpreted as 'the angle with sine equal to x'. $\cos^{-1}x$ and $\tan^{-1}x$ are similarly the inverse cosine and tangent functions.

Examples

(a)
$$\cos 45° = \frac{\sqrt{2}}{2}$$

hence
$$\cos^{-1}\left(\frac{\sqrt{2}}{2}\right) = 45°$$

(b)
$$\tan 50° = 1·192 \text{ so } 50° = \tan^{-1}(1·192)$$

Note: Since different angles can have the same sine, cosine or tangent, the domains must be restricted in order that the inverse functions may exist.

Examples

1. Find the range of values of the functions
$$f(x) = 2(\sin x)^2 \quad \text{and} \quad g(x) = 1 + 3\cos x$$
and solve the equations

(a) $f(x) = \frac{1}{2}$ (b) $g(x) = 4$

for x in the range $0 \leqslant x \leqslant 180°$.

Answer   Since $-1 \leqslant \sin x \leqslant 1$ then $0 \leqslant (\sin x)^2 \leqslant 1$
and so
$$0 \leqslant 2(\sin x)^2 \leqslant 2$$
Also $-1 \leqslant \cos x \leqslant 1$ and hence
$$1 - 3 \leqslant 1 + 3\cos x \leqslant 1 + 3$$
$$-2 \leqslant 1 + 3\cos x \leqslant 4$$

(a)
$$2(\sin x)^2 = \frac{1}{2}$$
$$(\sin x)^2 = \frac{1}{4}$$
$$\sin x = \frac{1}{2} \quad \text{or} \quad \sin x = -\frac{1}{2}$$

$0° \leqslant x \leqslant 180°$, so x is in the first two quadrants $\Rightarrow \sin x$ is positive.
Hence,
$$\sin x = \frac{1}{2}$$
$$x = \sin^{-1}\frac{1}{2}$$
$$x = 30° \quad \text{or} \quad x = 150°$$

$\mathrm{Sin}^{-1}\,\frac{1}{2}$ can be found by

    (i) knowledge of the values on page 269, or
    (ii) use of a calculator, or
    (iii) tables (see page 383)

(b)
$$1 + 3\cos x = 4$$
$$3\cos x = 3$$
$$\cos x = 1$$

x must be in the first quadrant and so $x = 0$.

2.

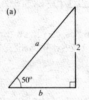

(a)

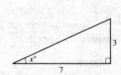

(b)

(a) Calculate a and b,

(b) calculate x,

giving your answers to three sig. fig.

Answer (a) $\tan 50° = \dfrac{\text{opposite}}{\text{adjacent}} = \dfrac{2}{b}$

so that
$$b = \frac{2}{\tan 50°}$$

$$= \frac{2}{1 \cdot 1918}$$

$$= 1 \cdot 678$$

so $b = 1 \cdot 68\,\text{cm}$ to 3 sig. fig.

Side a can be calculated using $\sin 50°$ or $\cos 50°$, or using Pythagoras' theorem

$$a^2 = 2^2 + b^2$$
$$a^2 = 2^2 + 1 \cdot 68^2$$
$$a^2 = 4 + 2 \cdot 822$$
$$= 6 \cdot 822$$
$$a = \sqrt{6 \cdot 822}$$
$$a = 2 \cdot 61$$ to 3 sig. fig.

(b) The known sides are the opposite and adjacent.

$$\tan x = \frac{\text{opposite}}{\text{adjacent}} = \frac{3}{7}$$

$$\tan x = 0 \cdot 4286$$

$$x = \tan^{-1}(0 \cdot 4286)$$

$$x = 23 \cdot 2 \qquad \text{to 3 sig. fig.}$$

3.

$ABCDE$ is a regular hexagon of side 5 cm.
Calculate

  (i) $\angle BAF$, (ii) $\angle AFB$, (iii) BF (iv) FC

Answer The exterior angle of a regular

hexagon is $\dfrac{360°}{6} = 60°$ and so

each interior angle is $180° - 60° = 120°$ (see page 223)

  (i) $\angle BAF = 120°$

  (ii) AFB is an isosceles triangle, and so

$$\angle AFB = \angle ABF = \frac{180° - 120°}{2} = \frac{60°}{2} = 30°$$

  (iii) Draw the perpendicular from A to BF, cutting the isosceles triangle
     AFB in half

     AFN is a right-angled triangle.

$$\cos 30° = \frac{FN}{5}, \text{ so } FN = 5 \cos 30°$$

$$= \frac{5\sqrt{3}}{2} \text{ cm}$$

$$BF = 2FN = 2\left(\frac{5\sqrt{3}}{2}\right) = 5\sqrt{3} \text{ cm}$$

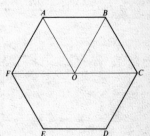

  (iv) AOF is an equilateral triangle, where
     O is the centre of the hexagon.
     Hence $FO = FA = 5$ cm,
     $FC = 2 \times FO = 10$ cm.

Examination questions

1. *The value of cos θ° is*

   (a) −0·8,   *(b)* −0·6,
   (c) 0·6,   *(d)* 0·8

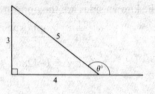

[SMP]

2. *ABCD is a parallelogram in which* $A\widehat{B}D = 90°$, $A\widehat{D}B = 60°$ *and* $AD = 20\,cm$. *ABN is a straight line and NC is parallel to BD. Calculate*

  (i) BD, (ii) AN, (iii) $A\widehat{C}N$ [CAM]

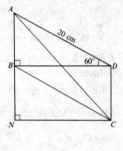

3.

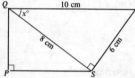

In the figure, the trapezium PQRS has PS parallel to QR, QR = 10 cm, RS = 6 cm, QS = 8 cm and $Q\widehat{S}R = Q\widehat{P}S = 90°$. *Write down (a)* sin x°, *(b)* cos x°, *and hence calculate (c) PQ (d) PS (e) area PQRS.*

[AEB]

4. *What is the value of cos x when* $\sin^2 x = \frac{1}{3}$ *and x is an acute angle?*

  A $\frac{2}{3}$, *B* $\frac{8}{9}$, *C* $\sqrt{\frac{2}{3}}$, *D* $\sqrt{\frac{8}{9}}$ [AEB]

5. *In* $\triangle ABC$, *the perpendicular CP is 6 cm long and PB is 8 cm long. Given angle PBC = angle ACP = x° find*

  (i) tan x°, *(ii) AP, (iii) area ABC.*   [AEB]

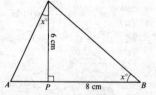

6.

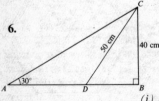

In $\triangle ABC$, $BC = 40\,cm$, $B\widehat{A}C = 30°$ *and* $A\widehat{B}C = 90°$. *The point D is an AB such that DC = 50 cm. Calculate*

  (i) AC (ii) $C\widehat{D}B$ *(iii)* $A\widehat{C}B$.   [CAM]

7. *The value of cos 143°, correct to 2 significant figures, is*
(a) −0·08,   *(b)* −0·79,   *(c)* −0·88,   *(d)* −0·60   [SMP]

8. *State the value of x in each of the following cases.*
   (i) 0 ⩽ x ⩽ 270; sin x° = −¹/₂,
   (ii) 90 ⩽ x ⩽ 360; cos x° = ¹/₂,
   (iii) 0 ⩽ x ⩽ 270; sin x° = −cos x°.   [CAM]

9. *Which of the following is not equal to any of the others?*
(a) −sin 20°   *(b)* sin 340°   *(c)* −cos 70°   *(d)* cos 790°.   [SMP]

10. $P\widehat{Q}R = 90°, PQ = 2x$ cm,
$PR = (x+13)$ cm.
   (i) *Given* ¹/₃ ⩽ cos Q P̂ R ⩽ ¹/₂,
      write down and simplify two
      inequalities each involving x.
   (ii) *Given that x is an integer, write*
      down the two possible values of
      x.
   (iii) *Given that QR is also an integer, find PQ, PR and QR.*   [CAM]

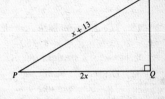

11. *p and q are numbers such that* 0 ⩽ p ⩽ 180, −90 < q < 90,
sin p° = sin 50° and cos q° = sin 30°. Calculate all the possible values of p
and q.

12. *The equation of the graph shown in*
the diagram could be
   (a) y = sin 2x°,   *(b)* y = 2 sin ¹/₂x°,
   (c) y = 2 sin x°,
   (d) y = 2 sin 2x°
            [SMP]

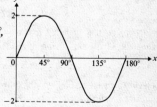

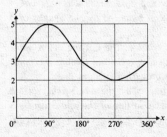

13. *The diagram shows part of a sine*
curve. Its equation referred to the given
axes is y = a + b sin x°. State the values
of a and b.   [SMP]

14. Functions *f, g* and *h* are defined by *f*: $x \mapsto \cos x°$ for $0 \leqslant x \leqslant 360$, *g*: $x \mapsto \frac{1}{2}x$ for all values of *x*, *h*: $x \mapsto x^2$ for all values of *x*.

The composite functions *p, q* and *s* are defined by *p*: $x \mapsto \cos \frac{1}{2}x°$, for $0 \leqslant x \leqslant 360$, *q*: $x \mapsto (\cos x°)^2$, for $0 \leqslant x \leqslant 360$, *s*: $x \mapsto \frac{1}{2}\cos(x^2)°$ for $0 \leqslant x \leqslant \sqrt{360}$.

  (i) The function *p* can be written in terms of *f* and *g*, that is $p = f \circ g$. Similarly, write each of the functions *q* and *s* in terms of some or all of *f, g* and *h*.
 (ii) The range of the function *p* is defined by $-1 \leqslant p(x) \leqslant 1$. Calculate the range of each of the functions *q* and *s* in a similar way.

Find the values of *x* in the interval $0 \leqslant x \leqslant 360$ for which

 (iii) $p(x) = 0$,   (iv) $q(x) = \frac{1}{4}$.   [AEB]

15. The diagram is the graph of
$y = \sin x°$ for $0 \leqslant x \leqslant 360$
together with a straight line *AB*.

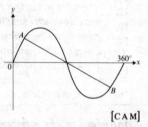

  (i) On the diagram
       (a) draw the line $y = 1$
       (b) sketch the graph of $y = \cos x°$.
 (ii) Given that *A* is (37, 0·6),
       write down the coordinates of *B*.   [CAM]

16. On squared paper, using a scale of 1 cm to represent 1 unit, draw axes to show values of *x* from -4 to 14 and values of *y* from 0 to 5. Draw the graph of the function *f* where

$$f: x \mapsto 1 + 2 \sin (15x)°   \text{ for }   0 \leqslant x \leqslant 14,$$

plotting values of $f(x)$ for $x = 0, 2, 4, 6, 8, 10, 12$ and 14. On the same diagram, draw the graph of the function *g* where

$$g: x \mapsto 1 - x   \text{ for }   -4 \leqslant x \leqslant 0.$$

Taking $f(4) = f(8) = 2·7$ and using the trapezoidal rule with interval of 2 units, estimate the total area of the region bounded by the graphs of *g* and *f*, the line $x = -4$ and the x-axis.

For a childrens game, a toy designer produces the outline of an adult fish by reflecting the graphs of *f* and *g* in the x axis and joining the point $(-4, g(-4))$ to its image under this reflection with a straight line.

Estimate the area enclosed by the outline   (a) the adult fish,   (b) a baby fish, which is obtained by enlarging the outline of the adult fish by a scale factor $\frac{1}{2}$.   [AEB]

Answers
 1. (a)
 2. (i) 10 cm   (ii) $20\sqrt{3}$ cm   (iii) 73·9°
 3. (a) 0·6   (b) 0·8   (c) 4·8   (d) 6·4   (e) 39·36
 4. C
 5. (i) 0·75   (ii) 4·5 cm   (iii) 37·5 cm²
 6. (i) 80 cm   (ii) 53·1°   (iii) 60°
 7. (b)
 8. (i) 210°   (ii) 300°   (iii) 135°
 9. (d)
10. (i) $3x \leqslant 13, 5x \geqslant 13$ (ii) 3, 4
    (iii) $PQ = 8$ cm, $PR = 17$ cm, $QR = 15$ cm
11. $p = 50, 130; q = -60, 60$
12. (d)
13. $a = 3, b = 2$
14. (i) $q = h \circ f, s = g \circ f \circ h$ (ii) $0 \leqslant q(x) \leqslant 1, -\tfrac{1}{2} \leqslant s \leqslant \tfrac{1}{2}$
    (iii) 180   (iv) 60, 120, 240, 300
15. (ii) $(323, -0\cdot6)$

Applications 1: Completing Triangles

The examples below show how the trigonometric functions can be used
to find the values of sides and angles of a triangle.

Examples
 1.

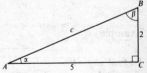

Side c can be found using Pythagoras' theorem.

$$c^2 = 5^2 + 2^2$$
$$c^2 = 25 + 4 = 29$$
$$c = \sqrt{29} = 5\cdot39 \qquad \text{to 3 sig. fig.}$$

Using the definition of tangent

$$\tan \alpha° = \frac{2}{5} = 0\cdot4$$

$$\therefore \; \alpha° = \tan^{-1}(0.4)$$
$$= 21.8°$$

(α must be acute, according to the diagram).

The angles of a triangle total 180°, so

$$\alpha° + \beta° + 90° = 180°$$
$$21.8° + \beta° + 90° = 180°$$
$$\beta = 180° - 90° - 21.8°$$
$$\therefore \; \beta = 68.2°$$

2. A right circular cone has slant height 12 cm and **semi-vertical angle** 16°. Find the radius of the base circle

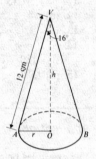

VAO is a right-angled triangle. VO is the perpendicular height and $\angle AVO$ is the semi-vertical angle.

$$\sin 16° = \frac{r}{12} \qquad \text{opposite} \div \text{hypotenuse}$$

so,
$$r = 12 \sin 16°$$
$$= 12 \times 0.2756$$
$$= 3.308$$

In order to use the definitions (**SOH, CAH, TOA**) the triangle must be right-angled.

Example

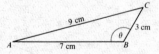

To find angle θ.

ABC is not a right-angled triangle. Drop a perpendicular from C to AB produced.

$\triangle BCN$ is right-angled, so $\sin \alpha = \dfrac{h}{3}$

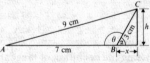

and
$$\cos \alpha = \frac{x}{3}$$

But $\sin \alpha = \sin \theta$, $\quad \cos \theta = -\cos \alpha$ page 271

So $h = 3 \sin \theta$ and $x = -3 \cos \theta$

From Pythagoras' theorem,
$$9^2 = (7+x)^2 + h^2$$
$$81 = 49 + 14x + x^2 + h^2$$
$$81 = 49 + 14x + 9\cos^2\theta + 9\sin^2\theta$$
$$81 = 49 + 14x + 9(\cos^2\theta + \sin^2\theta)$$

But $\sin^2\theta + \cos^2\theta = 1$, and so
$$81 = 49 + 14x + 9$$
$$14x = 81 - 49 - 9$$
$$= 23$$
$$x = \frac{23}{14}$$

so
$$-3\cos\theta = \frac{23}{14}$$

$$\cos\theta = -\frac{23}{42}$$

Note: that $\cos\theta$ is negative, since θ is obtuse.

So
$$\theta = \cos^{-1}\left(\frac{-23}{42}\right)$$
$$\theta = 123 \cdot 20°$$

If this method is used for a general triangle
the result is the **cosine rule**
$$a^2 = b^2 + c^2 - 2bc\cos A$$
similarly
$$b^2 = a^2 + c^2 - 2ac\cos B$$
and
$$c^2 = a^2 + b^2 - 2ab\cos C$$

To find an angle of a triangle given the sides, rearrange as
$$\cos A = \frac{b^2 + c^2 - a^2}{2bc}, \text{ etc.}$$

We use whichever is most convenient.

Another useful result is the **sine rule**
$$\frac{\sin A}{a} = \frac{\sin B}{b} = \frac{\sin C}{c}$$

Sine is positive for both acute and obtuse angles. When using the sine rule it is important to know if an angle is acute or obtuse, since in general there are two angles with the same value of sine. (For example, if θ is an angle in a triangle such that $\sin \theta = 0 \cdot 5$, then either $\theta = 30°$ or $\theta = 150°$.)

A useful property of triangles is that the smallest angle is opposite the shortest side, the middle angle opposite the middle side and the largest angle opposite the longest side.

Since the angles total $180°$, a triangle can have at most one obtuse angle. Thus the angles opposite the shortest and middle sides are *always* acute.

The ambiguity does not arise when using the cosine rule, as cosine is positive for acute angles but negative for obtuse angles

Examples   Complete the triangles
1.

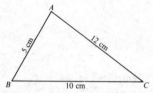

Find $\widehat{C}$ using the cosine rule.

$$\cos C = \frac{10^2 + 12^2 - 5^2}{2 \times 10 \times 12} = \frac{100 + 144 - 25}{240} = 0 \cdot 9125$$

$$\therefore \quad \widehat{C} = 24 \cdot 15° \qquad \text{(acute as it is opposite the shortest side)}$$

Using the sine rule with the acute angle $\widehat{A}$,

$$\frac{\sin A}{10} = \frac{\sin C}{5} \Rightarrow \sin A = \frac{10 \sin (24 \cdot 15°)}{5} = 0 \cdot 8182$$

$$\Rightarrow \widehat{A} = 54 \cdot 9°$$

Finally, since $\widehat{A} + \widehat{B} + \widehat{C} = 54 \cdot 9° + \widehat{B} + 24 \cdot 15° = 180°$, $\widehat{B} = 100 \cdot 95°$.

2.

From the cosine rule
$$7^2 = 2^2 + b^2 - 2 \times 2 \times b \cos 100°$$

which is a *quadratic* equation in b.
In this case, it is easier to use the sine rule.

$$\frac{\sin 100°}{7} = \frac{\sin B}{b} = \frac{\sin C}{2}$$

So,
$$\frac{2 \sin 100°}{7} = \sin C \qquad \text{first and last}$$

$$\sin C = 0·2814$$

$$C = 16·3° \qquad \text{C is acute since A is obtuse}$$

So,
$$B = 180° - 100° - 16·3°$$

$$= 63·7°$$

From the sine rule again

$$\frac{\sin 100°}{7} = \frac{\sin 63·7°}{b}$$

$$b = \frac{\sin 63·7°}{\sin 100°} \times 7$$

$$= \frac{0·8964 \times 7}{0·9848}1 = 6·37$$

(Remember to show all the steps of your working, including the values of sin 100 and sin 63·7 found from a calculator or tables.)

3. cosine rule

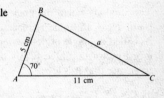

$$a^2 = 5^2 + 11^2 - 2 \times 5 \times 11 \cos 70°$$
$$a^2 = 25 + 121 - 110 \times 0·342$$
$$a^2 = 146 - 37·6$$
$$a^2 = 108·4$$
$$a = 10·4$$

Now use the sine rule

$$\frac{\sin 70°}{10·4} = \frac{\sin B}{11} = \frac{\sin C}{5}$$

C is clearly acute, since $5 < 11$, so using

$$\frac{\sin C}{5} = \frac{\sin 70}{10·4} = \frac{0·939\,7}{10·4}$$

$$\Rightarrow \sin C = \frac{5 \times 0·939\,7}{10·4} = 0·451\,8$$

$$\Rightarrow \quad \widehat{C} = 26·90$$

Hence $\widehat{B} = 180° - 70° - 26·9° = 83·1°$

A practical use of completion of triangles
is in measuring heights (of trees,
towers, etc.) and distances.

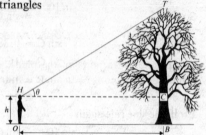

Example

The diagram shows a tree and an observer. We wish to find the height
of the tree.

Suppose that the tree is vertical and the ground horizontal.

Measure (a) the distance x m from the observer O to the base B of
the tree,

(b) the height, h m, of the eye-level of the observer,

(c) the angle that the line of sight HT of the top of the tree
makes with the horizontal.

This angle is called the **angle of elevation** of the top of the tree from the
point H. If an angle is measured *down* with respect to the horizontal,
its called an **angle of depression**. The angle θ is measured with a sextant,
a protractor mounted firmly on a base with devices such as spirit levels
to ensure that it is level.

Then
$$\tan \theta = \frac{TC}{HC}$$

$$= \frac{TC}{OB}$$

so that
$$TC = OB \tan \theta$$

$$= x \tan \theta$$

The height of the tree is then $h + x \tan \theta$.

If x is measured to be $50\,m$, θ is $35°$ and the observers eye-level is 1 m
above the ground, then the height of the tree is

$$(1 + 50 \tan 35°)\,\text{m} = (1 + 50 \times 0{\cdot}7002)\,\text{m}$$

$$= (1 + 35{\cdot}01)\,\text{m}$$

$$= (36{\cdot}01)\,\text{m}$$

$$= (36{\cdot}0)\,\text{m} \qquad\qquad \text{to 3 sig. fig.}$$

Applications 2: Polar Coordinates and Bearings

The position of a point in the plane, with respect to some fixed axes, can be given in terms of an angle θ and a distance r.

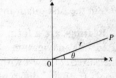

θ is the angle that OP makes with the *positive*
x-axis and r is the length OP.
   The ordered pair (r, θ) give the
                    polar coordinates
of the point P. The origin O is the **pole** and
the positive x-axis is the **initial line** (since it
corresponds to $\theta° = 0°$).

Examples
The points $A(2, 50°)$, $B(1, 170°)$, $C(4, 270°)$
and $D(2, 300°)$ are shown on the diagram.

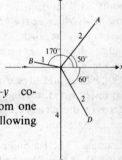

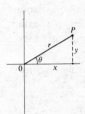

Polar coordinates and x–y coordinates can be converted from one
form to the other using the following
relations.

$$\cos \theta = \frac{x}{r} \quad \text{so} \quad x = r \cos \theta$$

$$\sin \theta = \frac{y}{r} \quad \text{so} \quad y = r \sin \theta$$

By Pythagoras' theorem, $r^2 = x^2 + y^2$, and also $\tan \theta = \dfrac{y}{x}$

Examples
1. Find the x–y coordinates of the point with polar coordinates
$(2, 60°)$.

$r = 2, \quad \theta = 60°$

$x = r \cos \theta = 2 \cos 60° = 2 \times \frac{1}{2} = 1$

$y = r \sin \theta = 2 \sin 60° = 2 \times \dfrac{\sqrt{3}}{2} = \sqrt{3}$ see page 269

2. Find the polar coordinates of the point with $x-y$ (cartesian) coordinates (3, 4).

$$r^2 = x^2 + y^2 = 3^2 + 4^2 = 9 + 16 = 25 \quad \text{so} \quad r = 5 \qquad \textit{positive root}$$

$$\tan \theta = \frac{y}{x} = \frac{4}{3} = 1 \cdot 3333 \qquad \qquad \text{so} \quad \theta = 53 \cdot 1°$$

θ is in the first quadrant, hence acute.

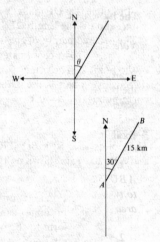

Bearings are a form of polar angle, used for navigation. The angle is measured *clockwise* with *north* as initial line (rather different from the usual convention of page 212).

To find the bearing of a point B from a point A, set up a north–south line at A. Measure the angle that AB makes with the north.

The diagram represents a point 15 km away on A on a bearing of 030°. Notice that all bearing angles are expressed with three digits, filling with Zeros on the left as necessary (so, 027° *not* 27°, 003° and *not* 3°).

Example   The bearing of A from B is 050° and the bearing of C from A is 140°. $AB = 7$ km and $AC = 10$ km.
Find the distance BC and the bearing of B from C.

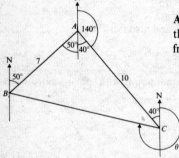

Answer   The angle $BAC = 90°$, since the north lines are all parallel. so, from Pythagoras' theorem

$$BC^2 = AB^2 + AC^2$$
$$= 7^2 + 10^2$$
$$= 49 + 100$$
$$= 149$$

So, $BC = \sqrt{149} = 12 \cdot 2$

To find θ, the bearing of B from C (clockwise from north) just find $\angle BCA$

$$\tan \angle BCA = \frac{7}{10}$$ *ABC* is right-angled

$$= 0.7$$

So, $$BCA = 35°$$ calculator

and so $$\theta = 360° - 40° - 35°$$

$$= 285°$$

The bearing of *B* from *C* is 285°.

Note: Always draw a clear diagram for problems involving bearings.

Bearings are always measured in a horizontal plane. Thus, for example, the bearing of the *top* of a tree from a point on the ground is taken as the bearing of the *base* of the tree from that point.

Examination questions

1. *A circle with centre O and radius 4 cm is drawn through the vertices ABCDE of a regular pentagon. Show that $\angle AOB = 72°$, and find, correct to two decimal places, the area, in cm², of $\triangle AOB$. Hence write down the area of the pentagon.* [LON]

2. *Calculate to the nearest whole number the values of*
(i) k, (ii) θ. [SMP]

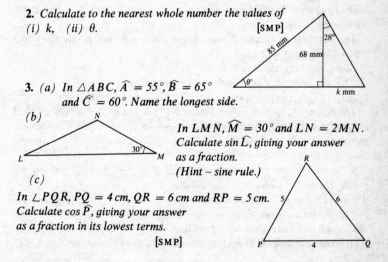

3. *(a) In $\triangle ABC$, $\widehat{A} = 55°$, $\widehat{B} = 65°$ and $\widehat{C} = 60°$. Name the longest side.*
(b)

In LMN, $\widehat{M} = 30°$ and $LN = 2MN$. Calculate $\sin \widehat{L}$, giving your answer as a fraction. (Hint – sine rule.)

(c)

In $\angle PQR$, $PQ = 4$ cm, $QR = 6$ cm and $RP = 5$ cm. Calculate $\cos \widehat{P}$, giving your answer as a fraction in its lowest terms. [SMP]

4. *A man stands on horizontal ground with his feet 50 m from the base of a vertical tower. He observes the angle of elevation of the top of the tower to be 12° and the angle of depression of the base of the tower to be 2°. Find, in metres, correct to one decimal place, the height of the tower.*

[LON]

5.

θ = 30°

×S

O ——————————————— θ = 0°

S is the point with polar coordinates (5, 25°). T is the image of S under reflection in the line θ = 30°. Find the polar coordinates of T.   [SMP]

6. *The polar coordinates of the reflection of (5, 30°) in the line θ = 90° are*

   (a) (5, −30°),   (b) (5, 150°),   (c) (5, 120°),   (d) (−5, 30°)

[SMP]

7. *A is due North of B. The bearing of C from B is 050°. If the distances of A and C from B are equal, then the bearing of C from A is*
   (a) 065°,   (b) 115°,   (c) 130°,   (d) 295°.   [SMP]

8. *The points P, S, O are on the same horizontal plane and are at the base of the Post Office Tower, the base of St Paul's Cathedral and at the Oval respectively.*
   The bearings of O and P from S are 200° and 290° respectively and PS = 2·7 km, SO = 3·6 km.
   Calculate   (i) the length, in km, of OP,
    (ii) the bearing of O from P to the nearest degree,
   (iii) the area, in hectares, of △PSO (1 hectare = 10 000 m²).
   The height of the Post Office Tower is 176 m and of St Paul's Cathedral is 111 m. Calculate, to the nearest 0·1°, the angle of depression of the highest point of St Paul's from the top of the Post Office Tower.   [LON]

9. *A, B and C are points on level ground. C is due North of A and B is due East of C. AB = 8 km and AC = 5 km. Calculate*
   (i) the length in cm of the line representing AB on a map of scale 1 : 50 000,
   (ii) the bearing of B from A.   [CAM]

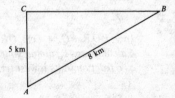

10. *The distance between the points with polar coordinates (5, 20°) and (5, 55°) is correct to two decimal places,*
  (a) 2·86, *(b)* 3·01, *(c)* 4·10, *(d)* 5·00.   **[SMP]**

Answers
  1. 7·61 cm², 38·04 cm²
  2. (i) 36   (ii) 53
  3. (a) *AC*   (b) ¼   (c) ⅛
  4. 12·4 m
  5. (5, 35°)
  6. (b)
  7. (b)
  8. (i) 4·5 km   (ii) 163°   (iii) 486 hectares, 1·4°
  9. (i) 16 cm   (ii) 51·3°
  10. (b)

Applications 3: Three-Dimensional Problems

Example *EFGH* is a square of side 10 cm on the horizontal ground. *EA* is a vertical post of height 10 m. The top, *A*, of the post is connected by taut cables to the points *G* and *H* on the ground. Calculate the lengths of the cables *AG* and *AH* and the angle *G* $\widehat{A}$ *H*.

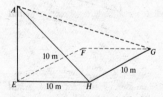
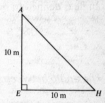

The triangle *AEH* is right-angled at *E*.

Using Pythagoras' theorem
$$AH^2 = 10^2 + 10^2 = 200$$
$$AH = \sqrt{200} \text{ cm}$$
$$= 14\cdot 1 \text{ cm}$$

Triangle *AEG* is right-angled at *E*.
AE = 10, *AG* and *EG* are unknown.

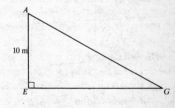

However, *EG* is the hypotenuse of triangle *EGH* and is equal to $\sqrt{200}$ m (since $\triangle EGH \equiv \triangle HAE$).

so,

$$AE^2 + EG^2 = AG^2 \qquad \text{Pythagoras' theorem}$$

$$10^2 + (\sqrt{200})^2 = AG^2$$

$$AG^2 = 300$$

$$AG = \sqrt{300}\,\text{cm}$$

$$AG = 17\cdot3\,\text{cm}$$

$\angle GAH$ appears in the right-angled triangle *AHG*

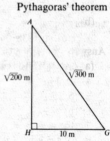

$$\sqrt{200} = \sqrt{300}\cos\angle GAH \qquad \text{see page 266}$$

$$\therefore \cos\angle GAH = \frac{\sqrt{200}}{\sqrt{300}} = 0\cdot8165$$

so

$$\angle GAH = 35\cdot3°$$

The angle between a line and a plane

Drop a perpendicular from a point *B* on the line to *C* on the plane. Then the angle is defined to be $\angle BAC$.

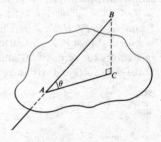

The angle between two planes

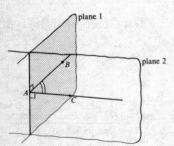

Suppose that the two planes intersect at the line *l*. Take a point *A* on this line and draw a line *AB* in plane 1 perpendicular to *l* and a line *AC* in plane 2 perpendicular to *l*. The angle is defined to be $\angle BAC$.

Example $ABCD$ is a rectangle, $AB = 10$ cm and $AD = 15$ cm. V is vertically above the centre of the rectangle and $VABCD$ is a right pyramid. If $VA = VB = VC = VD = 20$ cm find

(a) the angle between the edge VA and the base $ABCD$,
(b) the angle between the face VAB and the base.

Answer Let X be the centre of the rectangle.

(a) The required angle is $\angle VAX$

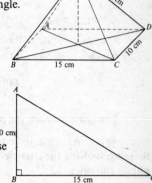

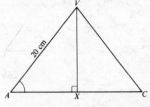

$AX = \frac{1}{2}AC$ and AC is the hypotenuse of the right-angled triangle ABC

$$AC^2 = AB^2 + BC^2 \qquad \text{Pythagoras' theorem}$$
$$= 10^2 + 15^2$$
$$= 100 + 225$$
$$= 325$$

so $\qquad AC = \sqrt{325} = 18\cdot03$

and so $\qquad AX = 9\cdot02$ cm

$$\cos \angle VAX = \frac{AX}{AV} = \frac{9\cdot02}{20} = 0\cdot451$$

$$\angle VAX = 63\cdot2°$$

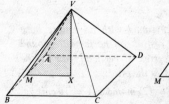

(b) The angle between the planes VAB and $ABCD$ is found by forming the right-angled triangle VMX where M is the mid-point of AB.

$$MX = \tfrac{1}{2}BC = \tfrac{1}{2} \times 15 = 7{\cdot}5 \text{ cm}$$

VX can be found from triangle VAX

$$\sin \angle VAX = \frac{VX}{20}$$

so
$$VX = 20 \sin \angle VAX$$
$$= 20 \times 0{\cdot}8927$$
$$= 17{\cdot}85 \text{ cm}$$

And so
$$\tan \angle VMX = \frac{VX}{MX} = \frac{17{\cdot}85}{7{\cdot}5}$$

$$\tan \angle VMX = 2{\cdot}38$$

$$VMX = 67{\cdot}2°$$

The angle between the planes is $67{\cdot}2°$.

Note: When referring to a triangle in the pyramid, draw a separate diagram showing the triangle 'full face'. Use this diagram for calculating angles and sides.

Examination questions

1. *PQRS is a rectangle. V is vertically above the point of intersection (X) of diagonals PR and QS. VP = VQ = VR = VS = 20 cm. Calculate to 3 sig. fig.,*

  (i) P X and V X,

  (ii) ∠ PVX,

  (iii) the angle between sloping faces VPQ and VQR.

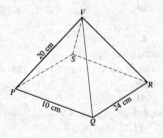

2. *A pyramid with its square base ABCD resting on horizontal ground has its vertex V vertically above the centre M of the base.*

  AB = 12 cm and VA = 19 cm.

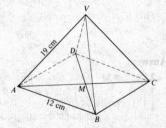

   (i) Using letters on the figure, name the angle between VA and the horizontal.

   (ii) Calculate the angle $V\widehat{A}B$.

   (iii) Calculate the height VM.   [CAM]

3. The diagram represents the outer vertical walls of a castle. The horizontal floor *ABCD* is a square of side 65 m. *XYZW* is the horizontal level of the tops of the walls. From the mid-point of *XY*, the angle of depression of the mid-point of the horizontal upper floor line *PQ* on the wall *CDWZ* is 5°.

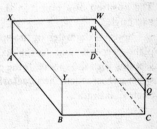

   (a) Calculate the depth of PQ below ZW, giving your answer in metres to one decimal place.

The line *PQ* is 12 m above the line *CD*.

   (b) Calculate the angle of depression of D from X, giving your angle correct to one decimal of a degree.

   (c) Calculate AC, in metres, correct to one decimal place.

For an acrobatic event, a taut cable is to be fixed from *X* to *C*.

   (d) Find, correct to the nearest metre, the length of cable required.

                                      [LON]

4. The diagram shows the outline of a bungalow. *AD, BE, CPF, RQ* are horizontal. All sloping planes make the same angle with the horizontal.

$AC = AB = DF = DE = CR = RP$
$= 4\cdot30$ m, $CB = FE = 6\cdot80$ m.

   (i) Calculate the angle between plane ACFD and the horizontal.

   (ii) Show that the height of R above CP is 2·6 m.

   (iii) Calculate (a) RQ, (b) QC, (c) the angle between QC and the horizontal.   [SMP]

Answers

  2. (i)$V\widehat{A}M$ (ii) 71·6°   (iii) 17 cm

  3. (a) 5·7   (b) 15·2°   (c) 91·9   (d) 94

  4. (i) 37·7°   (iii) (a) 3·4   (b) 5·5   (c) 28·3°

Latitude and Longitude

The position of a point on the surface of a sphere can be specified by two angles.

Choose a diameter of the sphere as a reference axis (north–south). A plane perpendicular to this axis forms a **circle of latitude** at the intersections with the sphere. If the plane also passes through the centre of the sphere, it is called the **equatorial plane** and corresponds to the **equator** circle of latitude.

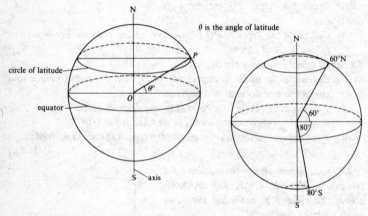

A point on the surface of the sphere lies on one and only one circle of latitude. A line from the centre O of the circle to the given point P forms an acute angle with the equatorial plane. This angle is called the **angle of latitude**, and is the same for all points on a circle of latitude. If the radius OP points northward (so that P is on the upper hemisphere) then the angle is given in degrees *north*. If P is in the lower hemisphere, the angle is given in degrees *south*.

A plane which contains the N–S axis forms **circles of longitude** on the surface of the sphere. One such circle is taken as the initial circle (or meridian) (the initial meridian of the Earth passes through Greenwich, London). Any other longitude circle forms an angle with this meridian, called the **angle of longitude**. This angle is specified as either east or west of the initial meridian.

A point on the surface of the sphere lies at the intersection of a latitude circle and a longitude circle.

Example G is the point with angle of latitude 60°N and angle of longitude 100°E.

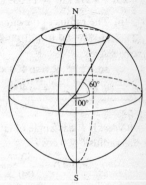

Distances along circles of latitude and longitude can be calculated using the formulae for arc length (page 214).

Any circle with centre at the centre of the sphere is called a **great circle**.

Example A has angles of latitude and longitude 25°N, 30°E respectively. B is 40°S and 20°W. Calculate

(a) The distance travelled when following a circle of longitude from A to the latitude circle of B and then along this circle to B by the minor arc.

(b) The distance travelled by going west from A along the latitude circle and then due south along the meridian to B.

Take the earth as a sphere of radius 6 400 km.

Answer

(a) The distance along the arc AC is

$$\frac{65}{180} \times \pi \times 6400 = 7261 \text{ km (page 214)}$$

The distance along arc BC is

$$\left(\frac{20+30}{180}\right) \times \pi r \text{ where } r \text{ is the radius}$$

of the circle of latitude, $r = BD$.

r can be found from triangle ODB

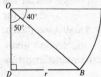

$$r = 6400 \cos 40°$$
$$= 6400 \times 0 \cdot 7660 = 4903 \text{ km}$$

The arc BC is then $\dfrac{50}{180} \times \pi \times 4903 = 4278 \text{ km}$

The total distance travelled is

$7\,261 + 4\,278\,\text{km} = 11\,539\,\text{km}$

(b) The radius of the circle of latitude of
A is found from triangle OPQ

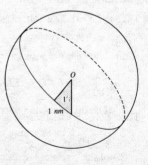

so $R = 6\,400 \times \sin 65°$

$= 6\,400 \times 0 \cdot 9063$

$= 5\,800\,\text{km}$

Note: If P has angle of latitude λ, then the circle of latitude through P has radius $6\,400 \cos \lambda$.

$$\text{arc } AD = \frac{50}{180} \times \pi \times 5\,800$$

$$= 5\,062\,\text{km}$$

$$\text{arc } DB = \frac{65}{180} \times \pi \times 5\,062$$

$$= 5\,742\,\text{km}$$

The total distance travelled is $10\,804\,\text{km}$.

Nautical miles

A convenient unit of distance is the **nautical mile**, defined to be the length of an arc
of a great circle which subtends an angle
of $1'$ at the centre ($1' = \frac{1}{60}$th of a degree).

Since one revolution $= 360° = 360 \times 60'$

$= 21\,600'$

then the distance around the circumference of a great circle is $21\,600\,\text{nm}$ (nautical miles).

Example   The points X and Y have positions $(35°N, 15°W)$ and $(70°S, 15°W)$ respectively. (The first angle gives the latitude, the second gives the longitude.) Calculate the shortest distance along the meridian from X to Y.

Answer

The angle subtended by XY
at the centre of the earth is

$$(35 + 70)° = 105° = 105 \times 60'$$
$$= 6300'$$

The distance along arc XY is
6 300 nm (since a meridian is
a great circle).

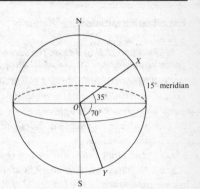

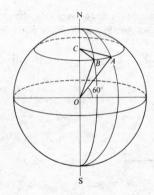

Example The points A and B lie on the
circle of latitude 60°N. The shorter distance AB along this circle is 1 500 nm.
Calculate the difference between the
angles of longitude of A and B.

Answer
The radius of the earth R

$$= \frac{360 \times 60}{2\pi} \text{ nm}$$

$$= \frac{21\,600}{2\pi} \text{ nm}$$

The radius of the circle of latitude of A and B is

$$r = R \cos \lambda = \frac{21\,600}{2\pi} \cos 60° = \frac{21\,600}{2\pi} \times \tfrac{1}{2} = \frac{10\,800}{2\pi} \text{ nm}$$

Hence $2\pi r = 10\,800$. Using the arc length formula (page 214)

$$1\,500 = \frac{\theta}{360} \times 2\pi r = \frac{\theta}{360} \times 10\,800 = \frac{\theta}{360} \times 30 \times 360$$

$$\theta = 50$$

The angles of longitude of A and B differ by 50°.

Examination questions

1. *Two points P and Q on the surface of the earth have positions (20°N, 10°W) and (59°N, 10°W) respectively.*
  (i) *State the latitude and longitude of the point on the surface of the earth diametrically opposite to P (i.e. at the opposite end of a diameter of the sphere).*
 (ii) *Calculate, in nautical miles, the shorter distance PQ measured along the meridian.*
(iii) *The point R lies due east of Q and the distance QR measured along the circle of latitude 59°N is 1 600 nautical miles. Find, in degrees and minutes, the longitude of R.*   [CAM]

2. *The shortest distance from X to Y, measured along the surface of the earth over the north pole, is 3 000 nautical miles. Given that X is the point (64°N, 157°W), calculate*
  (i) *the longitude of Y,*   (ii) *the latitude of Y.*   [CAM]

3.

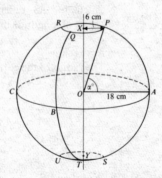

A lampshade is in the shape of part of a sphere. The diagram shows part of its wire frame.

The wire circles PQR (centre X), ABC (centre O) and STU (centre Y) are horizontal. PAS, QBT and RCU are three of the ten equal connecting wires, each of which lies in a vertical plane and is shaped as part of a semi-circle with centre O.

$$XP = YS = 6\,cm, \quad OA = OP = 18\,cm.$$

  (i) *Calculate the height (XY) of the shade.*
 (ii) *Angle POA = α°. Calculate α.*

(iii) Given that the length of wire in circle ABC is 113 cm, calculate (a) the length of wire in circle PQR, (b) the length of the connecting wire PAS; and hence (c) the total length of wire used in the frame (correct to the nearest centimetre). [SMP]

4. *Two points A, B on the earth's surface have positions (20°N, 120°E), (20°N, 60°W) respectively. Find the distances in nautical miles between A and B (i) over the North Pole, (ii) along the parallel of latitude.*

[SMP]

Answers

1. (i) (20°S, 10°W) (ii) 2 340 nm (iii) 16°40′E
2. (i) 157°W (iii) 66°N
3. (i) 33·9 cm (ii) 70·5° (iii) (a) 37·7 cm (b) 44.3 cm (c) 631 cm
4. (i) 8 400 nm (ii) 3 230 nm

Section 15: Networks and Matrices

Networks and Topological Equivalence

Professor Riemann is trying to find his way to a conference of mathematicians at the Mathematical Institute in Cowbridge. He stops in the town centre to ask the way to the Institute. The first person he asks tells him:

'Walk 500 metres down this street, turn left and continue for 325 metres when you should turn right. Go on a further 410 metres and the Institute is on the left.'

Not being able to measure distances so accurately, the Professor asks a second person the way, who answers:

'Take the third turning on the left, then the first on the right and finally the second turning on the left.'

With this information, Professor Riemann was able to find the Institute.

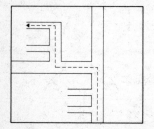 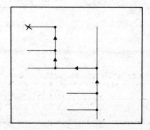

The second set of instructions made no mention of distances but told the Professor what to do at each junction. He could just as easily have found his way with the more schematic map on the right.

The road junctions are represented by dots (called **nodes**) and the streets by **arcs**. The length and shape of the arcs is irrelevant, the following two diagrams present the same information.

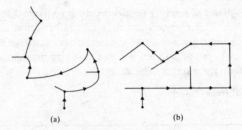

(a)   (b)

These diagrams are **topologically equivalent.**

Two diagrams are topologically equivalent if one can be formed from the other just by changing the lengths and shapes of the arcs. The nodes can be moved around but the number of nodes and the way that they are connected cannot be altered. Arcs must not be cut.

The following two diagrams are *not* equivalent.

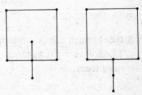

The first one has a node with four arcs coming from it while the second does not.

Examples of equivalent diagrams

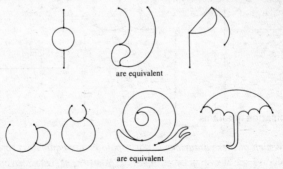

are equivalent

are equivalent

An arc must be terminated by two nodes.

The nodes are indicated here with 'blobs' but are often not printed. They should nevertheless be understood to be present.

The map of the London Underground system is topologically equivalent to the network of railway lines.

A wiring diagram used by an electrician is equivalent to the arrangement of wires. This diagram can only give information about how the wires interconnect, and not about the thicknesses and lengths of the wires.

A particular type of diagram is a **tree**, in which the number of nodes is one more than the number of arcs.

Examples of trees

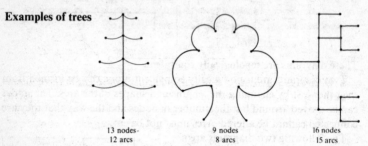

13 nodes
12 arcs

9 nodes
8 arcs

16 nodes
15 arcs

A tree cannot contain a **loop**.
   The following diagrams
are *not* trees.

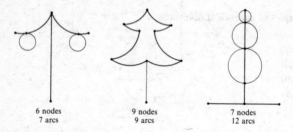

6 nodes
7 arcs

9 nodes
9 arcs

7 nodes
12 arcs

Examination questions

1. *Which of these diagrams is not topologically equivalent to any of the others?*   [SMP]

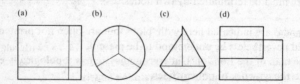

(a)   (b)   (c)   (d)

2. *A continuous network in which the number of nodes is one more than the number of arcs is called a* tree.

Which of the following is not *a tree?* [SMP]

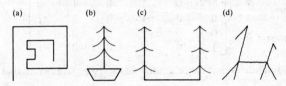

(a)   (b)   (c)   (d)

3. *Which of the following is* not *topologically equivalent in three dimensions to any of the other three?* [SMP]

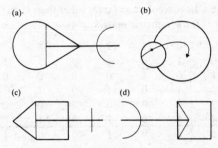

(a)   (b)

(c)   (d)

Answers
1. (d)
2. (b)
3. (a)

Matrices

A **matrix** is an array of numbers, or **data**, enclosed between large brackets (they may be square or round). A matrix can represent a relation between sets.

Examples
1. If $A = \{1, 2, 3, 4, 5\}$ and $B = \{10, 11, 12, 13, 14, 15\}$ with relation 'is a factor of', that is, a mapping from A to B associating a number in A with its multiples in B (see page 19), the **relation matrix** is

$$
\begin{array}{c}
\textit{elements of B} \\
\begin{array}{cccccc}
10 & 11 & 12 & 13 & 14 & 15
\end{array} \\
\textit{elements} \\ \textit{of A} \quad
\begin{array}{c} 1 \\ 2 \\ 3 \\ 4 \\ 5 \end{array}
\left[
\begin{array}{cccccc}
1 & 1 & 1 & 1 & 1 & 1 \\
1 & 0 & 1 & 0 & 1 & 0 \\
0 & 0 & 1 & 0 & 0 & 1 \\
0 & 0 & 1 & 0 & 0 & 0 \\
1 & 0 & 0 & 0 & 0 & 1
\end{array}
\right]
\end{array}
$$

where a 1 indicates that the relation holds and a zero indicates that it does not.

This relation is not symmetric, we cannot say that 10 is a factor of 5. The matrix is not symmetric about the **main diagonal** (top left to bottom right).

2. The relation 'have a common factor other than 1' on the set {10, 11, 12, 13, 14, 15} has the **symmetric matrix**

$$
\begin{array}{c}
\begin{array}{cccccc}
10 & 11 & 12 & 13 & 14 & 15
\end{array} \\
\begin{array}{c} 10 \\ 11 \\ 12 \\ 13 \\ 14 \\ 15 \end{array}
\left[
\begin{array}{cccccc}
1 & 0 & 1 & 0 & 1 & 1 \\
0 & 1 & 0 & 0 & 0 & 0 \\
1 & 0 & 1 & 0 & 1 & 1 \\
0 & 0 & 0 & 1 & 0 & 0 \\
1 & 0 & 1 & 0 & 1 & 0 \\
1 & 0 & 1 & 0 & 0 & 1
\end{array}
\right]
\end{array}
$$

main diagonal

The relation can also be represented by a mapping diagram of {10, 11, 12, 13, 14, 15} to itself:

where a 1 in the matrix shows that the pair of nodes is connected by an arc.

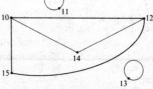

We may wish to take account of the *number* of arcs between pairs of nodes.

Example   The network

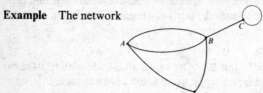

has corresponding matrix

$$
\begin{array}{c c c c c}
 & A & B & C & D \\
A & \begin{bmatrix} 0 & 2 & 0 & 1 \\ B & 2 & 0 & 1 & 1 \\ C & 0 & 1 & 2 & 0 \\ D & 1 & 1 & 0 & 0 \end{bmatrix}
\end{array}
$$

Notes: 1. A is not connected to itself, the entry is 0.
2. C is connected to itself by a loop, the entry is 2.
3. The matrix is symmetric about the main diagonal.
4. The sum of the A row (or column) gives the number of arcs connected to A.
5. Only 'one stage' paths are counted.

This is called the **route matrix** of the network. A network can be drawn once the route matrix is given.

Example   A network connecting points A, B and C has matrix

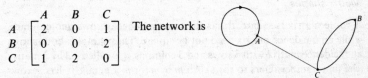

$$
\begin{array}{c c c c}
 & A & B & C \\
A & \begin{bmatrix} 2 & 0 & 1 \\ B & 0 & 0 & 2 \\ C & 1 & 2 & 0 \end{bmatrix}
\end{array}
$$ The network is

Any other topologically equivalent (see page 307) network would also correspond to this matrix.

A symmetric route matrix corresponds to an **undirected** network – the arcs can be followed in either direction (as in example 2 on page 310). If the network has 'one way' arcs, which can only be followed in one direction, the matrix is not symmetric. The network is then said to be **directed**.

Example
The directed network
has route matrix

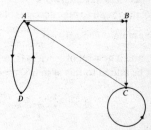

$$
\begin{array}{c c c c c c}
 & & & \text{'to' node} & & \\
 & & A & B & C & D \\
\text{'from'} & A & \begin{bmatrix} 0 & 1 & 0 & 1 \\ \text{node} & B & 0 & 0 & 1 & 0 \\ & C & 1 & 1 & 1 & 0 \\ & D & 1 & 0 & 0 & 0 \end{bmatrix}
\end{array}
$$

The total along a row gives the number of arcs leading from the node, while the column total gives the number of arcs leading to the node.

If the arcs of a network are labelled, an **incidence matrix** showing how the nodes and arcs are connected can be made

Example   The network

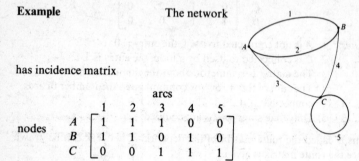

has incidence matrix

$$
\begin{array}{c}
\text{nodes}
\end{array}
\begin{array}{c}
\\ A \\ B \\ C
\end{array}
\begin{array}{c}
\overset{\text{arcs}}{}\\
\begin{array}{ccccc}
1 & 2 & 3 & 4 & 5
\end{array}\\
\left[
\begin{array}{ccccc}
1 & 1 & 1 & 0 & 0 \\
1 & 1 & 0 & 1 & 0 \\
0 & 0 & 1 & 1 & 1
\end{array}
\right]
\end{array}
$$

Matrix shapes

A route matrix is **square**, it has the same number of rows and columns, while an incidence matrix need not be square. The example above shows an incidence matrix with 3 rows and 5 columns, it is called a **3 by 5** matrix (the first number refers to rows). An *m* **by** *n* (or *m* × *n*) matrix has *m* rows and *n* columns, with *mn* elements altogether.

Addition of matrices

A route matrix could show the bus services between different parts of a town. Suppose that the existing services have network

Existing services

and a new set of services is to be added to this system

New routes

The extended network of services is then

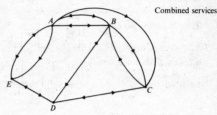

Combined services

The corresponding route matrices are

$$
\begin{array}{c} \\ A \\ B \\ C \\ D \\ E \end{array}
\begin{array}{ccccc} A & B & C & D & E \end{array}
\left[
\begin{array}{ccccc}
0 & 1 & 0 & 0 & 2 \\
1 & 0 & 1 & 1 & 0 \\
0 & 1 & 0 & 1 & 0 \\
0 & 0 & 1 & 0 & 1 \\
1 & 0 & 0 & 1 & 0
\end{array}
\right]
\text{ and }
\begin{array}{c} \\ A \\ B \\ C \\ D \\ E \end{array}
\begin{array}{ccccc} A & B & C & D & E \end{array}
\left[
\begin{array}{ccccc}
0 & 1 & 1 & 0 & 0 \\
1 & 0 & 0 & 0 & 0 \\
1 & 0 & 0 & 0 & 0 \\
0 & 1 & 0 & 0 & 0 \\
0 & 0 & 0 & 0 & 0
\end{array}
\right]
$$

combining to form

$$
\begin{array}{c} \\ A \\ B \\ C \\ D \\ E \end{array}
\begin{array}{ccccc} A & B & C & D & E \end{array}
\left[
\begin{array}{ccccc}
0 & 2 & 1 & 0 & 2 \\
2 & 0 & 1 & 1 & 0 \\
1 & 1 & 0 & 1 & 0 \\
0 & 1 & 1 & 0 & 1 \\
1 & 0 & 0 & 1 & 0
\end{array}
\right]
$$

The third matrix can be formed by adding the elements of the first two.

In general, if two matrices *have the same shape*, they can be added (or subtracted) by adding (or subtracting) the separate elements.

Examples

1.
$$
\begin{bmatrix} 1 & 2 & 3 \\ 4 & 5 & 6 \end{bmatrix} + \begin{bmatrix} 2 & 1 & 3 \\ 0 & 1 & 0 \end{bmatrix} = \begin{bmatrix} 1+2 & 2+1 & 3+3 \\ 4+0 & 5+1 & 6+0 \end{bmatrix}
$$

$$
= \begin{bmatrix} 3 & 3 & 6 \\ 4 & 6 & 6 \end{bmatrix}
$$

2.
$$
\begin{bmatrix} 1 & 2 \\ 3 & 4 \end{bmatrix} - \begin{bmatrix} 1 & 0 \\ 0 & 1 \end{bmatrix} = \begin{bmatrix} 1-1 & 2-0 \\ 3-0 & 4-1 \end{bmatrix} = \begin{bmatrix} 0 & 2 \\ 3 & 3 \end{bmatrix}
$$

If the number of bus services between all the points were doubled, the effect would be to double all the elements of the matrix.

In general, a matrix can be multiplied (or scaled) by a number (**scalar**) by multiplying each element separately.

Examples

1.
$$3\begin{bmatrix} 1 & 2 \\ 3 & 4 \end{bmatrix} = \begin{bmatrix} 3 & 6 \\ 9 & 12 \end{bmatrix}$$

2.
$$-2\begin{bmatrix} 0 & 1 \\ 2 & 3 \end{bmatrix} = \begin{bmatrix} 0 & -2 \\ -4 & -6 \end{bmatrix}$$

Other matrices

A matrix could show any numerical information.

Example   This matrix shows the marks obtained in three grading tests by five students where each paper is marked out of 10.

		Test		
		I	II	III
	Ahmed	5	7	6
	Bob	4	3	5
Student	Carol	8	8	9
	David	7	7	7
	Elina	8	5	7

The row total gives the overall score in the three tests. Suppose that the tests are of varying difficulty, so that the first paper should only count half as much as the others. The marks should be **weighted** $\frac{1}{5}$, $\frac{2}{5}$, $\frac{2}{5}$. To find an overall mark, multiply the scores by the weights and add to find the **weighted average** (see page 351).

Ahmed: $5 \times \dfrac{1}{5} + 7 \times \dfrac{2}{5} + 6 \times \dfrac{2}{5} = \dfrac{5}{5} + \dfrac{14}{5} + \dfrac{12}{5} = \dfrac{31}{5} = 6 \cdot 2$

We say that the row [5   7   6] has been *multiplied* by the column

$$\begin{bmatrix} \dfrac{1}{5} \\ \dfrac{2}{5} \\ \dfrac{2}{5} \end{bmatrix}$$

and we call this **row by column multiplication**.

Continuing for the other students

Bob: $\quad [4 \quad 3 \quad 5] \times \begin{bmatrix} \dfrac{1}{5} \\[4pt] \dfrac{2}{5} \\[4pt] \dfrac{2}{5} \end{bmatrix} = 4 \times \dfrac{1}{5} + 3 \times \dfrac{2}{5} + 5 \times \dfrac{2}{5}$

$$= \frac{4 + 6 + 10}{5} = \frac{20}{5} = 4$$

Carol: $\quad [8 \quad 8 \quad 9] \times \begin{bmatrix} \dfrac{1}{5} \\[4pt] \dfrac{2}{5} \\[4pt] \dfrac{2}{5} \end{bmatrix} = \dfrac{8}{5} + \dfrac{16}{5} + \dfrac{18}{5} = 8 \cdot 4$

and so on (David has 7 and Elina has 6·4).

A matrix showing the weighted averages can be made

$$\begin{array}{cc} & \textit{average} \\ \begin{array}{l} \text{Ahmed} \\ \text{Bob} \\ \text{Carol} \\ \text{David} \\ \text{Elina} \end{array} & \begin{bmatrix} 6 \cdot 2 \\ 4 \cdot \\ 8 \cdot 4 \\ 7 \cdot \\ 6 \cdot 4 \end{bmatrix} \end{array}$$

so,

$$\begin{bmatrix} 5 & 7 & 6 \\ 4 & 3 & 5 \\ 8 & 8 & 9 \\ 7 & 7 & 7 \\ 8 & 5 & 7 \end{bmatrix} \times \begin{bmatrix} \dfrac{1}{5} \\[4pt] \dfrac{2}{5} \\[4pt] \dfrac{2}{5} \end{bmatrix} = \begin{bmatrix} 6 \cdot 2 \\ 4 \cdot 0 \\ 8 \cdot 4 \\ 7 \cdot 0 \\ 6 \cdot 4 \end{bmatrix}$$

the matrices have been multiplied to form a new matrix. (Make sure you understand how the final matrix was calculated.)

Not all matrices can be multiplied together. The number of elements in a *row* of the first matrix must correspond to the number of elements in the *column* of the second.

A 5×3 matrix multiplied by a 3×1 matrix gives a 5×1 matrix. In general $(m \times n) \times (n \times p)$ gives $m \times p$; the so-called 'domino rule'.

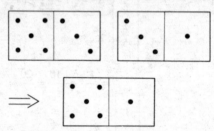

Example   Two types of cake are sold in a shop. The quantities sold each day are recorded in a matrix.

$$
\begin{array}{c}
 \\
\\
M \\
T \\
W \\
T \\
F
\end{array}
\begin{array}{cc}
 & Type \\
I & II \\
\begin{bmatrix}
3 & 5 \\
2 & 7 \\
3 & 4 \\
1 & 2 \\
0 & 4
\end{bmatrix}
\end{array}
$$

The prices of each cake are

$$
Type \quad
\begin{array}{c}
I \\
II
\end{array}
\begin{array}{c}
Price \\
\begin{bmatrix}
1 \cdot 20 \\
2 \cdot 30
\end{bmatrix}
\end{array}
\quad \text{in pounds}
$$

The first matrix is 5×2 and the second is 2×1 and so they can be multiplied to form a 5×1 matrix.

$$
\begin{bmatrix}
3 & 5 \\
2 & 7 \\
3 & 4 \\
1 & 2 \\
0 & 4
\end{bmatrix}
\begin{bmatrix}
1 \cdot 20 \\
2 \cdot 30
\end{bmatrix}
=
\begin{bmatrix}
3 \times 1 \cdot 20 + 5 \times 2 \cdot 30 \\
2 \times 1 \cdot 20 + 7 \times 2 \cdot 30 \\
3 \times 1 \cdot 20 + 4 \times 2 \cdot 30 \\
1 \times 1 \cdot 20 + 2 \times 2 \cdot 30 \\
0 \times 1 \cdot 20 + 4 \times 2 \cdot 30
\end{bmatrix}
=
\begin{bmatrix}
15 \cdot 10 \\
18 \cdot 50 \\
12 \cdot 80 \\
5 \cdot 80 \\
9 \cdot 20
\end{bmatrix}
$$

The entries in the final matrix show the total sales (in £) of cakes for each day.

When the second matrix has more columns, repeat the procedure for each column.

Examples

1. $\begin{bmatrix} 1 & 2 \\ 3 & 5 \end{bmatrix} \begin{bmatrix} 2 & 1 \\ 0 & 2 \end{bmatrix} = \begin{bmatrix} 1 & 2 \\ 3 & 5 \end{bmatrix} \begin{bmatrix} 2 \\ 0 \end{bmatrix} \begin{bmatrix} 1 \\ 2 \end{bmatrix}$ split into columns

Now $\left.\begin{array}{l} \begin{bmatrix} 1 & 2 \end{bmatrix} \begin{bmatrix} 2 \\ 0 \end{bmatrix} = 1 \times 2 + 2 \times 0 = 2 \\ \begin{bmatrix} 3 & 5 \end{bmatrix} \begin{bmatrix} 2 \\ 0 \end{bmatrix} = 3 \times 2 + 5 \times 0 = 6 \end{array}\right\}$ giving $\begin{bmatrix} 2 \\ 6 \end{bmatrix}$

and $\left.\begin{array}{l} \begin{bmatrix} 1 & 2 \end{bmatrix} \begin{bmatrix} 1 \\ 2 \end{bmatrix} = 1 \times 1 + 2 \times 2 = 1 + 4 = 5 \\ \begin{bmatrix} 3 & 5 \end{bmatrix} \begin{bmatrix} 1 \\ 2 \end{bmatrix} = 3 \times 1 + 5 \times 2 = 3 + 10 = 13 \end{array}\right\}$ giving $\begin{bmatrix} 5 \\ 13 \end{bmatrix}$

So $\begin{bmatrix} 1 & 2 \\ 3 & 5 \end{bmatrix} \begin{bmatrix} 2 & 1 \\ 0 & 2 \end{bmatrix} = \begin{bmatrix} 2 & 5 \\ 6 & 13 \end{bmatrix}$

2. $\begin{bmatrix} 2 & 5 \\ 3 & 7 \end{bmatrix} \begin{bmatrix} 1 & 2 & 0 \\ 2 & 1 & 2 \end{bmatrix} = \begin{bmatrix} 2 & 5 \\ 3 & 7 \end{bmatrix} \begin{bmatrix} 1 \\ 2 \end{bmatrix} \begin{bmatrix} 2 \\ 1 \end{bmatrix} \begin{bmatrix} 0 \\ 2 \end{bmatrix}$

$= \begin{bmatrix} 2 \times 1 + 5 \times 2 & 2 \times 2 + 5 \times 1 & 2 \times 0 + 5 \times 2 \\ 3 \times 1 + 7 \times 2 & 3 \times 2 + 7 \times 1 & 3 \times 0 + 7 \times 2 \end{bmatrix}$

$= \begin{bmatrix} 12 & 9 & 10 \\ 17 & 13 & 14 \end{bmatrix}$

3. Given that $\begin{bmatrix} 2 & 1 \\ p & q \end{bmatrix} \begin{bmatrix} 3 & 0 \\ 0 & 2 \end{bmatrix} = \begin{bmatrix} 6 & 2 \\ 9 & 8 \end{bmatrix}$

find p and q.

Answer

$\begin{bmatrix} 2 & 1 \\ p & q \end{bmatrix} \begin{bmatrix} 3 & 0 \\ 0 & 2 \end{bmatrix} = \begin{bmatrix} 2 \times 3 + 1 \times 0 & 2 \times 0 + 1 \times 2 \\ p \times 3 + q \times 0 & p \times 0 + q \times 2 \end{bmatrix}$

$= \begin{bmatrix} 6 & 2 \\ 3p & 2q \end{bmatrix}$

comparing with $\begin{bmatrix} 6 & 2 \\ 9 & 8 \end{bmatrix}$, $p = 3$ and $q = 4$.

If a matrix is *square* $(n \times n)$ then it can be multiplied by itself.

If $\mathbf{A} = \begin{bmatrix} 1 & 2 \\ 0 & 1 \end{bmatrix}$ then $\mathbf{A}^2 = \mathbf{AA} = \begin{bmatrix} 1 & 2 \\ 0 & 1 \end{bmatrix} \begin{bmatrix} 1 & 2 \\ 0 & 1 \end{bmatrix}$

$$= \begin{bmatrix} 1 \times 1 + 2 \times 0 & 1 \times 2 + 2 \times 1 \\ 0 \times 1 + 1 \times 0 & 0 \times 2 + 1 \times 1 \end{bmatrix}$$

$$= \begin{bmatrix} 1 & 4 \\ 0 & 1 \end{bmatrix}.$$

This is *not* the same as squaring the separate elements!

4. Some of the following matrices can be multiplied. Evaluate the products for those that are possible.

$$\mathbf{A} = \begin{bmatrix} 1 & 2 & 3 \end{bmatrix}, \quad \mathbf{B} = \begin{bmatrix} 1 & 2 \\ 3 & 4 \\ 0 & 1 \end{bmatrix}$$

$$\mathbf{C} = \begin{bmatrix} 1 & 2 \\ 3 & 5 \end{bmatrix}, \quad \mathbf{D} = \begin{bmatrix} 0 \\ 1 \\ 2 \end{bmatrix}$$

Answer $\mathbf{AB}$ is possible $(1 \times 3) \times (3 \times 2)$ gives 1×2

$$\begin{bmatrix} 1 & 2 & 3 \end{bmatrix} \begin{bmatrix} 1 & 2 \\ 3 & 4 \\ 0 & 1 \end{bmatrix} = \begin{bmatrix} 1 \times 1 + 2 \times 3 + 3 \times 0 & 1 \times 2 + 2 \times 4 + 3 \times 1 \end{bmatrix}$$

$$= \begin{bmatrix} 7 & 13 \end{bmatrix}$$

$\mathbf{AC}$ is not possible

$\mathbf{AD}$ is possible $(1 \times 3) \times (3 \times 1)$ gives 1×1

$$\begin{bmatrix} 1 & 2 & 3 \end{bmatrix} \begin{bmatrix} 0 \\ 1 \\ 2 \end{bmatrix} = 8$$

$\mathbf{BA}$ and $\mathbf{BD}$ are not possible, but $\mathbf{BC}$ is $(3 \times 2) \times (2 \times 2)$ gives 3×2

$$\begin{bmatrix} 1 & 2 \\ 3 & 4 \\ 0 & 1 \end{bmatrix} \begin{bmatrix} 1 & 2 \\ 3 & 5 \end{bmatrix} = \begin{bmatrix} 7 & 12 \\ 15 & 26 \\ 3 & 5 \end{bmatrix}$$

CA, **CB** and **CD** are all impossible.
DA is possible $(3 \times 1) \times (1 \times 3)$ give 3×3

$$\begin{bmatrix} 0 \\ 1 \\ 2 \end{bmatrix} \begin{bmatrix} 1 & 2 & 3 \end{bmatrix} = \begin{bmatrix} 0 & 0 & 0 \\ 1 & 2 & 3 \\ 2 & 4 & 6 \end{bmatrix}$$

AA, **BB** and **DD** are not possible, but **CC** is since **C** is square

$$\mathbf{C}^2 = \mathbf{CC} = \begin{bmatrix} 1 & 2 \\ 3 & 5 \end{bmatrix} \begin{bmatrix} 1 & 2 \\ 3 & 5 \end{bmatrix} = \begin{bmatrix} 7 & 12 \\ 18 & 31 \end{bmatrix}$$

Matrices are denoted by bold capital letters, such as **A**, **M**. Matrix multiplication is not in general commutative (page 18).

Example If $\mathbf{A} = \begin{bmatrix} 1 & 1 \\ 0 & 1 \end{bmatrix}$ and $\mathbf{B} = \begin{bmatrix} 1 & 2 \\ 3 & 4 \end{bmatrix}$

find the matrix products **AB** and **BA**.

Answer
$$\mathbf{AB} = \begin{bmatrix} 1 & 1 \\ 0 & 1 \end{bmatrix} \begin{bmatrix} 1 & 2 \\ 3 & 4 \end{bmatrix} = \begin{bmatrix} 4 & 6 \\ 3 & 4 \end{bmatrix}$$

$$\mathbf{BA} = \begin{bmatrix} 1 & 2 \\ 3 & 4 \end{bmatrix} \begin{bmatrix} 1 & 1 \\ 0 & 1 \end{bmatrix} = \begin{bmatrix} 1 & 3 \\ 3 & 7 \end{bmatrix}$$

so that $\mathbf{AB} \neq \mathbf{BA}$.

An **identity** matrix is square and has 1s down the main diagonal and 0s elsewhere.

Examples

1. $\begin{bmatrix} 1 & 0 \\ 0 & 1 \end{bmatrix}$ is the 2×2 identity

$$\begin{bmatrix} 1 & 0 \\ 0 & 1 \end{bmatrix} \begin{bmatrix} 2 & 3 \\ 4 & 5 \end{bmatrix} = \begin{bmatrix} 1 \times 2 + 0 \times 4 & 1 \times 3 + 0 \times 5 \\ 0 \times 2 + 1 \times 4 & 0 \times 3 + 0 \times 5 \end{bmatrix} = \begin{bmatrix} 2 & 3 \\ 4 & 5 \end{bmatrix}$$

2. $$\begin{bmatrix} 1 & 0 & 0 \\ 0 & 1 & 0 \\ 0 & 0 & 1 \end{bmatrix} \begin{bmatrix} 1 & 2 \\ 3 & 4 \\ 5 & 6 \end{bmatrix} = \begin{bmatrix} 1 & 2 \\ 3 & 4 \\ 5 & 6 \end{bmatrix}$$

Notice that only *square matrices* can be identity matrices.

Route matrices are square, and can be multiplied together.

Let $\mathbf{M} = \begin{bmatrix} 2 & 0 & 1 \\ 0 & 0 & 2 \\ 1 & 2 & 0 \end{bmatrix}$

be the route matrix of the example on page 311

then $\mathbf{M}^2 = \begin{bmatrix} 2 & 0 & 1 \\ 0 & 0 & 2 \\ 1 & 2 & 0 \end{bmatrix} \begin{bmatrix} 1 & 0 & 1 \\ 0 & 0 & 2 \\ 1 & 2 & 0 \end{bmatrix} = \begin{matrix} A \\ B \\ C \end{matrix} \begin{bmatrix} \overset{A}{5} & \overset{B}{2} & \overset{C}{2} \\ 2 & 4 & 0 \\ 2 & 0 & 5 \end{bmatrix}$

This matrix shows the number of 'two stage' paths between points. For example, the AB entry is 2, and there are two routes from A to B which consist of 2 arcs.

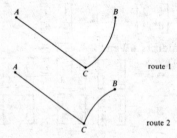

route 1

route 2

Transpose

If a matrix is reflected in its main diagonal, the **transpose** is formed.

Example

The transpose of $\begin{bmatrix} 1 & 2 & 3 \\ 4 & 5 & 6 \\ 7 & 8 & 9 \end{bmatrix}$ is $\begin{bmatrix} 1 & 4 & 7 \\ 2 & 5 & 8 \\ 3 & 6 & 9 \end{bmatrix}$

The transpose of $\mathbf{A}$ is denoted by $\mathbf{A}^\mathrm{T}$.

If $\mathbf{A}$ is a relation matrix, then $\mathbf{A}^\mathrm{T}$ represents the inverse relation (see page 82).

Inverse matrices

The inverse of a 2×2 matrix can be easily found by the formula:

If
$$\mathbf{A} = \begin{bmatrix} a & b \\ c & d \end{bmatrix}$$

then
$$\mathbf{A}^{-1} = \frac{1}{(ad-bc)} \begin{bmatrix} d & -b \\ -c & a \end{bmatrix}$$

Example   If
$$\mathbf{A} = \begin{bmatrix} 1 & 2 \\ 0 & 2 \end{bmatrix}$$

$a = 1$ $b = 2$ $c = 0$ $d = 2$ $ad - bc = 2$

$$\mathbf{A}^{-1} = \tfrac{1}{2} \begin{bmatrix} 2 & -2 \\ 0 & 1 \end{bmatrix} = \begin{bmatrix} 1 & -1 \\ 0 & \tfrac{1}{2} \end{bmatrix}$$

We can check this by calculating

$$\mathbf{A}^{-1}\mathbf{A} = \begin{bmatrix} 1 & -1 \\ 0 & \tfrac{1}{2} \end{bmatrix} \begin{bmatrix} 1 & 2 \\ 0 & 2 \end{bmatrix}$$

$$= \begin{bmatrix} 1 \times 1 + -1 \times 0 & 1 \times 2 - 1 \times 2 \\ 0 \times 1 + \tfrac{1}{2} \times 0 & 2 \times 0 + \tfrac{1}{2} \times 2 \end{bmatrix}$$

$$= \begin{bmatrix} 1 & 0 \\ 0 & 1 \end{bmatrix}$$

which is the identity, as required.

If the quantity $(ad - bc)$, called the **determinant** of the matrix

$$\mathbf{A} = \begin{bmatrix} a & b \\ c & d \end{bmatrix}$$

is zero, then the inverse cannot be found.

$\mathbf{A}$ is then said to be a **singular matrix.** For example $\begin{bmatrix} 2 & 6 \\ 1 & 3 \end{bmatrix}$ is singular.

The set of non-singular 2×2 matrices forms a *group* under row $\times$ $\times$ column multiplication. (But note that to prove we have a group we should show that *all* 2×2 non-singular matrices satisfy these conditions.)

Exercise: Check that the group axioms (page 62) hold, by testing them with particular matrices.

The inverse of *AB*

If **A** and **B** have inverses $\mathbf{A}^{-1}$ and $\mathbf{B}^{-1}$, then $(\mathbf{AB})^{-1} = \mathbf{B}^{-1}\mathbf{A}^{-1}$ (note the order).

Proof:

$$\begin{aligned}
(\mathbf{AB})^{-1}(\mathbf{AB}) &= (\mathbf{B}^{-1}\mathbf{A}^{-1})(\mathbf{AB}) \\
&= (\mathbf{B}^{-1})(\mathbf{A}^{-1}\mathbf{A})\mathbf{B} && \text{associativity} \\
&= \mathbf{B}^{-1}\mathbf{I}\mathbf{B} && \mathbf{A}^{-1}\mathbf{A} = \mathbf{I} \\
&= \mathbf{B}^{-1}\mathbf{B} && \mathbf{I}\mathbf{B} = \mathbf{B}, \mathbf{I} \text{ is the identity} \\
&= \mathbf{I}
\end{aligned}$$

and so $\mathbf{B}^{-1}\mathbf{A}^{-1}$ is the inverse of **AB**.

Examination questions

1.

$$\begin{array}{c@{\quad}c}
 & \begin{array}{cccc} A & B & C & D \end{array} \\
\begin{array}{c} A \\ B \\ C \\ D \end{array} &
\begin{bmatrix} 0 & 1 & 0 & 0 \\ 1 & 0 & 2 & 2 \\ 0 & 2 & 0 & 1 \\ 0 & 2 & 1 & 0 \end{bmatrix}
\end{array}$$

This is the route matrix of a network with no one-way routes.
Draw the network.   [SMP]

2. *If* $\mathbf{X} = \begin{bmatrix} -2 & 1 \\ 3 & -1 \end{bmatrix}$ *then* $\mathbf{X}^2$ *is*

(a) $\begin{bmatrix} 7 & -3 \\ -9 & 4 \end{bmatrix}$,   (b) $\begin{bmatrix} 4 & 1 \\ 9 & 1 \end{bmatrix}$,   (c) $\begin{bmatrix} 7 & -9 \\ -3 & 4 \end{bmatrix}$,   (d) $\begin{bmatrix} 7 & -1 \\ -9 & 4 \end{bmatrix}$.

[SMP]

3. $\mathbf{A} = \begin{bmatrix} 2 & 0 \\ 3 & 4 \end{bmatrix}$ $\mathbf{B} = \begin{bmatrix} k & 0 \\ 2 & 1 \end{bmatrix}$

Work out the matrix products **AB** *and* **BA**.
Given that $\mathbf{AB} = \mathbf{BA}$, *find the value of* k.   [LON]

4. *The inverse of the matrix* $\begin{bmatrix} 1 & 2 \\ 3 & 4 \end{bmatrix}$ *is*

$A \begin{bmatrix} -2 & 1 \\ 3/2 & -1/2 \end{bmatrix}$ $B \begin{bmatrix} 2 & -1 \\ 3/2 & 1/2 \end{bmatrix}$ $C \begin{bmatrix} -4 & 2 \\ 3 & -1 \end{bmatrix}$ $D \begin{bmatrix} 4 & -2 \\ -3 & 1 \end{bmatrix}$

$E \begin{bmatrix} 4 & -3 \\ -2 & 1 \end{bmatrix}$

[LON]

5. *Given that* $\begin{bmatrix} 3 & 1 \\ 2 & 0 \end{bmatrix}\begin{bmatrix} x \\ y \end{bmatrix} = \begin{bmatrix} 8 \\ 6 \end{bmatrix}$ *then* $\begin{bmatrix} 1 & 3 \\ 0 & 2 \end{bmatrix}\begin{bmatrix} x \\ y \end{bmatrix} =$

$A \begin{bmatrix} -8 \\ -8 \end{bmatrix}$ $B \begin{bmatrix} 0 \\ 6 \end{bmatrix}$ $C \begin{bmatrix} 6 \\ 8 \end{bmatrix}$ $D \begin{bmatrix} 10^{2/3} \\ 6 \end{bmatrix}$ $E \begin{bmatrix} 13^{1/3} \\ 8 \end{bmatrix}$

[LON]

6. *(a) Express as a single matrix* $\begin{bmatrix} 3 \\ 7 \end{bmatrix} - 2\begin{bmatrix} -2 \\ 4 \end{bmatrix}$

   (b) Given that $\begin{bmatrix} x & 2 \\ 3 & 4y \end{bmatrix}\begin{bmatrix} 1 \\ 5 \end{bmatrix} = \begin{bmatrix} 10 \\ 23 \end{bmatrix}$, *find x and y.*

[CAM]

7. *(a) Evaluate the matrix products (i)* $\begin{bmatrix} 1 & 0 \end{bmatrix}\begin{bmatrix} 0 \\ 1 \end{bmatrix}$ *(ii)* $\begin{bmatrix} 0 \\ 1 \end{bmatrix}\begin{bmatrix} 1 & 0 \end{bmatrix}$

   (b) **A** *is the* 2×2 *matrix such that*

$$\mathbf{A} - 2\begin{bmatrix} 1 & -1 \\ 0 & 1 \end{bmatrix} = 3\begin{bmatrix} 1 & 1 \\ -1 & 0 \end{bmatrix}$$

   Find **A**.

[CAM]

8. **I** *is the identity matrix* $\begin{bmatrix} 1 & 0 \\ 0 & 1 \end{bmatrix}$ *and* **A** *is a* 2×2 *matrix such that*

$\mathbf{A}^2 = \mathbf{I}$. *Write down two possible matrices* **A**, *other than* **I**.

[CAM]

9. *Given that* $\mathbf{A} = \begin{bmatrix} 4 & 7 \\ 1 & 2 \end{bmatrix}$ *and* $\mathbf{B} = \begin{bmatrix} 2 & -3 \\ 4 & -1 \end{bmatrix}$ *calculate*

   (a) $\mathbf{A} + 3\mathbf{B}$,   *(b)* $\mathbf{A}^{-1}$.

[CAM]

10. *Given that* $\mathbf{A} = \begin{bmatrix} 4 & 3 \\ 1 & 1 \end{bmatrix}$ $\mathbf{B} = \begin{bmatrix} 2 & 0 \\ 2 & 0 \end{bmatrix}$ *and* $\mathbf{C} = \begin{bmatrix} 1 & 3 \end{bmatrix}$,

evaluate (a) $\mathbf{A} + \mathbf{B}$, *(b)* $\mathbf{A}^2$, *(c)* $\mathbf{CB}$

(d) the matrix $\mathbf{D}$ *such that* $\mathbf{AD} = \begin{bmatrix} 1 & 0 \\ 0 & 1 \end{bmatrix}$ [AEB]

11. *Matrices* $\mathbf{P}$ *and* $\mathbf{I}$ *are defined by*

$$\mathbf{P} = \begin{bmatrix} 0 & -1 \\ -1 & 0 \end{bmatrix} \text{ and } \mathbf{I} = \begin{bmatrix} 1 & 0 \\ 0 & 1 \end{bmatrix}$$

Show that $\{\mathbf{P}, \mathbf{I}\}$ *forms a group under matrix multiplication.*

12. *A road construction contractor, having finished a housing estate in Francistown, moved to Newtown where only roundabouts A, B, C and their associated road outlets and inlets had been built.*

Details are shown in the diagram.

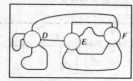
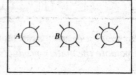

Francistown Estate   Newtown Estate

(i) Write down the route matrix for the roads of the Francistown estate.
(ii) (a) No further junctions, flyovers or dead ends are allowed in Newtown. Find the maximum number of roads that can be built if all the outlets must be used.
    (b) With roads as arcs and A, B, C, as nodes, a route matrix $\mathbf{M}$ *for the Newton estate can be drawn up.*
    One solution for $\mathbf{M}$ *begins*

$$\begin{array}{c} \\ A \\ B \\ C \end{array} \begin{array}{ccc} A & B & C \\ \begin{bmatrix} 0 & 2 & \\ & 0 & \\ & & \end{bmatrix} \end{array}$$

    Copy and complete $\mathbf{M}$, *and draw the network corresponding to it.*

(iii) The matrix
$$\begin{array}{c} A \\ B \\ C \end{array}\begin{bmatrix} \overset{A}{0} & \overset{B}{p} & \overset{C}{3} \\ & q & \\ & r & \end{bmatrix}$$
is another partial solution for a route

matrix which represents a network of roads in Newtown.
This matrix can be completed in two different ways.
(a) Write down the value of p and hence the value of q + r.
(b) Hence complete the matrix in two possible ways and draw the
two networks represented.   [SMP]

13. *Easibild Greenhouses are available in three models: Standard, Special
and Super. The glass for these comes in various packs labelled P, Q, R. The
number of packs needed for each model are given by the matrix*

$$\mathbf{X} = \begin{array}{c} \text{standard} \\ \text{special} \\ \text{super} \end{array}\begin{bmatrix} \overset{P}{2} & \overset{Q}{1} & \overset{R}{1} \\ 3 & 2 & 0 \\ 3 & 2 & 1 \end{bmatrix}$$

*The glass is cut in different sizes denoted by A, B, C, D. The numbers of pieces
of each size contained in each pack are given by the matrix.*

$$\mathbf{Y} = \begin{array}{c} P \\ Q \\ R \end{array}\begin{bmatrix} \overset{A}{8} & \overset{B}{0} & \overset{C}{1} & \overset{D}{0} \\ 0 & 1 & 0 & 8 \\ 4 & 0 & 0 & 3 \end{bmatrix}$$

 (i) *Evaluate the product* **XY** *and describe what information the result
displays.*
 (ii) *Find a matrix* **T** *such that* **XYT** *gives the total number of pieces of
glass needed for each model separately.*
(iii) *Evaluate* **XYT***.*
 (iv) *The mass, in kilograms, of each piece of glass is given by the matrix*

$$\mathbf{M} = \begin{array}{c} A \\ B \\ C \\ D \end{array}\begin{bmatrix} 4 \\ 1 \\ 2 \\ 4 \end{bmatrix}$$

Which of the expressions **MXY, MYX, XYM, YXM, YMX**
*can be evaluated? State and evaluate the one which gives the mass
of glass needed for each model.*
 (v) *A department store orders 100 Standards, 50 Specials and 20
Supers. Find the total mass of glass involved.*   [SMP]

14. *Messages are coded as follows:*

Letters are replaced by numbers as shown in the table.

A	B	C	D	E	F	G	H	I	J	K	L	M
1	2	3	4	5	6	7	8	9	10	11	12	13

N	O	P	Q	R	S	T	U	V	W	X	Y	Z
−1	−2	−3	−4	−5	−6	−7	−8	−9	−10	−11	−12	−13

The message is then written in two rows and the matrix so formed is multiplied on the left by $\begin{bmatrix} 2 & 5 \\ 1 & 3 \end{bmatrix}$

For example, $SMPRULESOK$ is coded by working out

$$\begin{bmatrix} 2 & 5 \\ 1 & 3 \end{bmatrix} \begin{bmatrix} -6 & 13 & -3 & -5 & -8 \\ 12 & 5 & -6 & -2 & 11 \end{bmatrix} \text{ which comes to}$$

$$\begin{bmatrix} 48 & 51 & -36 & -20 & 39 \\ 30 & 28 & -21 & -11 & 25 \end{bmatrix}$$

(i) Write the message $TINKER$ in code.

(ii) State the inverse of $\begin{bmatrix} 2 & 5 \\ 1 & 3 \end{bmatrix}$

(iii) Decode the message $\begin{bmatrix} 46 & -8 & -7 \\ 29 & -5 & -6 \end{bmatrix}$

[SMP]

Answers

2. (a)

3. $k = -\frac{1}{2}$

4. A

5. C

6. (a) $\begin{bmatrix} 7 \\ -1 \end{bmatrix}$ (b) $x = 0, y = 1$

7. (i) (0)   (ii) (0, 0)

8. $\begin{bmatrix} -1 & 0 \\ 0 & -1 \end{bmatrix}, \begin{bmatrix} 0 & 1 \\ 1 & 0 \end{bmatrix}$

9. (a) $\begin{bmatrix} 10 & -2 \\ 13 & -1 \end{bmatrix}$ (b) $\begin{bmatrix} 2 & -7 \\ -1 & 4 \end{bmatrix}$

10. (a) $\begin{bmatrix} 6 & 3 \\ 3 & 1 \end{bmatrix}$ (b) $\begin{bmatrix} 19 & 15 \\ 5 & 4 \end{bmatrix}$ (c) $\begin{bmatrix} 8, & 0 \end{bmatrix}$ (d) $\begin{bmatrix} 1 & -3 \\ -1 & 4 \end{bmatrix}$

$$
\begin{array}{cc}
 & D\ E\ F \\
\textbf{12. (i)} &
\begin{array}{c}
D \\
E \\
F
\end{array}
\begin{bmatrix}
4 & 1 & 1 \\
1 & 0 & 4 \\
1 & 4 & 0
\end{bmatrix}
\end{array}
\quad \text{(ii)(a) 7} \quad \text{(iii)(a) 1, 4}
$$

14. (i) $\begin{bmatrix} 41 & 43 & -27 \\ 26 & 24 & -16 \end{bmatrix}$ (ii) $\begin{bmatrix} 3 & -5 \\ -1 & 2 \end{bmatrix}$ (iii) *TAILOR*

Section 16: Vectors and Transformations

Vectors

A translation can be described by its effect on the coordinates of a point.

Example
The translation $T: (x, y) \mapsto (x+4, y+5)$
translates the point $P(1, 3)$ by 4 units in the
x direction and 5 units in the y direction.

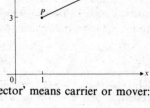

It is only necessary to specify the x shift,
4, and y shift, 5. These shifts can be stored
in a 2×1 matrix, or **column vector** $\binom{4}{5}$. We
can also call $\binom{4}{5}$ a **displacement vector** ('vector' means carrier or mover:
the translation moves points).

A displacement is represented in the
x–y plane by an arrow connecting a point
P and its image Q.

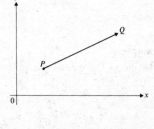

We write this as $\overrightarrow{PQ} = \binom{4}{5}$.

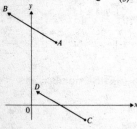

> The choice of initial point is not impor-
> tant. Any two arrows which are parallel
> and have the same length represent the
> same displacement vector.

$\overrightarrow{AB} = \overrightarrow{CD} = \binom{-1}{3}$

The length of a displacement vector is called the **modulus** of the vector,
written as $|\overrightarrow{AB}|$ or AB for example. We can use Pythagoras' theorem to
calculate the modulus.

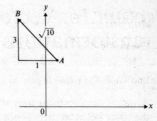

$$|\overrightarrow{AB}|^2 = 1^2 + 3^2 = 10$$

and so $\qquad |\overrightarrow{AB}| = \sqrt{10}$

Two translations can be added by composition of mappings (page 80). If translation T has displacement vector $\binom{1}{3}$ and translation S has vector $\binom{-1}{5}$, then the combined translation ST has vector

$$\binom{-1}{5} + \binom{1}{3} = \binom{0}{8} \qquad \text{using matrix addition (page 312)}$$

To add two vectors, add the elements (or **components**) separately. Column vectors can also be multiplied by scalars, for example

$$2\binom{1}{3} = \binom{2}{6}$$

If $\binom{1}{3}$ represents vector $\overrightarrow{AB}$, then $\binom{2}{6}$ represents a vector which is parallel to, and twice the length of, $\overrightarrow{AB}$.

Examples

1. $$2\binom{1}{3} + 5\binom{-1}{2} = \binom{2}{6} + \binom{-5}{10} = \binom{2-5}{6+10} = \binom{-3}{16}$$

2. $$3\binom{1}{4} - \tfrac{1}{2}\binom{2}{6} = \binom{3}{12} - \binom{1}{3} = \binom{3-1}{12-3} = \binom{2}{9}$$

Note: When a displacement is multiplied by a negative number, the direction is reversed.

$$-\overrightarrow{AB} = \overrightarrow{AB'}$$

Arithmetic

Examples

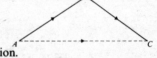

   1. $\vec{AB} + \vec{BC} = \vec{AC}$

known as the **triangle rule** of vector addition.

A vector displacement only takes account of the initial and final points; the route between them is not important.

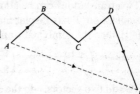

   2. $\vec{AB} + \vec{BC} + \vec{CD} + \vec{DE} = \vec{AE}$

Any number of displacements can be added

   3. $\vec{AA}$ is the zero or null displacement, with column vector $\binom{0}{0}$.

   4. $\vec{AB} + \vec{BA} = \vec{AA}$

                             $= 0$

and so $\vec{BA} = -\vec{AB}$

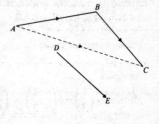

   5. Displacements can be added even when the letters do not match up.

   $\vec{AB} + \vec{DE} = \vec{AB} + \vec{BC} = \vec{AC}$

where C is a point such that $DE = BC$ and DE is parallel to BC (since vectors which are parallel and of the same length are equal).

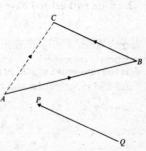

   6. Subtraction can also be performed

$\vec{AB} - \vec{PQ} = \vec{AB} + \vec{QP}$ as $\vec{QP} = -\vec{PQ}$

           $= \vec{AB} + \vec{BC}$ see diagram

           $= \vec{AC}$

Vectors form a group under addition (see page 62).

Displacement vectors can also be denoted by single, bold small letters (**a**, **b**, **r**, **p**).

Examples
1.

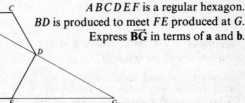

ABCDEF is a regular hexagon.
BD is produced to meet *FE* produced at *G*.
Express $\vec{BG}$ in terms of **a** and **b**.

Answer

$$\vec{BG} = \vec{BD} + \vec{DG}$$ find a route from *B* to *G*

and $$\vec{BD} = \vec{BA} + \vec{AD}$$ find a route from *B* to *D* which

$$= -\vec{AB} + \vec{AD}$$ takes directions parallel to **a** and **b**

$$= -\mathbf{a} + 2\mathbf{b}$$ *AD* ∥ *BC* and *AD* = 2*BC*

$$= 2\mathbf{b} - \mathbf{a}$$

Also $$\vec{DG} = \vec{DE} + \vec{EG}$$

$$= -\mathbf{a} + \vec{EG}$$ *DE* ∥ *BA*, and *DE* = *BA*

From triangle *DEG*

$$120° - 30° = 90° \quad \therefore \; B\widehat{D}E = 90°$$

$$\frac{DE}{EG} = \sin 30° = \frac{1}{2} \quad \text{the hexagon is regular}$$

so, $$\vec{EG} = 2\vec{BC} = 2\mathbf{b}$$ *EG* ∥ *BC*

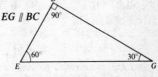

Putting these together

$$\vec{BG} = 2\mathbf{b} - \mathbf{a} + (-\mathbf{a} + 2\mathbf{b})$$

$$= 2(2\mathbf{b} - \mathbf{a})$$

Notice that the routes between points were chosen to follow paths parallel to the given vectors **a** and **b**. Much use was made of the equality of vectors which are parallel and have the same length.

2.

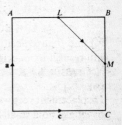

L is the mid-point of *AB*, *MC* = ⅓*BC*.
Find $\vec{LM}$ in terms of **a** and **c**.

Answer $$\vec{LM} = \vec{LB} + \vec{BM}$$

$$= \frac{1}{2}\mathbf{c} + (-\frac{2}{3}\mathbf{a})$$

$$= \frac{1}{2}\mathbf{c} - \frac{2}{3}\mathbf{a}$$

Position vectors

Any point in the plane defines a vector
with one end at the origin O.

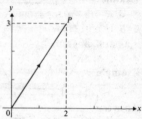

Point $P(2, 3)$ determines the vector $\overrightarrow{OP}$.
$\overrightarrow{OP}$ is called the **position vector** of P.
$\overrightarrow{OP} = \binom{2}{3}$.

In this way, the set of points in the plane can be represented by the set of
column vectors. A point (x, y) has position vector $\binom{x}{y}$.

Basis vectors

The vectors $\mathbf{i} = \binom{1}{0}$ and $\mathbf{j} = \binom{0}{1}$ corresponding to the points $I(1, 0)$ and
$J(0, 1)$ on the axes, are called **basis vectors**. Any vector can be expressed in
terms of $\mathbf{i}$ and $\mathbf{j}$, for example

$$\binom{2}{3} = 2\binom{1}{0} + 3\binom{0}{1} = 2\mathbf{i} + 3\mathbf{j}$$

Any two vectors which are not parallel form a basis.

Example If $\mathbf{a} = \binom{1}{1}$ and $\mathbf{b} = \binom{2}{-1}$ then we can express $\mathbf{c} = \binom{4}{7}$ in
terms of $\mathbf{a}$ and $\mathbf{b}$.

$$\mathbf{c} = 6\binom{1}{1} - \binom{2}{-1} = 6\mathbf{a} - \mathbf{b}$$

There is only one way to express $\mathbf{c}$ in terms of $\mathbf{a}$ and $\mathbf{b}$. This means that,
for any two non-parallel vectors $\mathbf{a}$ and $\mathbf{b}$,

if $$\lambda \mathbf{a} + \mu \mathbf{b} = p\mathbf{a} + q\mathbf{b}$$

where $$\lambda, \mu, p, q, \in \mathbb{R}$$

then $$\lambda = p \quad \text{and} \quad \mu = q$$

If A and B have position vectors $\mathbf{a}$ and $\mathbf{b}$
with respect to an origin O, then
$$\overrightarrow{AB} = \mathbf{b} - \mathbf{a}$$

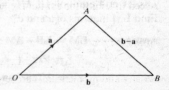

If C and D have position vectors $\mathbf{c}$ and $\mathbf{d}$, so that $\overrightarrow{CD} = \mathbf{c} - \mathbf{d}$ and if also $\mathbf{c} - \mathbf{d} = k(\mathbf{b} - \mathbf{a})$ for some $k \in \mathbb{R}$, then CD is parallel to AB and has length kAB. In particular when $k = 1$, AB and CD are equal in length and $ABCD$ is a parallelogram.

Example

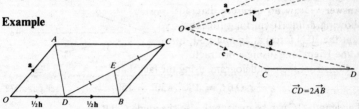

$\overrightarrow{CD} = 2\overrightarrow{AB}$

$OACB$ is a parallelogram. $\overrightarrow{OA} = \mathbf{a}$ and $\overrightarrow{OB} = \mathbf{b}$. D is the mid-point of OB and E is the mid-point of DC. Prove that AD is parallel to EB and find the ratio $AD : EB$.

Answer $\overrightarrow{AD} = \frac{1}{2}\mathbf{b} - \mathbf{a}$

$\overrightarrow{EB} = \overrightarrow{ED} + \overrightarrow{DB} = \frac{1}{2}\overrightarrow{CD} + \overrightarrow{DB} = \frac{1}{2}(\overrightarrow{CB} + \overrightarrow{BD}) + \overrightarrow{DB}$

$\quad = \frac{1}{2}(-\mathbf{a} - \frac{1}{2}\mathbf{b}) + \frac{1}{2}\mathbf{b} = \frac{1}{4}\mathbf{b} - \frac{1}{2}\mathbf{a} = \frac{1}{2}(\frac{1}{2}\mathbf{b} - \mathbf{a})$

Hence $AD \parallel EB$ and $AD : EB = 1 : \frac{1}{2} = 2 : 1$

The parallelogram rule

If two vectors $\mathbf{a}$ and $\mathbf{b}$ are added, then the sum $\mathbf{a} + \mathbf{b}$ is called the **resultant** vector. The resultant can be found by completing the parallelogram with $\mathbf{a}$ and $\mathbf{b}$ as adjacent sides: it is the diagonal of this parallelogram

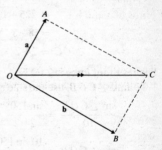

Notice that $|\mathbf{a} + \mathbf{b}| \leqslant |\mathbf{a}| + |\mathbf{b}|$, because the side OC of triangle OAC cannot exceed in length the sum of the lengths of the other two sides.

Applications

Physical quantities which have associated directions, such as force, velocity and momentum, can be represented by vectors.

Examples

1. A force of 10 N and a force of 15 N act at the same point and make an angle of 30°. Find the magnitude of the resultant force, and the angle that this resultant makes with the 15 N force.

Answer   Draw an *accurate* diagram showing a line 10 cm long (to represent the 10 N force) at an angle 30° to a line 15 cm long (using a protractor).

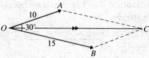

Construct the parallelogram, using the fact that

$$\angle OBC = 180° - 30° = 150° \qquad \text{see page 222}$$

The length OC can be measured, also the angle COB.

$$OC = 24.2 \text{ cm} \quad \text{and} \quad \angle COB = 12°$$

Notice that the lengths of the vectors **OA** and **OB** represent the magnitudes of the forces.

The resultant can also be found by calculation, using the sine and cosine rules (page 287).

   In $\triangle OBC$

$$
\begin{aligned}
OC^2 &= OB^2 + BC^2 - 2OB \cdot BC \cos 150° \\
&= 15^2 + 10^2 - 2 \times 15 \times 10 \times (-0.866) \\
&= 225 + 100 + 259.8 \\
&= 584.8 \\
\therefore OC &= 24.2
\end{aligned}
$$

The resultant force is 24.2 N.

   To find $\angle COB$, use the sine rule

$$\frac{\sin \angle COB}{10} = \frac{\sin 150°}{24.2}$$

$$
\begin{aligned}
\sin \angle COB &= \frac{10 \sin 150°}{24.2} \\
&= \frac{10 \times 0.5}{24.2} \\
&= 0.2066
\end{aligned}
$$

$$\therefore \angle COB = \sin^{-1}(0.2066) = 12° \qquad \text{to the nearest degree}$$

$$\widehat{COB} < \widehat{AOB} \text{ and so is acute}$$

2.
A man cycles along a straight road at a
speed of 5 m/s. A gust of wind blows in a
direction making an angle of 45° with his
direction of motion, with a speed of 2 m/s.

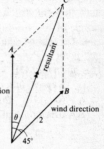

Find the resultant speed and direction of
the cyclist.

Answer The speed is found from the parallelogram. Measuring the
diagonal, the speed is 6·6 m/s. The direction makes an angle of $\theta°$ with
the original direction of the cyclists path. Measuring with a protractor,
$\theta = 13·1°$.
The triangle OBC is called the **triangle of velocities** for the problem.

Examination questions

1. *Given that* $\overrightarrow{OA} = \binom{4}{4}$, $\overrightarrow{AB} = \binom{-3}{-8}$ *then* $\overrightarrow{OB} =$
   A $\binom{-6}{-10}$ *B* $\binom{-2}{-4}$ *C* $\binom{2}{4}$ *D* $\binom{6}{10}$

2. *(a)* $OABC$ *is a parallelogram.* $\overrightarrow{OA} = \mathbf{a}$ *and* $\overrightarrow{OC} = \mathbf{c}$.
   (i) Express $\overrightarrow{AC}$ *in terms of* $\mathbf{a}$ *and* $\mathbf{c}$.
   (ii) Given that $|\overrightarrow{OA}| = 2$, $|\overrightarrow{OC}| = 3$, *find the value of* $|3\mathbf{a}| + |2\mathbf{c}|$.
   Given that $\mathbf{u}$ *and* $\mathbf{v}$ *are non-parallel vectors and that*

   $$(p - 2q)\mathbf{u} = (p + q - 3)\mathbf{v}$$

   find the values of p *and* q.   [CAM]

3. *$OACB$ is a parallelogram whose diagonals
intersect at E; the diagonal AB is produced to D
and OD and CD are joined.*
   Given that $\overrightarrow{OA} = \mathbf{a}$, $\overrightarrow{OB} = \mathbf{b}$ *and*
   $\overrightarrow{DB} = 2(\mathbf{a} - \mathbf{b})$, *express, as simply as
   possible, in terms of* $\mathbf{a}$ *and* $\mathbf{b}$.

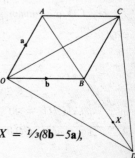

   (i) $\overrightarrow{AB}$, *(ii)* $\overrightarrow{ED}$, *(iii)* $\overrightarrow{OD}$, *(iv)* $\overrightarrow{CD}$.

Given also that X is the point on BD such that $OX = \frac{1}{3}(8\mathbf{b} - 5\mathbf{a})$, *find the value of* $\frac{BX}{BD}$. *If, in addition,* $|\mathbf{a}| = |\mathbf{b}| = 3$ *and* $A\widehat{O}B = 60°$, *find the numerical value of* $|\mathbf{b} - \mathbf{a}|$. [CAM]

4. *OPQ is an equilateral triangle. R is the mid-point of PQ and S is the mid-point of OR. It is given that* $\overrightarrow{OP} = \mathbf{p}$ *and* $\overrightarrow{OQ} = \mathbf{q}$.

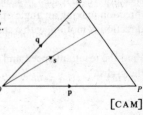

   (i) *Express in terms of* $\mathbf{p}$ *and* $\mathbf{q}$
       (a) $\overrightarrow{OR}$, (b) $\overrightarrow{OS}$.
   (ii) *Given that* $|\mathbf{p}| = 2$, *find the value of*
       (a) $|\mathbf{p} - \mathbf{q}|$, (b) $|\overrightarrow{OR}|$. [CAM]

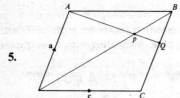

5.

In the parallelogram OABC, OP = ¾OB and APQ is a straight line. $\overrightarrow{OA} = \mathbf{a}$ *and* $\overrightarrow{OC} = \mathbf{c}$.

   (i) *Find* $\overrightarrow{OB}$, $\overrightarrow{OP}$ *and* $\overrightarrow{AP}$ *in terms of* $\mathbf{a}$ *and* $\mathbf{c}$.
   (ii) *By writing* $\overrightarrow{OQ}$ *as* $\overrightarrow{OA} + x\overrightarrow{AP}$ *express* $\overrightarrow{OQ}$ *in terms of* $\mathbf{a}$, $\mathbf{c}$ *and* x.
   (iii) *By writing* $\overrightarrow{OQ}$ *as* $\overrightarrow{OC} + y\overrightarrow{CB}$ *express* $\overrightarrow{OQ}$ *in terms of* $\mathbf{a}$, $\mathbf{c}$, *and* y.
   (iv) *Find the value of* x *which makes the terms in* $\mathbf{c}$ *equal in the two expressions for* $\overrightarrow{OQ}$. *Hence find the value of* y.
   (v) *Use the value of* y *to find* $\frac{CN}{QB}$ [SMP]

6. *ABCD is a parallelogram. A is the point (1,7) and B is the point (3,4).*

Express $\overrightarrow{CD}$ *as a column vector.* [SMP]

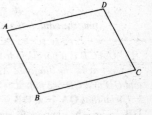

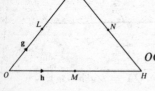

7. *In the triangle OGH the mid-points of OG, OH and GH are L, M and N respectively.* $\overrightarrow{OG} = \mathbf{q}$, $\overrightarrow{OH} = \mathbf{h}$.

(i) *Write down expressions, in terms of* **q** *and* **h**, *for*

    (a) $\overrightarrow{OL}$ *(b)* $\overrightarrow{GN}$ *(c)* $\overrightarrow{ON}$ *(d)* $\overrightarrow{OG} + \overrightarrow{OM} + \overrightarrow{ON}$

(ii) *(a)* *Use the vector equation* $\overrightarrow{OG} + \overrightarrow{GM} = \overrightarrow{OM}$ *to express* $\overrightarrow{GM}$ *in terms of* **g** *and* **h**.

    (b) *By a similar method, express* $\overrightarrow{HL}$ *in terms of* **g** *and* **h**.

    (c) *Hence obtain an expression for* $\overrightarrow{GH} + \overrightarrow{HL} + \overrightarrow{ON}$ *and simplify it.*

(iii) *(a)* *Use your results from (ii) to express* $\overrightarrow{GM} - \overrightarrow{HL}$ *in terms of* **g** *and* **h**.

    (b) *K is a point, not shown on the diagram, such that* $\overrightarrow{OK} = \overrightarrow{GM} - \overrightarrow{HL}$. *What can you say about* $\overrightarrow{OK}$ *and* $\overrightarrow{GH}$?

                                                               [SMP]

8. *A man at O (0, 0) is exercising his dog. Initially the dog is at A (0, 25) and it begins to run in a straight line so that t seconds later it is at P where the position vector* $\overrightarrow{OP}$ *is given by* $\overrightarrow{OP} = \begin{pmatrix} 4t \\ 25 - 3t \end{pmatrix}$ *for* $0 \leqslant t \leqslant 10$. *(All distances are measured in metres.)*

(i) *If the dog is at R after 3 s, find the coordinates of R.*

(ii) *Write* $\overrightarrow{RA}$ *as a column vector and verify that* $\overrightarrow{RA}$ *is perpendicular to* $\overrightarrow{OA}$.

    Hence calculate the shortest distance between the man and his dog during the interval $0 \leqslant t \leqslant 10$.

(iii) *Write down and simplify an expression for* $|\overrightarrow{OP}|^2$ *in terms of t. Deduce the period of time in the interval* $0 < t \leqslant 10$ *for which the dog is at least 25 m away from the man.*   [AEB]

9. *(a)* *A river has a constant width of 2 km and flows at 3 km/h from west to east, between parallel banks. A girl at the point G on one bank is capable of rowing at 4 km/h in still water. She wishes to row directly across the river to the point D on the other bank.*

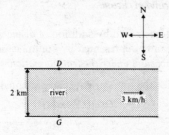

Either *by drawing, using 2 cm to represent 1 km/h, or by calculation find (i) the bearing of the course which she must steer, (ii) the time, in minutes, which it will take her to reach D.*

(b) e *and* n *are unit vectors at right angles.*

The vector $(13n - 4e)$ *is the sum of the vectors* $h(2n + e)$ *and* $k(n - 3e)$ *where h and k are constants. Write down two equations, each involving both h and k and hence find the values of h and k.* [CAM]

10. *In regular hexagon O P Q R S T,* $\overrightarrow{OP} = $ p *and* $\overrightarrow{OT} = $ t. *Express* $\overrightarrow{PT}$ *in terms of* p *and* t *and show that*

(a) $\overrightarrow{PS} = 2$t,   (b) $\overrightarrow{OS} = $ p $+ 2$t.

Given that $PX = \frac{2}{3}PT$, *show that X lies on OS and find the value of* $\frac{OX}{XS}$. [LON]

Answers

1. B
2. (i) c$-$a   (ii) 12, $p = 2, q = 1$
3. (i) b$-$a   (ii) $\frac{3}{2}$(a$-$b)   (iii) 2a$-$b   (iv) a$-$2b
4. (i) (a) $\frac{1}{2}$(p$+$q)   (b) $\frac{1}{4}$(p$+$q)   (ii) (a) 2   (b) $\sqrt{3}$
6. $\binom{-2}{3}$
7. (i) (a) $\frac{1}{2}$g   (b) $\frac{1}{2}$(h$-$g)   (c) $\frac{1}{2}$(h$+$g)   (d) h$+\frac{3}{2}$g
   (ii) (a) $\frac{1}{2}$h$-$g   (b) $\frac{1}{2}$g$-$h   (c) $-\frac{3}{2}$g   (iii) (a) $\frac{3}{2}$h$-\frac{3}{2}$g
   (b) **OK** $\parallel$ **GH** and **OK** $= \frac{3}{2}$(**GH**)
8. (i) $R(12, 16)$ (ii) $\binom{-12}{9}$, 20m   (iii) $25t^2 - 150t + 625, t > 6$ secs
9. (a) $228 \cdot 6°, 45 \cdot 3$ mins   (b) $h = 5, k = 3$

Transformation Matrices

Translations are represented by addition of displacement vectors. Other transformations can be represented by multiplication by 2×2 matrices, *if the origin O is invariant under the transformation.*

Example   Describe the transformation represented by the matrix

$$\begin{bmatrix} -1 & 0 \\ 0 & 1 \end{bmatrix}$$

Answer We must find out what effect the transformation has on the points in the plane. We see what happens to the vertices of the unit square $O(0,0)$, $I(1,0)$, $K(1,1)$, and $J(0,1)$.

The image of a point is found by multiplying the corresponding position vector by the matrix.

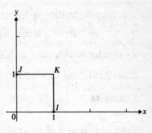

O:
$$\begin{bmatrix} -1 & 0 \\ 0 & 1 \end{bmatrix}\begin{pmatrix} 0 \\ 0 \end{pmatrix} = \begin{pmatrix} 0 \\ 0 \end{pmatrix}$$
as it should!

I:
$$\begin{bmatrix} -1 & 0 \\ 0 & 1 \end{bmatrix}\begin{pmatrix} 1 \\ 0 \end{pmatrix} = \begin{pmatrix} -1 \\ 0 \end{pmatrix}$$
$I'(-1,0)$

K:
$$\begin{bmatrix} -1 & 0 \\ 0 & 1 \end{bmatrix}\begin{pmatrix} 1 \\ 1 \end{pmatrix} = \begin{pmatrix} -1 \\ 1 \end{pmatrix}$$
$K'(-1,1)$

J:
$$\begin{bmatrix} -1 & 0 \\ 0 & 1 \end{bmatrix}\begin{pmatrix} 0 \\ 1 \end{pmatrix} = \begin{pmatrix} 0 \\ 1 \end{pmatrix}$$
$J'(0,1)$

O and J are invariant under the transformation. The image of $OIKJ$ is $OI'K'J$.

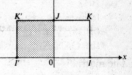

We can see that the transformation is reflection in the y-axis.

Example Describe the transformation with matrix $\begin{bmatrix} 1 & 3 \\ 0 & 1 \end{bmatrix}$.

Answer Find the image of the square $OIKJ$.

I:
$$\begin{pmatrix} 1 \\ 0 \end{pmatrix} \rightarrow \begin{bmatrix} 1 & 3 \\ 0 & 1 \end{bmatrix}\begin{pmatrix} 1 \\ 0 \end{pmatrix} = \begin{pmatrix} 1 \\ 0 \end{pmatrix}$$

K:
$$\begin{pmatrix} 1 \\ 1 \end{pmatrix} \rightarrow \begin{bmatrix} 1 & 3 \\ 0 & 1 \end{bmatrix}\begin{pmatrix} 1 \\ 1 \end{pmatrix} = \begin{pmatrix} 4 \\ 1 \end{pmatrix}$$

J:
$$\begin{pmatrix} 0 \\ 1 \end{pmatrix} \rightarrow \begin{bmatrix} 1 & 3 \\ 0 & 1 \end{bmatrix}\begin{pmatrix} 0 \\ 1 \end{pmatrix} = \begin{pmatrix} 3 \\ 1 \end{pmatrix}$$

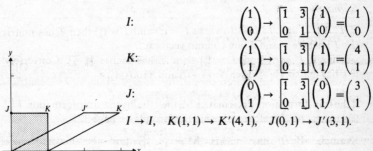

$I \rightarrow I$, $\quad K(1,1) \rightarrow K'(4,1)$, $\quad J(0,1) \rightarrow J'(3,1)$.

The transformation is a shear with the x-axis as invariant line. In general, $\begin{bmatrix} 1 & p \\ 0 & 1 \end{bmatrix}$ represents a shear which leaves the x-axis invariant and $\begin{bmatrix} 1 & 0 \\ q & 1 \end{bmatrix}$ is a shear for which the y-axis is invariant. Conversely, the matrix for a given transformation can be found from the images of the vectors $\binom{1}{0}$ and $\binom{0}{1}$

Examples

1. $$T: (x, y) \to (2x, 3y)$$

First note that $T(0,0) = (0,0)$, and so it is possible to find a matrix.

$\binom{1}{0}$ is position vector of $(1,0) \xrightarrow{\;T\;} (2,0)$ with vector $\binom{2}{0}$.

$\binom{0}{1}$ is position vector of $(0,1) \xrightarrow{\;T\;} (0,3)$, with vector $\binom{0}{3}$. The matrix for T is $\begin{bmatrix} 2 & 0 \\ 0 & 3 \end{bmatrix}$. In general, if $T\binom{1}{0} = \binom{a}{b}$ and $T\binom{0}{1} = \binom{c}{d}$ then T has matrix $\begin{bmatrix} a & c \\ b & d \end{bmatrix}$.

2. Let R be reflection in the line $y = x$.

$$R(1,0) = (0,1)$$
$$R(0,1) = (1,0)$$

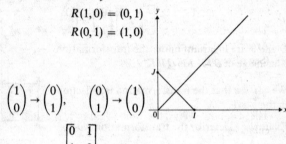

$$\binom{1}{0} \to \binom{0}{1}, \qquad \binom{0}{1} \to \binom{1}{0}$$

The matrix is
$$\begin{bmatrix} 0 & 1 \\ 1 & 0 \end{bmatrix}$$

Summary

If $T: I \mapsto I'$ and $T: J \mapsto J'$ where $I = \binom{0}{1}$ and $J = \binom{0}{1}$ then T has matrix $(I' : J')$ (where I' and J' are column vectors).

Thus if $I' = \binom{a}{b}$ and $J' = \binom{c}{d}$ then T has matrix $\begin{bmatrix} a & c \\ b & d \end{bmatrix}$. Conversely, if T has matrix $\begin{bmatrix} a & c \\ b & d \end{bmatrix}$ then $T: I \mapsto \binom{a}{b}$ and $T: J \mapsto \binom{c}{d}$.

If the transformation T has matrix **M**, then the inverse transformation T^{-1} has matrix $\mathbf{M}^{-1}$ (calculated using the formula on page 321).

Example If T has matrix $\mathbf{M} = \begin{bmatrix} 1 & 2 \\ 0 & 1 \end{bmatrix}$, find the matrix which represents T^{-1}.

Answer   Using the formula (page 321) with $a = 1$, $b = 2$, $c = 0$ and $d = 1$

$$ad - bc = 1 - 0 = 1$$

$$\mathbf{M}^{-1} = \frac{1}{1} \begin{bmatrix} 1 & -2 \\ 0 & 1 \end{bmatrix}$$

$$= \begin{bmatrix} 1 & -2 \\ 0 & 1 \end{bmatrix}$$

The determinant of a matrix gives the scaling factor for *areas* under the transformation. $\begin{bmatrix} 1 & 2 \\ 0 & 1 \end{bmatrix}$ represents a shear, which preserves area (page 245) and the determinant is indeed 1.

Example   The matrix $\begin{bmatrix} 2 & 0 \\ 0 & 2 \end{bmatrix}$ represents an enlargement (about O) with scale factor 2, since

$$\begin{bmatrix} 2 & 0 \\ 0 & 2 \end{bmatrix} \begin{bmatrix} x \\ y \end{bmatrix} = \begin{bmatrix} 2x \\ 2y \end{bmatrix} = 2 \begin{bmatrix} x \\ y \end{bmatrix}$$

The determinant of $\begin{bmatrix} 2 & 0 \\ 0 & 2 \end{bmatrix}$ is $2 \times 2 - 0 = 4$.
Areas are scaled by a factor of 4.
(See page 235.)

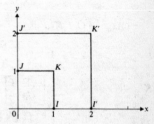

The diagram shows the unit square $OIKJ$ and its image under the enlargement.

If transformation S is represented by matrix $\mathbf{M}$, and transformation T is represented by matrix $\mathbf{N}$, then the composition ST (T followed by S) is represented by $\mathbf{MN}$.

(*Note*:   that the order is important, matrix multiplication is *not* commutative.)

Example   Find the image of the unit square $O(0, 0)$, $I(1, 0)$, $K(1, 1)$, $J(0, 1)$ under the transformation with matrix $A \begin{bmatrix} 1 & -2 \\ 0 & 1 \end{bmatrix}$. Label this image $O'I'K'J'$. Find the image of $O'I'K'J'$ under the transformation with matrix $B = \begin{bmatrix} -1 & 0 \\ 0 & 2 \end{bmatrix}$, label it $O''I''K''J''$. Verify that the image of $OIKJ$ under the transformation with matrix BA is $O''I''K''J''$.

Answer   Find the images of O, I, K and J.

I:
$$\begin{bmatrix} 1 & -2 \\ 0 & 1 \end{bmatrix} \begin{pmatrix} 1 \\ 0 \end{pmatrix} = \begin{pmatrix} 1 \\ 0 \end{pmatrix}$$

K:
$$\begin{bmatrix} 1 & -2 \\ 0 & 1 \end{bmatrix} \begin{pmatrix} 1 \\ 1 \end{pmatrix} = \begin{pmatrix} -1 \\ 1 \end{pmatrix}$$

J:
$$\begin{bmatrix} 1 & -2 \\ 0 & 1 \end{bmatrix} \begin{pmatrix} 0 \\ 1 \end{pmatrix} = \begin{pmatrix} -2 \\ 1 \end{pmatrix}$$

The image of $O' I' K' J'$ is

I':
$$\begin{bmatrix} -1 & 0 \\ 0 & 2 \end{bmatrix} \begin{pmatrix} 1 \\ 0 \end{pmatrix} = \begin{pmatrix} -1 \\ 0 \end{pmatrix}$$

K':
$$\begin{bmatrix} -1 & 0 \\ 0 & 2 \end{bmatrix} \begin{pmatrix} -1 \\ 1 \end{pmatrix} = \begin{pmatrix} 1 \\ 2 \end{pmatrix}$$

J':
$$\begin{bmatrix} -1 & 0 \\ 0 & 2 \end{bmatrix} \begin{pmatrix} -2 \\ 1 \end{pmatrix} = \begin{pmatrix} 2 \\ 2 \end{pmatrix}$$

Now
$$BA = \begin{bmatrix} -1 & 0 \\ 0 & 2 \end{bmatrix} \begin{bmatrix} 1 & -2 \\ 0 & 1 \end{bmatrix} = \begin{bmatrix} -1 & 2 \\ 0 & 2 \end{bmatrix}$$

$$\begin{bmatrix} -1 & 2 \\ 0 & 2 \end{bmatrix} \begin{pmatrix} 1 \\ 0 \end{pmatrix} = \begin{pmatrix} -1 \\ 0 \end{pmatrix}$$

$$\begin{bmatrix} -1 & 2 \\ 0 & 2 \end{bmatrix} \begin{pmatrix} 1 \\ 1 \end{pmatrix} = \begin{pmatrix} 1 \\ 2 \end{pmatrix}$$

$$\begin{bmatrix} -1 & 2 \\ 0 & 2 \end{bmatrix} \begin{pmatrix} 0 \\ 1 \end{pmatrix} = \begin{pmatrix} 2 \\ 2 \end{pmatrix}$$

The image is the same as that found above.

Simultaneous Equations and Matrices

The equations

$$2x + 3y = 5 \quad \text{(i)}$$
$$x - 2y = 7 \quad \text{(ii)}$$

can be written in matrix form as

$$\begin{bmatrix} 2 & 3 \\ 1 & -2 \end{bmatrix} \begin{pmatrix} x \\ y \end{pmatrix} = \begin{bmatrix} 5 \\ 7 \end{bmatrix}$$

and so

$$\begin{pmatrix} x \\ y \end{pmatrix} = \begin{bmatrix} 2 & 3 \\ 1 & -2 \end{bmatrix}^{-1} \begin{pmatrix} 5 \\ 7 \end{pmatrix}$$

But

$$\begin{bmatrix} 2 & 3 \\ 1 & -2 \end{bmatrix}^{-1} = \frac{1}{(-4-3)} \begin{bmatrix} -2 & -3 \\ -1 & 2 \end{bmatrix}$$

$$= \frac{1}{-7} \begin{bmatrix} -2 & -3 \\ -1 & 2 \end{bmatrix}$$

so

$$\begin{pmatrix} x \\ y \end{pmatrix} = -\frac{1}{7} \begin{bmatrix} -2 & -3 \\ -1 & 2 \end{bmatrix} \begin{pmatrix} 5 \\ 7 \end{pmatrix}$$

$$= -\frac{1}{7} \begin{pmatrix} -31 \\ 9 \end{pmatrix}$$

$$= \begin{pmatrix} 3\frac{1}{7} \\ -\frac{9}{7} \end{pmatrix}$$

Thus $x = 3\frac{1}{7}$, $y = -\frac{9}{7}$ are the solutions.

Examination questions

1. *On graph paper, using a scale of 2 cm to represent one unit on each axis and taking values of x from 0 to 7 and values of y from −5 to +5 draw the △ABC with vertices A (2, 2), B (6, 2) and C (2, 4).*

   (a) Given that $\mathbf{M} = \begin{bmatrix} \frac{1}{2} & \frac{1}{2} \\ -\frac{1}{2} & \frac{1}{2} \end{bmatrix}$, *find the coordinates of the images of A, B and C under the transformation whose matrix is* **M**. *Draw the image of* △ABC *and label the image triangle DEF.*

(b) Draw the image of $\triangle ABC$ under the transformation whose matrix is
$\mathbf{M}^2$. Label this image triangle GHJ.

(c) Find the value of the fraction $\dfrac{\text{area of } \triangle GHJ}{\text{area of } \triangle ABC}$.

(d) Find the matrix of the single transformation which will transform
$\triangle GHJ$ into $\triangle ABC$.   [LON]

2. Matrices $\mathbf{M}$ and $\mathbf{I}$ are defined by $\mathbf{M} = \begin{bmatrix} 1 & \frac{3}{5} \\ -1 & \frac{4}{5} \end{bmatrix}$ and $\mathbf{I} = \begin{bmatrix} 1 & 0 \\ 0 & 1 \end{bmatrix}$

(a) Find the image of the point $P(3,1)$ under the transformation
represented by $\mathbf{M}$. State the equation of the line through the origin
containing both the point P and its image under this transformation.

(b) Evaluate $\mathbf{M}^2$. Given that $\mathbf{I} = a\mathbf{M} + b\mathbf{M}^2$ where a and b are numbers,
find a pair of simultaneous equations in a and b and solve them.
Multiply through the equation $\mathbf{I} = a\mathbf{M} + b\mathbf{M}^2$ by $\mathbf{M}^{-1}$ to find an
expression for $\mathbf{M}^{-1}$ in terms of a, b and two matrices. Using your
values of a and b, evaluate this expression to find $\mathbf{M}^{-1}$.   [AEB]

3. *(a)* Given that $\mathbf{A} = \begin{bmatrix} 1 & 5 \\ 2 & 6 \end{bmatrix}$, find

   (i) the inverse of $\mathbf{A}$,   *(ii)* the value of x and y for which

$$\mathbf{A}\begin{pmatrix} x \\ y \end{pmatrix} = \begin{pmatrix} 11 \\ 10 \end{pmatrix}.$$

(b) Find the value of k for which $\mathbf{B} = \begin{bmatrix} 1 & k \\ 2 & 6 \end{bmatrix}$ has no inverse.
For this value of k

   (i) find the image of $(3,2)$ under the transformation represented
   by $\mathbf{B}$,

   (ii) prove that every point (x,y) in the plane is mapped onto the
   line $y = 2x$ under this transformation,

   (iii) deduce the value of p for which the solution set of the equation

$$\mathbf{B}\begin{pmatrix} x \\ y \end{pmatrix} = \begin{pmatrix} p \\ 10 \end{pmatrix}$$ is not empty and find three ordered pairs (x,y)

belonging to the solution set for this value of p.   [AEB]

4. *(i)* Using a scale of 1 cm for 1 unit on graph paper, draw axes
for $-10 \leqslant x \leqslant 10$ and $0 \leqslant y \leqslant 10$. Draw and label the triangle
with vertices $R(5,0)$, $S(10,0)$ and $T(10,5)$.

(ii) Find the images $R_1S_1T_1$ and $R_2S_2T_2$ or RST under the transformations represented by

$$\begin{bmatrix} 0 & 1 \\ -1 & 0 \end{bmatrix} \text{ and } \frac{1}{2}\begin{bmatrix} 2 & -1 \\ 1 & 2 \end{bmatrix}$$

Draw and label these images on your diagram. Describe fully the transformations represented by these matrices.

(iii) Find $\begin{bmatrix} 0 & 1 \\ -1 & 0 \end{bmatrix}^{-1}$ and solve the matrix equation

$$\begin{bmatrix} 0 & 1 \\ -1 & 0 \end{bmatrix} X = \frac{1}{2}\begin{bmatrix} 2 & -1 \\ 1 & 2 \end{bmatrix}$$

5. A shear represented by the matrix $\mathbf{A} = \begin{bmatrix} 1 & 0 \\ 2 & 1 \end{bmatrix}$ maps the vector $\binom{a}{b}$ onto the vector $\binom{8}{5}$. Find a and b. [SMP]

6. In this question use a scale of 2 cm to represent 1 unit on each axis, taking values of x from -1 to $+7$ and values of y from -5 to $+15$. Draw on graph paper $\triangle ABC$ where A, B, C are respectively the points $(2,2)$, $(6,2)$ and $(6,4)$.

The transformation E is an enlargement about the point $(4,0)$ with scale factor $-\frac{1}{2}$. The transformation R is a rotation through $180°$ about the point $(3,0)$.

Construct the images of $\triangle ABC$ under the transformation E, R, ER and RE marking your diagram carefully to distinguish the images. Describe in words the single transformation T such that $TRE = ER$. Write down the matrix of the transformation S such that $SRE = I$, where I is the identity transformation, and describe in words the transformation S. [LON]

7. (The whole of this question should be answered on graph paper or on squared paper.)

(i) Draw x- and y-axes for values of x from 0 to 24 and values of y from -8 to 16, using a scale of 1 cm to 2 units. On your diagram draw and label the arrowhead $A(7,-1)$, $B(16,2)$, $C(8,1)$, $D(4,8)$.

(ii) *The matrix for the transformation T is* $\frac{1}{5}\begin{bmatrix} 6 & 2 \\ 2 & 9 \end{bmatrix}$.

    (a) *Find the coordinates of T(A), T(B), T(C) and T(D).*

    (b) *On your diagram draw the arrowhead T(ABCD), labelling the vertices.*

(iii) (a) *The points P and Q have coordinates (6, −3) and (12, −6). Draw the line OPQ on your diagram and find the coordinates of T(P) and T(Q).*

    (b) *Describe T as fully as possible.*   [SMP]

8. (i) *Using a scale of 1 cm to 1 unit, draw x- and y- axes, taking values of x from 0 to 10 and values of* **y** *from 0 to 10. Draw and label the isosceles triangle S whose vertices are O (0,0), A (4,0), B (2,1).*

    (ii) **T** $=\begin{bmatrix} 2 & 1 \\ 1 & -2 \end{bmatrix}$. *Draw and shade the image of S under the transformation represented by* **T**. *Label A′, the image of A, on your diagram.*

    (iii) (a) *Find* **T** ^{2}.   (b) *Describe in words the single transformation represented by* **T** ^{2}.   [SMP]

9.

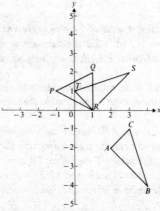

(i) *Triangle RST can be mapped onto triangle ABC by a rotation about O followed by a translation. State the magnitude and the direction of the angle of rotation and give the translation in the form* $\binom{a}{b}$.

(ii) *Triangle RST can also be mapped onto triangle ABC by the translation* $\binom{-2}{7}$ *followed by a rotation. Find the centre of the rotation.*

(iii) Triangle *R S T* is mapped onto triangle *R Q P* by a shear. By considering the images of *(1,0)* and *(0,1)* under the shear, or otherwise, find the matrix which represents the shear.

(iv) Calculate the area of triangle *R S T*.

(v) Triangle *R S T* is mapped onto triangle *L M N* by an enlargement, scale factor 2 and centre *(3,0)*. Write down the coordinates of *L, M* and *N*. [CAM]

Answers

1. (a) $(2, 0), (4, -2), (3, 1)$ (c) $\frac{1}{4}$ (d) $\begin{bmatrix} 0 & -\frac{1}{2} \\ \frac{1}{2} & 0 \end{bmatrix}$

2. (a) $\binom{6}{2}, y = \frac{1}{3}x$ (b) $\begin{bmatrix} -2 & 18 \\ -6 & 22 \end{bmatrix}, a = \frac{3}{4}, b = -\frac{1}{8}$

3. (a) (i) $\frac{1}{4}$ $\begin{bmatrix} -6 & 5 \\ 2 & -1 \end{bmatrix}$ (ii) $x = -4, \quad y = 3$ (b) $k = 3$ (i) $(9, 18)$

(iii) $p = 5$

5. $8, -11$

7. (ii) (a) $(8, 1), (20, 10), (10, 5), (8, 16)$ (iii) (a) $(6, -3), (12, -6)$

8. (iii) (a) $\begin{bmatrix} 5 & 0 \\ 0 & 5 \end{bmatrix}$ (b) an enlargement, scale factor 5, centre $(0, 0)$

Section 17: Statistics

The results of an experiment or survey are called data. Statistics is the study of general features and trends of the data.

Types of data

Qualitative data are not recorded in terms of numbers. Examples are colour, sound and texture.

If the measurements are numerical, then the data are called **quantitative**. Quantitative data are of two types, discrete and continuous.

Discrete Data

If the data can only take certain isolated values, then they are said to be **discrete**.

Examples
   1. The number of boys in a class of 20 children can only take values in the set $\{0, 1, 2, 3, 4, 5, \ldots, 18, 19, 20\}$.

   2. If a coin is tossed 100 times, the number of heads takes values in the set $\{0, 1, \ldots, 100\}$.

   3. Shoe sizes, for example $6\frac{1}{2}$, 7, $7\frac{1}{2}$, 8.

   4. The value of the money in your purse or pocket is of the form $£A.bc$.

Analysing discrete data

Averages give representative values of the data. There are three types of average in common use.

1. **Arithmetic mean** (or simply **mean**) of a set of numbers is the usual average

$$\text{mean} = \frac{\text{sum total of all items}}{\text{number of items}}$$

Example The mean of the set of 6 numbers 1, 2, 3, 5, 7 and 10 is

$$\frac{1+2+3+5+7+10}{6} = \frac{28}{6} = 4\frac{2}{3}$$

2. **Median** is the middle ranking number when the data are put in *ascending* or *descending* order.

Example The median of the numbers 1, 3, −2, 3, 7.
First , order the data, −2, 1, 3, 3, 7. The middle number is the third one, 3.

If there is an even number of items, there is no middle one. In this case, take the mean of the two middle ones.

Example 3, 1, 7, 2, 5, 4
First, order   1, 2, 3, 4, 5, 7
Middle two   3 and 4
Take mean, median is $\frac{3+4}{2} = 3\cdot5$

3. **Mode** is the most frequently occurring number.

Example The mode of the set of numbers 1, 2, 4, 3, 1, 3, 2, 1, 7, 9, 2, 1, 3, 1, 1 is 1.

It often helps to arrange the numbers in order

$$1, 1, 1, 1, 1, 1, 2, 2, 2, 3, 3, 3, 4, 7, 9$$

A set of data may have several, or no, modes.

The mean has the advantage of making use of all of the figures. The median is particularly useful when the exact values of the largest and smallest observations are unknown. The mode is most often used in commercial and Government planning, giving the most likely observation.

For a large number of data items, it is usual to form a **frequency table** showing how many times each number occurs. Do this by first making a **tally**, counting each number.

Example For the data 7, 8, 1, 3, 2, 1, 5, 2, 7, 9, 1, 3, 4, 7, 1, 5, 2, 3, 8, 6, 1, 2, 2, 6, 7, 5, 3, 4, 2, 4, 3, 2, 7, 6, 6, 2.

number	tally	frequency
1	|||||	5
2	||||||||	8
3	|||||	5
4	|||	3
5	|||	3
6	||||	4
7	|||||	5
8	||	2
9	|	1
total		36

To build up this table, read through the data, recording a tally mark every time you come across each number. The total of the tallies gives the frequencies. Total the frequencies as a check, they should come to the total number of data items.

The frequency table shows that the mode is 2 with a frequency of 8.

The mean can also be found using the frequency table. Multiply each number by its frequency, add up and divide by the total frequency.

number x	frequency f	$f \times x$
1	5	5
2	8	16
3	5	15
4	3	12
5	3	15
6	4	24
7	5	35
8	2	16
9	1	9
totals	36	147

The mean is $147/36 = 4 \cdot 08$ (to 2 decimal places).

The median is best found from a **cumulative frequency** table. Add the frequencies successively.

x	f	cumf
1	5	5
2	8 + =	13
3	5 + =	18
4	3 + =	21
5	3 + =	24
6	4 + =	28
7	5 + =	33
8	2 + =	35
9	1 + =	36
total	36	

The cumulative frequency of a value of x is the number of data items smaller than or equal to it in value. Thus 18 numbers are smaller than or equal to 3.

Note: that the final cumulative frequency (cumf) figure is equal to the total frequency, a useful check on your calculations.

The median is the average of the 18th and 19th numbers (even number of items). Since the cumf changes from 18 to 21 as x changes from 3 to 4, then the 18th number is equal to 3 and the 19th number is equal to 4. The median is $3 \cdot 5$.

In general, to find the median, find the number corresponding to a cumf of half of the total frequency. If the total is odd, add 1 before dividing by two.

Weighted average

Data may be *weighted* before averaging (see examples on page 314).

Example

x	weight	x × weight
1	1	1
2	1	2
3	2	6
4	2	8
5	3	15
totals	9	32

The weighted total, 32, is then divided by the total weight, 9.

$$\text{weighted average} = \frac{32}{9} = 3 \cdot 56$$

Note: The weights behave in the same way as frequencies; compare with the example on page 350.

Continuous Data

Quantities like height and weight can take any value within physical limits. They are not restricted to isolated values. For example, the weight of an apple may take any value between $0 \cdot 5$ and $1 \cdot 5$ kg. We say that the data takes values in a **continuous range**.

In practice, measurements are limited by the accuracy of the apparatus used. For example, if the mass can be weighed correct to two decimal places, then the result would be in the set $(0 \cdot 5, 0 \cdot 51, 0 \cdot 52, 0 \cdot 53, \ldots, 1 \cdot 49, 1 \cdot 50)$. When recording continuous data it is usual to split the range into intervals and write the frequency of measurements falling in each interval.

Example   A 'radar-gun' was used by a traffic monitoring group to measure the speeds of cars using a certain stretch of road. The speeds of 50 cars were measured and the data recorded in the table below.

speeds (mph)	number of cars	
0–20	1	0–20 means from 0 up to
20–30	2	*but not including* 20, etc.
30–35	16	The *limits* of this interval
35–40	20	are 0 and 20.
40–45	7	No speed higher than
45–50	2	60 mph was recorded.
50–55	1	
55–60	1	

The mean, median and mode for grouped data

The mean is found by using the *middle value* of each interval as the representative value. Thus the interval 0–20 is represented by 10. This value is often called the **mid-interval value**. In general the mid-interval value is the mean of the limits of the interval. For the data of the example above:

interval (mph)	mid-value (x)	frequency (f)	x × f	cumf
0–20	10	1	10·0	1
20–30	25	2	50·0	3
30–35	32·5	16	520·0	19
35–40	37·5	20	750·0	39
40–45	42·5	7	297·5	46
45–50	47·5	2	95·0	48
50–55	52·5	1	52·5	49
55–60	57·5	1	57·5	50
totals		50	1 832·5	

$$\text{Mean} = \frac{1\,832\cdot5}{50} = 36\cdot7 \qquad \text{(1 decimal place)}$$

Notice that this is an *estimate* for the mean. For an exact figure, you need to know the exact speeds of all 50 cars. Grouping the data makes the calculation easier at the expense of loss of accuracy.

The **modal class** is 35–40 corresponding to a frequency of 20. The **median class** is also 35–40, since the median is the average of the 25th and 26th items. The cumf value for this class is 25·5 and so both the 25th and 26th items are in this class.

In general, the median of n items corresponds to a cumf of $\frac{n+1}{2}$. The median class is the first class with a cumf greater than $\frac{n+1}{2}$. It is often useful to draw a diagram of the data and frequencies.

Statistical Diagrams

Discrete data

Bar chart (for either qualitative or quantitive data): for each data item, a strip is drawn with height showing the frequency.

Example

item	A	B	C	D
frequency	2	5	10	1

total frequency 18

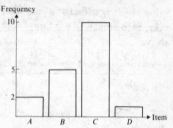

The diagram shows the relative frequencies of each item. When you want to see how the proportions of each item compare with the total frequency, draw a **proportionate** bar chart. This is a **vertical** bar chart. The bars could also be drawn **horizontally** if desired.

The proportions can also be shown as percentages of the total. This is particularly useful when two sets of data are to be compared.

Example   Draw percentage proportionate bar charts for the following figures.

The figures show the numbers of students in a certain school obtaining grades A, B, C, D, E and U in an examination in the years 1983 and 1984.

grade	1983	1984
A	10	12
B	15	14
C	25	30
D	10	11
E	10	10
U	15	14
totals	85	91

First express the frequencies as percentages of the total frequencies.

grade	1983	1984	
A	11·8	13·2	
B	17·6	15·4	
C	29·4	33·0	
D	11·8	12·1	
E	11·8	11·0	
U	17·6	15·4	
totals	100·0	100·0	(*as a check*)

A	B	C	D	E	U	
11·8%	17·6%	29·4%	11·8%	11·8%	17·6%	1983

A	B	C	D	E	U	
13·6%	15·9%	34·0%	12·5%	11·4%	12·5%	1984

Pie chart: This is a diagram of a circle divided into sectors with angles proportional to the frequencies.

Example   Draw a pie chart for the data for 1983 shown in the table of the last example. Use a circle of radius 2·5 cm.

Answer   First calculate the angles corresponding to the percentages by multiplying the percentages by 360°.

grade	frequency	%	angle
A	10	11·8	42·5
B	15	17·6	63·4
C	25	29·4	105·9
D	10	11·8	42·5
E	10	11·8	42·5
U	15	17·6	63·4
totals		100	360·2

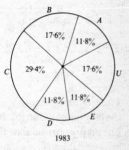

1983

When pie charts are drawn to compare two sets of data, we can illustrate the difference in total frequency by requiring the areas of the circles to be proportional to the total frequencies. Since the area of a circle of radius r is πr^2 (page 213) the radius should be proportional to the *square root* of the total frequency. If the 1983 and 1984 figures for the example above are to be compared using pie charts, the radius of the 1984 circle should be $\sqrt{91/85} \times$ that for 1983. The 1984 chart radius should then be $\sqrt{91/85} \times 2\cdot5 \approx 2\cdot6$ cm.

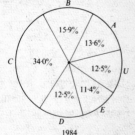

1984

Note: This should only be done when the charts are to reflect changes in total frequency. If you are just interested in the changes of proportion for each item, the circles should be the same size.

Continuous data

A type of bar chart called a **histogram** can be drawn for continuous data.

Histogram: The *x*-axis shows the values of the quantity being measured. This *continuous* range is divided into intervals which form the bases of the strips, or bars.

The frequencies are represented by the *areas* of the strips (unlike a bar chart where the frequency is measured by the *height* of the strips).

Example   The table below shows the lengths of 40 chicken feathers (in cm).

length (cm)	class width	frequency	frequency density (freq/cm)
0 to 1·5	1·5	1	0·67
1·5 to 3·0	1·5	3	2·00
3·0 to 5·0	2·0	12	6·00
5·0 to 7·0	2·0	15	7·50
7·0 to 10·0	3·0	9	3·00
		40	

The frequency density is calculated as frequency/class width. This gives the lengths of the strips. If the intervals are all of equal width, the frequency is then proportional to the length of the strip. The histogram is

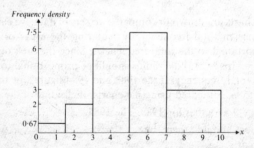

Frequency curve: A point can be plotted at the middle of the top of each strip of histogram. If the points are joined with straight line segments a *frequency polygon* is formed. If they are joined with a smooth curve, a **frequency curve** is formed. It is not necessary to draw the histogram first, plot the points with x coordinates given by the mid-interval values and y coordinates given by the heights of the strips.

Example The frequency polygon for the data of the example above

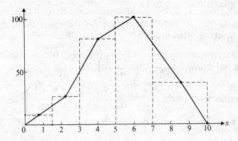

Cumulative frequency curve: These curves and polygons are drawn by plotting points with x coordinates given by the *upper limits* of the intervals and y coordinate given by the cumf.

As a general guide, a curve is drawn when at least 50 points are plotted, otherwise a polygon is drawn. An examination question will usually specify which is required. The curve or polygon is sometimes called an **ogive**.

The data of the example above has the frequency polygon shown on the right.

The median can be estimated from this cumf graph. Draw a line parallel to the x-axis at height $\left(\dfrac{N+1}{2}\right)$ where $N =$ total frequency. The point where this line meets the graph provides the median value.

The median for this data is estimated to be $5 \cdot 3$, corresponding to a cumf of $\dfrac{41}{2} = 20 \cdot 5$.

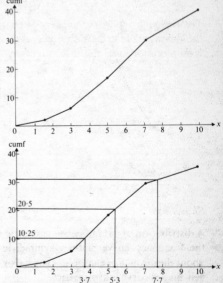

Notice how this is an improvement over the method of page 353, which gives only the median class.

Other measures are

the **lower quartile** with cumf $\frac{N+1}{4}$

the **upper quartile** with cumf $3\left(\frac{N+1}{4}\right)$

the **deciles** with cumf $\frac{N+1}{10}, 2\left(\frac{N+1}{10}\right), 3\left(\frac{N+1}{10}\right)\ldots$

the **percentiles** with cumf $\frac{N+1}{100}, 2\left(\frac{N+1}{100}\right), 3\left(\frac{N+1}{100}\right)\ldots$

The upper and lower quartiles of the data above are 3·7 and 7·7, respectively.

Dispersion measures the spread of the set of data. The **range** (= highest figure − lowest figure) is one measure of dispersion. A better measure is the **semi-interquartile range** (SIR) defined as (upper quartile–lower quartile) ÷ 2. The lower the dispersion, the more closely the date is grouped about the mean. (Sometimes the **interquartile range** = upper quartile − lower quartile is used.)

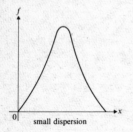
small dispersion

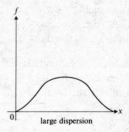
large dispersion

Skewness

A distribution of data may be symmetric, the frequency curve is then symmetric about the mean. For example, a **normal** or **bell-shaped** curve is symmetric:

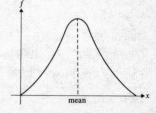
mean

A curve that is not symmetric is **skewed** either to the left or to the right.

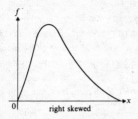

right skewed

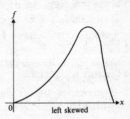

left skewed

When drawing frequency graphs, make sure that you produce clear and accurate diagrams. Follow the guidelines on page 150.

Examination questions

1. *In a test question, seven candidates obtained the marks 3, 4, 6, 8, 8, 3, 3.*
 (i) *State the modal mark.*
 (ii) *State the median mark.*
 (iii) *Calculate the mean mark.* [CAM]

2. *The heights of 5 boys are 1·25 m, 1·84 m, 1·60 m, 1·38 m and 1·43 m.*
 (i) *State the median height of the boys.*
 (ii) *Find the mean height.*
 (iii) *A sixth boy joins the group and the mean height of the six boys is 1·56 m. Calculate the height of the sixth boy.* [CAM]

3. *In forty games the scores occurred with the frequencies shown by the following table*

Score	1	2	3	4	5
Frequency	11	10	7	8	4

 (i) *Find* *(a)* *the median score,* *(b)* *the mean score.*
 (ii) *The mean score in the next ten games was 3·6. Find the mean score for all fifty games.* [CAM]

4. *(i)* *A group of students undertook a survey of trees in a wood. They reported as follows: 'We found 100 trees which we measured accurately. All the trees were taller than 2 m and the tallest was 20 m high.*

The median height was 14 m.
The upper quartile was 16 m.
The interquartile range was 6 m.'

Taking a vertical scale of 2 cm to represent 20 trees and a horizontal scale of 2 cm to represent 4 m of height, use these data to plot five points on a cumulative frequency graph. Draw a smooth curve through these points.

Given that 30 trees were taller than x metres, use your graph to estimate the value of x.

(ii) A second group of students undertook a similar survey in the same wood. They presented their results by means of the following histogram.

*Thus
the histogram
shows that there
are 5 trees of
height h, where
$16 < h \leqslant 17$.*

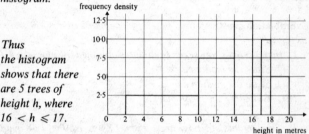

(a) Use the histogram to find the number of trees whose height was greater than 18 m.

(b) For one of the items listed in the first group's report, the second group found a different value. State which item this was, giving the reason for your answer.

(c) All the trees in the wood grow at a uniform rate of 0·5 m/year, and any of height greater than 20 m are cut down. Given that no new trees are planted, use the histogram to find the lower quartile six years after the survey was made.   [CAM]

5.

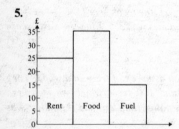

The bar chart illustrates the weekly expenditure of a family on rent, food and fuel. Sketch a pie chart to represent this information, marking the size of the angle in each sector.

[LON]

6. *The hours of sunshine per day were recorded at a seaside resort over a period of 52 days. The results were as follows:*

Hours of sunshine per day	5	6	7	8	9	10	11
Frequency of days		6	11	9	8	7	5	4

(a) *Write down the modal number of hours of sunshine per day.*
(b) *Find the median number of hours of sunshine per day.*
(c) *Calculate the mean number of hours of sunshine per day.* [AEB]

7. *Five integers between 3 and 8 have a mean of 4·4 and mode of 4. Find all possible values for the mean and mode when the numbers 3 and 8 are included.*

8. *The numbers of toffees in ten jars supplied to a sweet shop were listed as follows:*

542, 562, 562, 575, 582, 589, 591, 592, 596, 598

(i) *State the range of the data.*
(ii) *If the data are to be rearranged in the classes 540–549, 550–559, and so on to 590–599, state the modal class.* [SMP]

9. *In 1978 the average family spent 19·4% of its total expenditure on food and 1·1% on water services. Water services cost 85p per week.*
(i) *Calculate to the nearest degree the angle representing food in a pie chart showing all the expenditure.*
(ii) *Calculate the weekly cost of food to the nearest pound.* [SMP]

10.

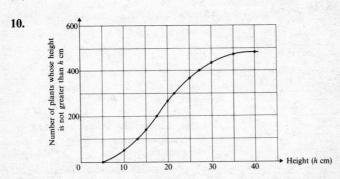

Above is a cumulative frequency graph for the heights of 480 plants. State
(i) *the median height;* (ii) *the interquartile range.* [SMP]

11.

The pie chart shows the sources of income of a local Trust for Nature Conservation. If the subscriptions amounted to £22 600, how much, correct to the nearest £10, was earned by sales?   [CAM]

Answers

1. (i) 3   (ii) 4   (iii) 5
2. (i) 1·43 m   (ii) 1·5   (iii) 1·86 m
3. (i) (a) 2   (b) 2·6   (ii) 2·8
4. (i) 15·5 (approx.)   (ii) 10 trees are taller than 18 m   (b) Interquartile range
5. 120°, 168°, 72°.
6. (a) 6   (b) 7·5   (c) 7·3
8. (i) 56   (ii) 590–599
9. (i) 70°   (ii) £15
10. (i) 20   (ii) 12
11. £8 860

Section 18: Probability

Events and Outcomes

Suppose that you throw a die. The number on the top face could be 1, 2, 3, 4, 5 or 6. Throwing a die is an **experiment** with **outcomes** in the **possibility space**.

$$\mathscr{E} = \{1, 2, 3, 4, 5, 6\}$$

For a fair die, each of these 6 outcomes is *equally likely*. Now suppose that you are playing a game in which you win when you throw a 1 or a 6. The set $A = \{1, 6\}$ of outcomes is called an **event**, it is a subset of the possibility space. A contains 2 of the 6 equally likely outcomes. We define the **probability** that A occurs as $p(A) = \frac{2}{6} \equiv \frac{1}{3}$. In general, $\mathscr{E}$ contains n equally likely outcomes and $n(A) = r$, then $p(A) = \frac{r}{n}$. The basic outcomes $\{1\}, \{2\}, \{3\}, \{4\}, \{5\}$ and $\{6\}$ each have a probability of $\frac{1}{6}$.

In practice, this means that, in a large number of throws, we expect $\frac{1}{6}$ of them to show a 6.

It follows from the definition of $p(A)$ that $0 \leqslant p(A) \leqslant 1$. If $p(A) = 0$ then A cannot happen. If $p(A) = 1$ then A must definitely happen.

Example As an experiment, toss a coin. The possible outcomes are head and tail. The possibility space is $\{$head, tail$\}$. If the coin is fair then these possibilities are equally likely and $p(\text{head}) = p(\text{tail}) = \frac{1}{2}$. If the coin is *biased* then $p(\text{head}) \neq p(\text{tail})$. For example, if $p(\text{head}) = \frac{2}{3}$ and $p(\text{tail}) = \frac{1}{3}$ then the coin is twice as likely to fall heads as tails.

If events A, B, C, ... include all possible outcomes, they are said to be *exhaustive*. If no two of them intersect (i.e. $A \cap B = \varnothing$, $B \cap C = \varnothing$, $A \cap C = \varnothing$, ...) they are said to be **mutually exclusive**.

For a set of mutually exclusive and exhaustive events A, B, C, ..., $p(A) + p(B) + p(C) + \ldots = 1$.

The complement, A', of set A contains all outcomes that are not in A (A' is read as 'not A'). Since A and A' are exhaustive and mutually exclusive

$$p(A) + p(A') = 1$$
$$\Rightarrow \qquad p(A') = 1 - p(A)$$

Example   A bag contains 10 red balls, 5 blue balls and 12 white balls. I choose a ball at random. The possible outcomes are {red, blue, white}. These are not equally likely outcomes since there are different numbers of each colour.

$$p(\text{red}) = {}^{10}\!/_{27}, \ p(\text{blue}) = {}^{5}\!/_{27} \text{ and } p(\text{white}) = {}^{12}\!/_{27}$$

So

$$p(\text{red}) + p(\text{blue}) + p(\text{white}) = \frac{10 + 5 + 12}{27} = 1.$$

(As expected, as {red}, {blue} and {white} are mutually exclusive and exhaustive.)

Combinations of Events

When throwing a die, the possibility space is {1, 2, 3, 4, 5, 6}. The event $A = $ {the score is even} is the combination of the events $B = $ {the score is 2}, $C = $ {the score is 4} and $D = $ {the score is 6}. The set theory notation of page 66 is used, and we draw Venn diagrams.

$A = B \cup C \cup D.$

We can translate the union
symbol $\cup$ as 'or'.

It turns out that

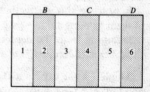

$$p(2 \text{ or } 4 \text{ or } 6) = p(2) + p(4) + p(6)$$
$$= \frac{1}{6} + \frac{1}{6} + \frac{1}{6} = \frac{3}{6} = \frac{1}{2}$$

This is the **addition rule** for probabilities.

In general, if A and B are two events that cannot happen at the same time (called **mutually exclusive**) then

$$p(A \cup B) = p(A) + p(B)$$

Examples

1. I choose at random one card from a pack of 52. What is the probability that I get either a jack or an ace?

Answer {jack} and {ace} are mutually exclusive events.

$$p(\text{jack or ace}) = p(\text{jack}) + p(\text{ace}) = \frac{4}{52} + \frac{4}{52}$$

(there are 4 jacks and 4 aces in the pack)

$$= \frac{8}{52} = \frac{2}{13}$$

2. Two dice, one red and one blue, are thrown and the scores added. Find the probability that the total score on one throw is (a) 7, (b) greater than 7. (Assume that the dice are fair.)

Answer It is useful to list the possibility space in the form of an array

				red die			
	score	1	2	3	4	5	6
	1	2	3	4	5	6	7
	2	3	4	5	6	7	8
blue die	3	4	5	6	7	8	9
	4	5	6	7	8	9	10
	5	6	7	8	9	10	11
	6	7	8	9	10	11	12

(a) There are 6 ways to score 7, and 36 possible outcomes altogether.

$$\text{Thus } p(7) = \frac{6}{36} = \frac{1}{6}$$

(b) 15 of the entries in the array are greater than 7.

$$p(\text{score} > 7) = \frac{15}{36} = \frac{5}{12}$$

We can look at this in another way. The event {score is 7} corresponds to the equally likely events {1 and 6}, {2 and 5}, and so on. These each have a probability of $\frac{1}{36}$, adding gives $\frac{6}{36}$; as required.

We also may wish to find the probability that two or more events happen.

Example   I toss a coin twice. What is the probability that I get a head both times?

Answer   The possibilities are

HH   head then head

HT   head then tail

TH   tail then head

TT   tail then tail

(the order is important). These events are equally likely. One of the four is two heads and so the probability is ¼. Notice that

$$\frac{1}{4} = \frac{1}{2} \times \frac{1}{2} = p(\text{H}) \times p(\text{H}).$$

If the events A and B are **independent** (so that the occurrence of one does not affect the probability of the other) then

$$p(A \text{ and } B) = p(A) \times p(B)$$

This is the **product rule** for independent events.

Examples

1. I choose one card from a pack of 52, look at it and then replace it in the pack. I then choose another card from the pack. Find the possibilities that   (a) both cards are red,
   (b) the first card is a jack and the second is not,
   (c) one card is a jack and the other is not,
   (d) at least one of the two cards is a jack.

Answer

(a) $p(\text{first is red}) = \frac{1}{2}$ since 26 of the 52 are red

               $p(\text{second is red}) = \frac{1}{2}$ since we have replaced the first

   so $p(\text{both are red}) = \frac{1}{2} \times \frac{1}{2} = \frac{1}{4}$

(b) $p(\text{first is a jack}) = \frac{4}{52} = \frac{1}{13}$

                     $p(\text{second is not jack}) = \frac{12}{13}$

Thus $p\text{(first jack, second not)} = \dfrac{1}{13} \times \dfrac{12}{13} = \dfrac{12}{169}$

(c) $p\text{(one jack)} = p\text{(first jack, second not or first not second is)}$

                 $= p\text{(jack, not jack)} + p\text{(not jack, jack)}$

$$= \frac{12}{169} + \frac{12}{169}$$

$$= \frac{24}{169}$$

(d) $p\text{(at least one jack)} = p\text{(jack, not jack)} + p\text{(both jacks)}$

$$= \frac{24}{169} + \frac{1}{13} \times \frac{1}{13} = \frac{25}{169}$$

We can also work this out using the rule $p(\text{not } A) = 1 - p(A)$. The opposite of at least one jack is no jacks. The probability of no jacks both times is

$$\left(\frac{12}{13}\right) \times \left(\frac{12}{13}\right) = \frac{144}{169}$$

So the probability of at least one jack is

$$1 - \frac{144}{169} = \frac{25}{169}$$

2. John and Mary each toss a fair die. The first one to get a 6 wins. Find the probability that John wins on his second toss, given that Mary goes first.

Answer   The outcomes must be

	Mary	John
first toss	not 6	not 6
second toss	not 6	6

$$p(6) = \tfrac{1}{6} \text{ for a fair die.}$$

So

$$p(\text{not } 6) = 1 - \tfrac{1}{6} = \tfrac{5}{6}.$$

For the 4 throws, multiplying

(independence) $p(\text{John wins on 2nd throw}) = (\tfrac{5}{6})(\tfrac{5}{6})(\tfrac{5}{6})(\tfrac{1}{6})$

$$= \frac{125}{1\,296}$$

3. A fly lands on a square tile with the following pattern on it. The corners are quadrants of a circle of radius 6 cm. If the fly is equally likely to land on any part of the tile, what is the probability that it lands in the shaded part?

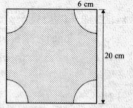

It then flies up and lands randomly on a tile with the same pattern. What is the probability that it lands in the shaded part both times?

Answer   The area of the four quadrants is $\pi \times 6^2 = 36\pi$

The shaded area is $20^2 - 36\pi = 286 \cdot 9$

The probability that it lands in the shaded part is

$$\frac{286 \cdot 9}{400} = 0 \cdot 72$$

The probability that it lands in the shaded part both times is

$$(0 \cdot 72)^2 = 0 \cdot 52$$

4. A bag contains 12 counters, three red and nine black. I choose two counters without replacing them. Find the probabilities that (a) they are both red, (b) they are both the same colour.

Answer

(a) p (first is red) $= \frac{3}{12} = \frac{1}{4}$. p (second is red) $= \frac{2}{11}$ (since there are then only two reds left and 11 counters in total),

$$p \text{ (both are red)} = \frac{1}{4} \times \frac{2}{11} = \frac{1}{22}$$

(b) The counters can either be both red or both black

$$p \text{ (both black)} = \frac{9}{12} \times \frac{8}{11} = \frac{6}{11}$$

$$p \text{ (both the same)} = p \text{ (both red)} + p \text{ (both black)}$$

$$= \frac{1}{22} + \frac{6}{11}$$

$$= \frac{13}{22}$$

Tree diagrams

When a sequence of experiments is performed it is often useful to draw a **tree diagram**. Each experiment is represented as a node and the possible outcomes as arcs leading from the nodes.

Examples

1. A coin is biased so that $p(H) = \frac{2}{3}$ and $p(T) = \frac{1}{3}$. Find the probability that in 3 tosses two heads are obtained.

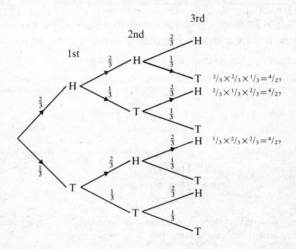

The result of the first toss is H or T. For each of these outcomes, the second toss results in a H or T, and again for the third toss. Each path from the first node to a final node represents a possible outcome for the 3 tosses. The probability of the outcome of *each* toss is written on the corresponding arc.

To calculate the probability for a particular outcome of the 3 tosses, multiply the probability on the corresponding path. Thus $p(H$ then H then $T) = \frac{2}{3} \times \frac{2}{3} \times \frac{1}{3} = \frac{4}{27}$. (Since the tosses are independent.) 3 paths correspond to 2H and 1T. Adding the probabilities (exclusive events) $\frac{4}{27} \times \frac{4}{27} \times \frac{4}{27} = \frac{4}{9}$. Thus the required probability is $\frac{4}{9}$.

2. A die is thrown and then a coin is tossed. Find the probability of getting a 6 and a head.

Answer

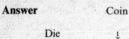

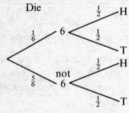

$$p(6 \text{ and } H) = \frac{1}{6} \times \frac{1}{2} = \frac{1}{12}$$

3. A box of chocolates contains three types. 6 hard centres, 12 soft centres and 6 all chocolate. What is the probability that if I choose two chocolates they are both soft centred?

Answer

From the diagram

$$p(\text{soft and soft}) = \frac{1}{2} \times \frac{11}{23} = \frac{11}{46}$$

Note: that at each node of a tree, the probabilities on the arcs branching off must total 1.

It is easy to make a calculation error when working out probabilities. It is a useful check to bear in mind that any probability is a number between 0 and 1 (so that if you calculate $p(A) = -2$, for example, then you know that you have made a mistake).

Examination questions

1. *A bag contains 100 discs which are identical except for colour. Of these discs, x are red, y are yellow and the rest are green.*

(i) A disc is selected at random from the bag. Given that the probability that it is red is $9/50$, find x.

(ii) A disc is selected at random from the 100 discs, is not replaced and a second disc is then selected at random. Given that the probability that the first disc is red and the second is yellow is $2/25$, find y.

(iii) Two discs are selected at random from the 100 discs. Find, as a fraction, the probability that one is red and the other is yellow.

[CAM]

2. Two dice are thrown and their scores are multiplied together to give a number x. Find, as a fraction, the probability that (i) $x = 5$, (ii) x is even, (iii) $x \leqslant 4$. [CAM]

3. The diagram represents a target consisting of two concentric circles. The probability that a shot which hits the target will land on the shaded area is $4/9$.

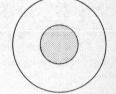

(i) Calculate the probability that a shot which hits the target will land on the unshaded area.

(ii) Given that the radius of the shaded circle is 5 cm find the radius of the target. [CAM]

4. Each of the 37 patients reporting to a doctor has at least one of the follow symptoms: a cold, a headache, a fever. In the Venn diagram, the expressions represent the number of patients in each subset.

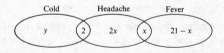

(i) Write down the total number of patients with a fever.

(ii) Express y in terms of x as simply as possible.

(iii) The number of patients with only a fever was three more than the number who had only a headache. Write down an equation in x and hence determine the number of patients who had both a fever and a headache.

(iv) Find the probability that a patient who had a fever also had a headache.

(v) *Two patients were chosen at random from all the patients. Calculate the probability that both patients had a fever, giving your answer as a fraction in its lowest terms.* [CAM]

5. *A family of two children can be represented by one of the following codes. BB, BG, GB, GG, where BG means that the elder child is a boy and the younger child is a girl, etc.*
(a) *Write down the 8 possible codes for a family of 3 children.*
Given that in all these families the probabilities of any child being a boy or a girl are equal, find the probability that
(b) *a family of 2 children will consist of one boy and one girl (in any order).*
(c) *a family of 3 children will consist of 2 boys and one girl   (i) in that order,   (ii) in any order.*
(d) *a family of 3 children will contain at least one girl.*
Two neighbouring families, the Smiths and the Browns, contain 3 children and 2 children respectively. Find the probability that there will be exactly 3 boys in the two families. [LON]

6. *In last year's mathematics examination, there were 20 000 candidates who were awarded grades as follows:*

Grade A	2 780
Grade B	4 360
Grade C	6 320
Grade D	1 600
Grade E	1 380
Unclassified	3 560

(a) *On graph paper, draw a bar chart to represent this information. Use 2 cm to represent 1 000 candidates and 1 cm to represent each grade.*
(b) *If the information were presented on a pie chart calculate the angle which would be used for the sector representing the grade C, giving your answer to the nearest °.*
(c) *Find, as a decimal correct to three decimal places, the probability that a candidate picked at random will have   (i) grade C,   (ii) grade A, B or C.*
(d) *If two candidates are to be picked at random, write down, but do not simplify, an expression for the probability that they will both have grade C.* [LON]

7. *The faces of a uniform regular octahedron are numbered from 1 to 8. If it is rolled as a die, state the probability of obtaining a score of 7 or less.*

[SMP]

8. *(i) Two regular pentagons are used as spinners in a game. The blue spinner has edges numbered 1, 2, 3, 4, 5, and the red spinner has edges numbered 1, 2, 2, 5, 5. What is the probability of a score of 2 on (a) the blue spinner, (b) the red spinner?*

(ii) A player uses both spinners and the separate scores are added to give the total score for that turn.

(a) Using a possibility space diagram, or otherwise, calculate the probability of getting a total score of 4.

(b) Calculate the probability that in a game between two players each has scored 4 after one turn.

(iii) 5 balls in a bag are numbered 1, 2, 2, 5, 5. Two balls are drawn at random from the bag and not replaced. Calculate the probability that the sum of the numbers on the balls is 7.

[SMP]

9. *A Roman die in the British Museum has 8 square faces and 6 triangular ones. If it is twice as likely to land on any given square face as on any given triangular one when thrown, find the probability that it will land on a triangular face.*

[SMP]

10. *From a starting point 0 on an open plane, a man walks a sequence of stages, each of 1 km either north or east. The direction of each stage is determined by spinning a coin: 'heads' due north, 'tails' due east.*

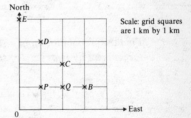

(i) How many different routes are possible from O to
    (a) P, (b) Q, (c) C?

(ii) p(A) denotes the probability that after 4 stages, the man will be at A, and so on. Calculate p(A), p(B), p(C), p(D) and p(E).

(iii) Calculate how far each point, A, B, C, D, and E is from O in a straight line.

(iv) What is the probability that the man ends up more than 3 km from O after 4 stages?

(v) When 20 men each walked 4 stages, it was noticed that 2 ended at A,

5 *at B, 5 at C, 4 at D and 4 at E. Find the average distance of the*
20 *men from O.*   [SMP]

11. *The probabilities that each of three marksmen, Tom, Dick and Harry,
will hit a target at a single attempt are* 0·19, 0·24 *and* 0·35 *respectively.*

(i) *If they all fire simultaneously at the target, find the probabilities
(correct to 3 decimal places) that   (a) Tom misses it;   (b) all
three men miss it;   (c) at least one man hits it.*

(ii) *They now prepare to fire once at the target in the order Tom, Dick,
Harry. Once the traget has been hit, no more shots are fired. Copy
and complete the tree diagram below, inserting all the outcomes
and one-stage probabilities in the correct places.*

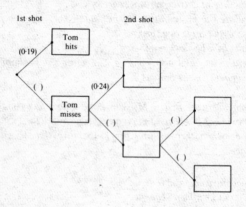

*Find the probabilities that   (a) the target is hit by Dick,   (b) the
target is hit by Harry,   (c) the target is hit.*   [SMP]

12.

*The blobs in the diagram represent villages and the connecting lines represent
roads.*

*I start walking from A. At B and C the probabilities are equal that I take
any of the roads forward. (I do not retrace my steps or stay at B or C).*

What is the probability that I arrive at D.   [SMP]

Answers

1. (i) 18   (ii) 44   (iii) $^4/_{25}$
2. (i) $^1/_{36}$ (ii) $^3/_4$ (iii) $^5/_{36}$
3. (i) $^5/_9$ (ii) 7·5 cm
4. (i) 21   (ii) $y = 14 - 2x$ (iii) 6   (iv) $^2/_7$ (v) $^{35}/_{101}$
5. (b) $^1/_2$ (c) (i) $^1/_8$ (ii) $^3/_8$ (d) $^7/_8$, $^5/_{16}$
8. (i) (a) $^1/_5$ (b) $^2/_5$ (ii) (a) $^3/_{25}$ (b) $^9/_{625}$ (iii) $^2/_5$
9. $^1/_{22}$
12. $^1/_{20}$

Section 19: Iterative Methods

Sequences

We recall that a *sequence* of numbers is a list of numbers with a rule for generating successive terms.

Examples

1. 1, 2, 4, 8, 16, ... (multiply each term by two to get the next term).

2. 1, 2, 5, 26, ... (square the term and add 1).

3. $1/2, 2/3, 3/4, 4/5, \ldots$ (keep adding one to both top and bottom).

Suppose that we want to find $\sqrt{2}$ without using a calculator or tables. One method is

Step 1: Since $1^2 = 1 < 2$ and $2^2 = 4 > 2$ then $\sqrt{2}$ must be between 1 and 2. Take 1·5 as a *first approximation* x_1.

Step 2: Since $1·5^2 = 2·25 > 2$, then $\sqrt{2}$ must be between 1 and 1·5. Take the average of 1 and 1·5 as the *second approximation*, $x_2 = 1·25$.

Step 3: Since $(1·25)^2 = 1·562\,5 < 2$, then $\sqrt{2}$ is between 1·25 and 1·5. Take $x_3 = 1·375$ (average of 1·25 and 1·5).

The sequence 1·5, 1·25, 1·375, ... is generated. The further along the sequence that you go, the closer you get to $\sqrt{2}$. Each step involves the same operations.

The method is called an **iterative process**.

Example (a) Use the relation $x_{n+1} = 7 - 1/x_n$, to find the terms x_2, x_3, x_4 and x_5 of a sequence, given that $x_1 = 7$.

Put $n = 1$ in the relation

$$x_2 = 7 - \frac{1}{x_1}$$

$$= 7 - \frac{1}{7}$$

$$= 6 \cdot 857\,14 \text{ (to 5 decimal places)}$$

Put $n = 2$ in the relation $x_3 = 7 - 1/x_2$, using the value of x_2 just calculated: $x_3 = 7 - 1/6 \cdot 857\,14 = 6 \cdot 854\,17$. Continuing in this way, $x_4 = 6 \cdot 854\,10$ and $x_5 = 6 \cdot 854\,10$ (all calculations to 5 decimal places).

(b) To 5 decimal place accuracy, this sequence of numbers approaches $6 \cdot 854\,10$. This number is a solution of the equation $x = 7 - 1/x$. We can obtain this equation by dropping the subscripts from the relation $x_{n+1} = 7 - 1/x_n$. The equation can be rearranged as $x^2 - 7x + 1 = 0$.

We call the number $6 \cdot 854\,10$ a *limit* of the sequence. We have found one solution as the limit of a sequence. We could find the second root of the quadratic equation by factorizing

$$x^2 - 7x + 1 = (x - 6 \cdot 854\,10)(x - a)$$

where $x = a$ is the second root of the equation (see page 119). Multiplying out the right-hand side

$$x^2 - (6 \cdot 854\,10 + a)x + 6 \cdot 854\,10a$$

Comparing this with the expression on the left

$$x^2 - 7x + 1$$

we must have $-7 = -(6 \cdot 854\,10 + a)$ and so $a = 0 \cdot 145\,90$ to five decimal places.

Flow Diagrams

An iterative process like this can often be most easily expressed by a **flow diagram**, similar to the function diagrams of page 92. The new feature is that we can *repeat* parts of the diagram by forming **loops**. These loops are indicated by arrows on the diagram.

The iterative process of the last example has the flow diagram

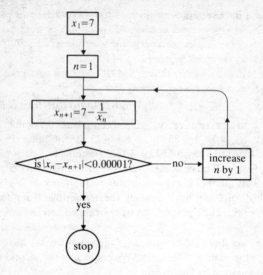

Note: $|x_n - x_{n+1}| \rightarrow$ positive part of $x_n - x_{n+1}$. Thus $|-2| = 2$, for example.

The diamond shape is called a **decision box**. It contains a **condition**. In this example, the decision box tests whether the accuracy of 5 decimal places has been reached. A decision box is used to change the **flow** of the process.

Flow charts are often used by computer programmers, in order to break a process down into steps which can then be written in a computer language.

Iterative methods can also be used to do calculations which are of use to company management. Predicted sales figures and costs based on performance to date are just two examples (see question 1 below). Most iterative methods are performed on computers for commercial and scientific uses. A computer can repeat calculations quickly and accurately.

In the following questions, follow the steps *exactly*, taking great care over the calculations.

Examination questions

1. *In 1982 the Standard Motor Production Company (SMPC) aims to sell 14% of the total number of cars sold in the state of OL.*

(i) (a) *By the end of September, 48 600 cars of all makes had been sold. Calculate the total number (T) that will be sold by the end of December if sales continue at the same average monthly rate.*

(b) *By the end of September, S M P C has sold 5 709 cars. Show that, in order to reach its target, S M P C must sell on average 1 121 cars per month for the rest of the year.*

(ii)

n	x	y	P	S	T	M
9	—	—	5 709	48 600		1 121
10	1 022	7 272				
11	1 393	5 175				

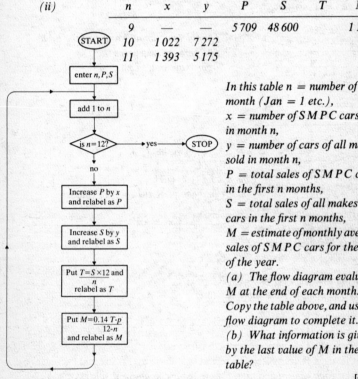

In this table n = number of the month (Jan = 1 etc.),

x = number of S M P C cars sold in month n,

y = number of cars of all makes sold in month n,

P = total sales of S M P C cars in the first n months,

S = total sales of all makes of cars in the first n months,

M = estimate of monthly average sales of S M P C cars for the rest of the year.

(a) *The flow diagram evaluates M at the end of each month. Copy the table above, and use the flow diagram to complete it.*

(b) *What information is given by the last value of M in the table?*

[SMP]

2. *The flow diagram [overleaf] is based on a method (attributed to Archimedes) for finding the value of π.*

(i) *Copy the table below, and use the flow diagram (starting with n = 6, s = 1, p = 6) to complete column 2. (All results should be recorded correct to 4 decimal places.)*

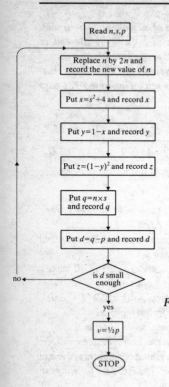

Column	1	2	3	4
n	6	12	24	48
x	—			
y	—			
z	—			
s	*1*			
q	—	6·211 7		
d	—	6·211 7		
p	6	6·211 7		

(ii) *Complete columns 3 and 4 of the table.*
(Note: $v = \frac{1}{2}p$ gives the
approximation to π.)

[SMP]

Flowchart:

- Read n, s, p
- Replace n by $2n$ and record the new value of n
- Put $x = s^2 \div 4$ and record x
- Put $y = 1 - x$ and record y
- Put $z = (1-y)^2$ and record z
- Put $q = n \times s$ and record q
- Put $d = q - p$ and record d
- is d small enough — no → (loops back)
- yes
- $v = \frac{1}{2}p$
- STOP

3. (i) Find s_1 and t_1 if $\begin{pmatrix} 1 & 2 \\ 1 & 1 \end{pmatrix}\begin{pmatrix} 1 \\ 1 \end{pmatrix} = \begin{pmatrix} s_1 \\ t_1 \end{pmatrix}$.

(ii) $\begin{pmatrix} 1 & 2 \\ 1 & 1 \end{pmatrix}\begin{pmatrix} s_1 \\ t_1 \end{pmatrix} = \begin{pmatrix} s_1 \\ t_1 \end{pmatrix}$.

Find s_2 and t_2. (iii) $\begin{pmatrix} 1 & 2 \\ 1 & 1 \end{pmatrix}\begin{pmatrix} s_n \\ t_n \end{pmatrix} = \begin{pmatrix} s_{n+1} \\ t_{n+1} \end{pmatrix}$.

Copy and complete the table of values:

n	1	2	3	4	5
s_n					
t_n					

(iv) $R_1 = s_1/t_1$, $R_2 = s_2/t_2$, $R_3 = s_3/t_3, \ldots$
Copy and complete the table of values

n	1	2	3	4	5
R_n					
$(R_n)^2$					

in each case giving all the digits your calculator displays.

(v) *The trend shown by the values in the table in part (iv) is known to continue indefinitely.*

(a) *Without evaluating R_{52}, R_{53}, write 2, $(R_{52})^2$, $(R_{53})^2$ in order of size, smallest first.*

(b) *To what irrational number does the table for R_n give an approximation?*

[SMP]

Section 20: Using Calculators and Tables

Calculators and tables are an invaluable aid when used correctly. When performing a calculation, write down the result of each step in your working. It is *not* enough to simply state the final numerical answer.

Calculators

Your calculator should have keys for $+$, $-$, $\times$, $\div$, $\sqrt{}$, x^2, $+/-$, SIN, COS, TAN as well as INV or SECOND FUNCTION for $\sin^{-1}$ etc. A $1/x$ key is also useful, as is a LOG key and its inverse often appears as 10^x. Some calculators do not have a $\sqrt{}$ key, but roots can be found by pressing INV and then x^2.

Check the manual for your calculator. Calculators often have a x^y key also.

Examples

1. To find $\sqrt{156}$. Key in 156 and press $\sqrt{}$. The displayed answer should be $12 \cdot 489\,995$ (for a 9 digit calculator).

2. To find 15^2. Key in 15 and press the x^2 key (or INV, $\sqrt{}$).

3. To evaluate

(a) $1 - \sqrt{35^2 + 1}$. Press the keys

$\boxed{3}$ $\boxed{5}$ $\boxed{x^2}$ $\boxed{+}$ $\boxed{1}$ $\boxed{=}$ $\boxed{\sqrt{}}$ $\boxed{+/-}$ $\boxed{+}$ $\boxed{1}$ $\boxed{=}$

Note how the $+/-$ key is used to put $-$ in front of the square root, and the use of the $=$ to display the results of each stage.

(b) $\dfrac{1}{5^2+7}$ | 5 | | x^2 | | + | | 7 | | = | | $1/x$ |.

4. To find the sine of an angle, key in the angle and *then* press the sine key.

$$\sin 35°: \boxed{3}\ \boxed{5}\ \boxed{\text{SIN}}\ \text{displaying } 0·573\,574\,6$$

Make sure that the mode selector is set to *deg* and not *rad* or *grad*.

5. Given a value of sine, cosine or tangent, to find the corresponding angle use the | INV | | SIN | keys, etc.

$\sin^{-1}(0·2)$: | 0 | | . | | 2 | | INV | | SIN | giving $11·536\,959$

which would normally be rounded to a given number of decimal places. To two decimal places, the answer is $11·54°$.

6. To calculate $(1·1)^5$, | 1 | | . | | 1 | | x^y | | 5 | | = |

Remember to press each key carefully and firmly. Use the | = | key to show the results of each stage of the calculation and write down all of these partial results in your working.

Tables

Logarithm tables can be used for multiplications and divisions. Some books of tables have two sets of logarithms, natural logarithms (Napierian) and logarithms to base 10. You should always use logs to base 10. Tables are either 3 figure or 4 figure.

To find the log of a number:

   (i) Put the number in standard index form (page 37). For example $12·8 = 1·28 \times 10^1, 0·2346 = 2·346 \times 10^{-1}$.

  (ii) Look up the **number** part in the tables. The corresponding figure from the tables is called the **mantissa** of the log. Write the mantissa after a decimal point.

 (iii) Take the power of 10 and write it in front of the decimal point of the mantissa. This is called the **characteristic** of the log.

If the power is negative, then the minus sign should be shown as a *bar* above the characteristic. The mantissa is always positive.

Example   To find the log of $0.2346 = 2.346 = 2.346 \times 10^{-1}$.
To find the mantissa from your tables:

  (a) Find the first two digits in the left-hand column.
  (b) Move to the column with the third digit above it. Write down the entry in the table.
  (c) In the same row, move to the column of the section on the far right which has the fourth digit above. Add the entry here to the result of (b).

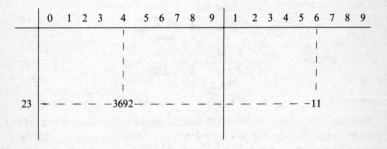

The mantissa is $3692 + 11 = 3703$.

    The characteristic is -1, written as $\bar{1}$. The log of 0.2346 is $\bar{1}.3703$.

This is for *four figure tables*. If you are using three figure tables, write the number to three significant figures (0.235) and ignore the instructions for the last digit above (part (c)).

    When *multiplying* two numbers, find their logs, add them, and then find the **antilog** of the sum. If your tables have antilog, follow the same rules as above for finding logs. Remember that the characteristic gives the power of 10 – look up the mantissa in the tables. If you do not have antilog tables, look for the mantissa in the body of the log tables. The figures can then be read off from the left of the row and the top of the column.

    When dividing two numbers, subtract their logs and find the antilog of the result.

You can remember these rules as

$$\log(xy) = \log x + \log y$$

and

$$\log\left(\frac{x}{y}\right) = \log x - \log y.$$

To raise a number to a given power, multiply the log of the number by the power and then antilog the result

$$\log(x^n) = n\log(x)$$

When using log tables, set out your working in a table.

Example   To find $\dfrac{1\cdot 234 \times 54\cdot 8}{0\cdot 234\,6}$

Set this out as

	number	log	
	1·234	0·091 3	
×	54·8	1·738 8	+
		1·830 1	
÷	0·234 6	1·370 3	−
	288·2	2·459 8	(antilog)

Squares: These tables are used in exactly the same way as log tables. The decimal point is ignored in the tables, it is up to you to decide where it should go in your answer. The best way to do this is to write the number in standard index form, doubling the power gives the position of the point.

Example $123\cdot 6 = 1\cdot 236 \times 10^2$
From the tables, 1 236 corresponds to 1 528. Doubling the power of 10, $2 \times 2 = 4$. The answer is $1\cdot 528 \times 10^4$ which can be written as 15 280.

Square roots: The tables are sometimes split up. One for numbers between 0 and 10, another for numbers between 10 and 100. The first table is used again for numbers between 100 and 1000, the second table for numbers between 1000 and 10 000, and so on.

Examples

(i) $\sqrt{1\,210} = \sqrt{12\cdot 1 \times 100} = \sqrt{12\cdot 1} \times \sqrt{100} = 3\cdot 464\,1 \times 10$
$$= 34\cdot 64$$

(ii) $\sqrt{0\cdot 008\,1} = \sqrt{\dfrac{81}{10\,000}} = \dfrac{\sqrt{81}}{\sqrt{10\,000}} = \dfrac{9}{100} = 0\cdot 09$

(iii) $\sqrt{25\,600} = \sqrt{2\cdot 56 \times 10\,000} = \sqrt{2\cdot 56} \times \sqrt{10\,000}$
$$= 1\cdot 6 \times 100 = 160$$

The trigonometric functions: The tables are often called *natural* sines, etc.
When the angle is expressed as a decimal of a degree, use the tables in the
same way as for logs. The figure in the right-hand section of the tables,
corresponding to the fourth digit, is *subtracted* for cosines. If the angle is
in degrees and minutes, look for the column which has the nearest number
of minutes *less* than those given. Make up to the correct figure by adding
from the right hand section of the table.

Example   To find the sine of 45° 20′.

	0′	6′	12′	18′	24′	30′	36′	42′	48′	54′	1′	2′	3′	4′	5′
45	–	–	–	–	– 7108 –	–	–	–	–	–	–	–	–4		

So sin 45° 20′ = 0·710 8 + 0·000 4 = 0·711 2.

To find the angle with a given sine, cosine or tangent, look for the given
value in the body of the tables and read off the degrees from the left-hand
column and the minutes from the top of the table.

Section 21: Scale Drawings

Some problems can be solved by drawing an accurate diagram and making measurements (for example the vectors problems of page 334). You should draw diagrams accurately, using a sharp pencil and taking care to measure distances. A protractor should be used to measure angles.

Example

A right-angled triangle has two sides 25 cm and 31·5 cm, which form the right angle. Draw a scale diagram, taking 1 cm to represent 5 cm. Measure the length of the hypotenuse and state the length of the corresponding hypotenuse of the full-size triangle. The lengths are 8·04 cm and 40·2 cm.

5 cm

6·03 cm

Plan and elevation

Example
1. The three-dimensional shape in which $AB = BC = AC = CD$

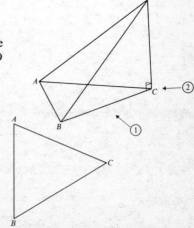

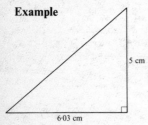

has **plan**
when viewed from directly above.

The **elevation** from a particular direction is the view seen from the given direction. It is a **two-dimensional projection**.

Elevation 1

Elevation 2.

2.

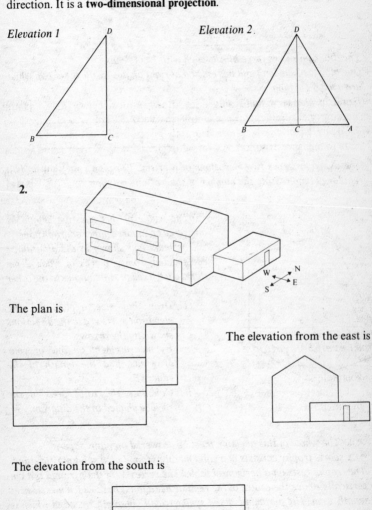

The plan is

The elevation from the east is

The elevation from the south is

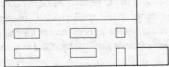

Examination questions

1.

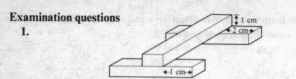

The diagram shows three blocks each with 1 cm² ends.
One block is 5 cm long and lies on, and at right angles to, the other two which are each 3 cm long.
Draw the plan view, half size.   [SMP]

2.

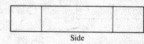

Front   Side

The diagram shows two elevations of a prism. The plan (not shown) is a regular polygon. State the number of sides of this polygon.   [SMP]

3.

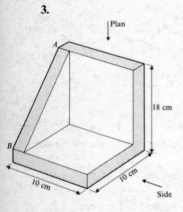

(The whole of this question should be answered on squared paper or graph paper.)

The book end shown in the diagram is constructed from 3 pieces of wood 2 cm thick, each fixed at right angles to the other two.

(i) Draw, half size, a plan and side elevation as viewed in the directions shown by the arrows.

By measurement on one of your drawings, find the length of the edge AB.

(ii) Calculate the total area of the surface shaded in the diagram.

4. *The whole of this question must be answered on plain paper.*

A sports trophy consists of a solid metal pyramid on a solid plastic stand. The trophy rests on a horizontal table. The vertex V of the pyramid is 4 cm vertically above the centre of the regular hexagonal base which has sides of length 2 cm. The pyramid is fixed symmetrically on a plastic stand which is part of a cone. The radius of the upper circular face of the stand is 3 cm and the radius of the lower circular face of the stand is 4 cm. The vertical height of the stand is 3 cm.

Draw full size   (i) the plan of the complete trophy.
(ii) its elevation on a vertical plane parallel to AB.
Use your drawing to find the true length *of VA.*

[CAM]

5. The base of a simple toy is a block of wood measuring 8 cm by 6 cm with a thickness of 1 cm. The base stands on a horizontal table and a solid cylinder of height 12 cm and diameter 3 cm is glued centrally to the upper surface of the block so that its axis is vertical as shown in the diagram.

A solid sphere of diameter 8 cm has a hole of diameter 3 cm drilled symmetrically through it so that the sphere will just fit on to the rod.

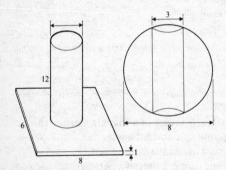

The sphere is placed on to the rod and rests on the base, forming the complete toy.

Draw full sized and correctly positioned in relation to each other
  (i) the plan of the complete toy,
  (ii) the elevation of the complete toy on a vertical plane parallel to the fixed base (i.e. the 8 × 1 part of the toy).

Measure and write down the length of that part of the cylinder which is outside the sphere.   [CAM]

Technical Terms and Definitions

A   absolute error   the absolute difference between the measured or calculated value and the actual value of a quantity

      acceleration   rate of change of velocity

      acute angle   an angle between 0° and 90°

      acute-angled triangle   has three acute angles

      algebraic fraction   for example, $\dfrac{x+1}{x-1}$

      alternate angles

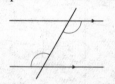

      altitude   line from a vertex of a triangle meeting the opposite side at right angles

      arc   (1) part of a circle
              (2) line forming part of a network

      argument   unknown quantity in a formula (also variable)

B   bar chart   diagram showing frequency by the height of the bars

      basis vectors   usually $\binom{1}{0}$ and $\binom{0}{1}$; any vector can be formed as a combination of basis vectors

      bearing   angle giving position from a fixed reference point

      binary number   base 2 number: 110_2 for example

      binary operation   rule for combining two elements of a set

      boundary   the edge of a region of the plane

C   cartesian product   of sets A and B, $A \times B$ is the set of all ordered pairs (a, b)

chord	a line joining two points on the circumference of a circle
circle	the locus of points all of which are a given distance from a fixed point
circumference	the perimeter of a circle
closed	a set is closed under a binary operation if all of the products are also in the set
coefficient	of a term is its numerical part
column vector	for example, $\binom{2}{3}$
commutative operation	satisfies $a*b = b*a$ for all a and b
complement	of a set A, A' is the set of elements not in A
completing the square	method for solving quadratic equations
component	one of the numbers of a column vector
composition	method of combining two mappings or functions
compound interest	is paid both on the investment and on accumulated interest
cone	solid on a circular base which tapers to a point
congruence	equation of the form $a \equiv b \pmod{n}$
congruent	(1) numbers have the same remainder on division by a given number
	(2) figures have the same shape and size
continuous data	can take any value within given limits
coordinate axes	reference lines for a system of coordinates
coordinates	numbers giving the position of a point
corresponding angles	

cosine	for an acute angle θ, $\cos \theta = \dfrac{\text{adjacent side}}{\text{hypotenuse}}$
cube	(1) a box with equal width, length and height
	(2) power 3
cube root	$b = \sqrt[3]{a}$ means that $b^3 = a$
cyclic quadrilateral	quadrilateral with vertices on a circle
cylinder	prism with circular base

D   data   numbers to be analysed in statistics
    decimal numbers   for example, 2·36
    decimal places   the number of digits after the decimal point
    definite integral $\int_a^b y\,dx$ with limits a and b; for calculating
                            areas below graphs
    degree (°)   unit of angular measurement, $360° =$ one
                            revolution
    denominator   bottom part of a fraction
    depression   the angle that the line of sight makes below
      (angle of)   the horizontal
    determinant   of the matrix $\begin{pmatrix} a & b \\ c & d \end{pmatrix}$ is $ad-bc$
    diagonal   line joining opposite vertices of a figure
    diameter   chord of a circle which passes through the
                            centre
    differentiation   method for calculating gradients
    discrete data   can only take certain values
    distributive law $a*(b\circ c) = (a*b)\circ(a*c)$
    divisor   factor
    domain   the elements that a mapping acts on

E   element   member of a set; number in matrix
    elevation   view of a solid figure from a given direction
    elevation (angle of)   angle that the line of sight makes above the
                            horizontal
    ellipse   shape like a flattened circle
    empty set   set with no elements
    enlargement   transformation which changes the size but not
                            the shape of a figure
    equation   condition for a variable to satisfy, containing
                            an equals sign
    equator   circle of latitude in a plane perpendicular to
                            the north–south axis passing through the
                            centre of the earth
    equilateral   having equal sides
    even number   divisible by 2
    event   subset of possibility space

	exponential function	function which has the variable in the index: 2^x for example
F	factor	divides a quantity exactly with no remainder
	factorize	express as a product of factors
	finite set	the elements can all be listed
	flow chart	diagram showing the sequence of steps of a calculation or process
	function	associates an image number with a given number
G	gradient	measures the rate of change of a function
	graph	the set of points corresponding to the ordered pairs of a function
	group	a set with a binary operation satisfying the group axioms of page 62
H	HCF	highest common factor to two or more quantities
	heptagon	seven-sided figure
	hexagon	six-sided figure
	histogram	form of bar chart for continuous data, where frequency is given by the areas of the strips
	hypotenuse	the side of a right-angled triangle opposite to the right angle
I	identity element	has no effect when combined with other elements of the set
	image	the result of a mapping or transformation
	incidence matrix	shows how the nodes and arcs of a network are connected
	independent events	the occurrence of one event does not affect the probability of the other
	index	or power: 2^3 has index 3
	inequality	for example, $2 + x < 6$
	infinite set	has uncountably many elements
	integer	whole number
	integration	opposite of differentiation
	intercept	point where a graph cuts an axis

	intersection	elements common to two or more sets
	invariant	unaffected by a given transformation
	inverse	combines with the element to give the identity; the inverse of a function reverses that function
K	kite	quadrilateral with two pairs of adjacent equal sides
L	latitude (angle of)	the angle of elevation or depression of a point on the surface of the earth from the centre
	LCM	smallest number containing the given quantities as factors
	like terms	have the same variables with the same powers
	linear	general form $ax + b$
	locus	set of possible positions of a point subject to given restrictions
	longitude (angle of)	the angle that the great circle passing through a point on the earth makes with the zero meridian
	lowest terms	when the top and bottom of a fraction have no common factors
M	many-to-many	mapping can have several images for each domain element
	many-to-one	mapping has one image only for each element of the domain
	mapping	association between the elements of two sets
	mapping diagram	illustrates the association of the sets by joining corresponding elements with arrows
	matrix	an array of numbers in brackets
	maximum point	'top of the hill' on a graph
	mean	average
	median	(1) middle of a set of numbers in ascending or descending order (2) line joining a vertex of a triangle to the mid-point of the opposite side
	mid-interval value	average of the end points of an interval
	minimum point	'bottom of a valley' on a graph

	mixed number	has an integer part and a fraction part: $2\frac{1}{2}$ for example
	mode	the most frequent of a set of numbers
	modulus	the length of a vector
	mutually exclusive	events that cannot happen at the same time
N	natural numbers	positive whole numbers (including zero)
	net	pattern of shapes which fold to form a polyhedron
	network	pattern of connecting lines
	node	end point of an arc in a network
	number base	number used to find the value of a number gives its digits
	numerator	top of a fraction
O	obtuse	angle between 90° and 180°
	octagon	eight-sided figure
	odd number	not divisible by 2
	one-to-many	mapping, an element may be mapped to several images, but each image comes from only one element
	one-to-one	mapping, arrows can only connect single pairs
	onto	map, each range element comes from a domain element
	operation	see binary
	ordered pair	pair of elements in brackets, the order being important: (x, y)
	ordered triple	three elements in brackets, the order being important: (x, y, z)
P	parallel	lines in a plane which do not meet
	parallelogram	quadrilateral formed by two pairs of parallel lines
	pentagon	five-sided figure
	percentage (%)	fraction with denominator 100
	perimeter	the outside edges of a figure
	pie chart	statistical diagram, frequencies are given by the angles in the sectors of the circle

plan	view of the base of a solid
plane	flat two dimensional surface
polar coordinates	$P(r, \theta)$, r = distance OP, θ = angle OP makes with the positive x-axis
polygon	figure formed by line segments
pole	the origin of polar coordinates
polyhedra	solid with polygonal faces
polynomial	an expression which has terms in the variable added together: $4x^3 - 3x^2 + 2x - 9$
possibility space	a list of all possible outcomes
power	index, the number of times a quantity appears in a product
prime number	has no factors other than 1 and itself
prism	solid object which has the same cross-section for any cut parallel to the base
proportional	$y \propto x^n$ means that $y = kx^n$, for some constant k
pyramid	solid tapering to a point
Pythagoras' theorem	the square on the hypotenuse of a right-angled triangle is equal to the sum of the squares on the other two sides

Q	quadrant	sector of a circle formed by an angle of $90°$
	quadratic equation	general form $ax^2 + bx + c = 0$
	quadratic expression	$ax^2 + bx + c$
	quadrilateral	four-sided figure
	qualitative	describing quality rather than quantity
	quantitative	measurable by numbers
	quartile	(1) upper, corresponding to 75% cumf
		(2) lower, corresponding to 25% cumf

R	radius	line from the centre of a circle to its circumference
	range	possible images for a mapping or function
	ratio	division into fractional parts: $2:3$
	rational number	a fraction
	real number	any number
	reciprocal	of a quantity is formed when the quantity divides into 1: reciprocal of a is $1/a$

	rectangle	quadrilateral with all angles 90°
	recurring decimal	a sequence of digits in the decimal expansion is repeated indefinitely
	reflection	in a given axis produces a mirror image
	reflex angle	between 180° and 360°
	regular polygon	all the sides are equal and all the angles are equal
	relation	mapping
	relation matrix	describes the relation between two sets
	relative error	absolute error ÷ actual value
	remainder	quantity left when one number is divided out from another
	repeated factor	factor with a power: x^2, a^4
	rhombus	equal-sided quadrilateral
	right angle	90°
	rotation	when all points are moved through a given angle
	route matrix	describes the connections in a network
	row vector	for example, (1 2), (3 4 5)
S	scale	(1) units of distances on x and y axes
		(2) enlargement factor
	secant	line crossing a circle
	sector	part of a circle formed between two radii
	segment	part of a circle cut off by a chord
	semi-interquartile range	½(upper quartile − lower quartile)
	semi-vertical angle	of a cone is the angle that a straight line from the vertex to the circumference of the base makes with the vertical height
	sequence	list of numbers and a rule for generating them
	set	collection of items
	shear	transformation which distorts shapes in proportion to the height above a fixed line
	significant figures	number of digits counting from the first non-zero one on the left
	simple interest	interest paid only on the original investment
	simultaneous equations	more than one equation to be satisfied by the variables

sine	for an acute angle θ, $\sin\theta = \dfrac{\text{opposite side}}{\text{hypotenuse}}$
singular	having no inverse
skew	not symmetric
slope	gradient
solution set	set of solutions to a problem
speed	rate of change of displacement
sphere	ball shape
square	(1) equal-sided rectangle
	(2) power 2
square root	$b = \sqrt{a}$ if $b^2 = a$
standard index form	numbers in the form $A \times 10^n$ where $1 \leqslant A \leqslant 10$ and $n \in \mathbb{Z}$
subgroup	subset of a group which itself forms a group
subset	set contained in a larger set
subtend	form an angle
supplementary	angles add up to $180°$
symmetric	invariant under a reflection or under a rotation
symmetry group	of a figure are the transformations under which the figure is invariant

T

tangent	(1) line which touches a curve
	(2) for an acute angle θ, $\tan\theta = \dfrac{\text{opposite side}}{\text{adjacent side}}$
tessellation	repeating pattern of shapes covering a plane
tetrahedron	solid with four triangular faces
topologically equivalent	networks which have the same pattern of connections
translation	movement of all points by given amounts
transpose	reflection of a matrix in its main diagonal
trapezium	quadrilateral with one pair of parallel sides
tree	branching diagram
triangle	three-sided figure
turning point	maximum or minimum

U

union	set formed from all the elements of the component sets
universal set	contains all elements for a problem

V variable   quantity in an expression which can have
                       different values
   Venn diagram   illustrates relations between sets by
                       overlapping circles or other shapes
   vertex   point where lines or faces meet

W weighted average   calculated by multiplying individual items by
                       a weight before averaging (see page 351)